DISCOVERING CALCULUS

A Preliminary Version
II Multi Variable

Alan L. Levine
George M. Rosenstein, Jr.
Franklin and Marshall College

McGraw-Hill, Inc.
College Custom Series

*New York St. Louis San Francisco Auckland Bogotá
Caracas Lisbon London Madrid Mexico Milan Montreal
New Delhi Paris San Juan Singapore Sydney Tokyo Toronto*

McGraw-Hill's College Custom Series consists of products that are produced from camera-ready copy. Peer review, class testing, and accuracy are primarily the responsibility of the author(s).

DISCOVERING CALCULUS: A Preliminary Version
II Multi Variable

3 4 5 6 7 8 9 0 HAM HAM 9 0 9 8 7 6 5 4

ISBN 0-07-037582-8

Editor: Margaret A. Hollander

Cover Design: Mark Anderson

Printer/Binder: HAMCO Corporation

PREFACE TO INSTRUCTORS

In recent years, a nationwide movement ("Calculus Reform") has called for a dramatic change in the way calculus is taught. Many schools have responded to the challenge by experimenting and revising the traditional course content. While these revised courses vary widely in nature, most concentrate on making calculus more applied, teaching more problem solving skills, and incorporating modern computer/calculator technology. Many make use of existing textbooks, while supplementing them with their own innovative materials. This retro-fit approach carries all of the disadvantages of the traditional texts while minimizing the benefits of the new ideas.

We felt that no meaningful reform could take place within the framework of an existing text. We decided to restructure the calculus course from the ground up and write a book that fit the course as we envisioned it.

The biggest problem students face when learning calculus is that they confuse "doing" with "understanding". The reason for this confusion is that their entire mathematical education has focused on learning mechanical procedures, not concepts—that is, on the "how", not the "what" and "why" of mathematics. Combating this problem requires a change in pedagogy. Students must become more active in the learning process and teachers must do more than just lecture. Assessment of student abilities must focus on important ideas rather than easy-to-grade procedures.

Our book addresses these issues from several points of view. First comes the question of content. We have selected a set of topics that we feel are central to the understanding of calculus; these form the core of the text. There are many topics (such as techniques of integration) ordinarily found in calculus texts that are largely mechanical and do not enhance the underlying concepts. These have either been de-emphasized, omitted entirely, or placed in the student projects at the end of each chapter.

We also believe that students will show more interest in mathematics if they can truly visualize and understand its applications. Consequently, we have included sections which illustrate the application of calculus to areas such as fluid dynamics, biology, physics, chemistry, engineering, economics and astronomy. In addition, our student projects are designed to motivate learning through activities in individual and group settings.

Many of the applications involve differential equations, a topic not normally given much emphasis in beginning calculus courses. We introduce first-order differential equations in Chapter 5 and use them to motivate exponential and logarithmic functions. Second-order equations are introduced in Chapter 7 and are used to motivate trigonometric functions. Chapter 11 on infinite series is motivated by the problem of determining power series solutions of differential equations.

Traditionally, calculus has been taught in a lecture/recitation format with little input from the students. Our book is written in a way that is flexible and encourages other teaching styles to be used. The language we use is less formal, minimizing much of the rigor and technical jargon that can make the standard texts so formidable. We have found that with a little encouragement, students can read our book in advance of class and come prepared to discuss the material. To help students with their reading and comprehension, we have interspersed "Test Your Understanding" sections strategically throughout the presentation. These questions allow students to check whether they really understand what they have read before going on to the next topic.

Most existing texts advertise 5000 exercises, many of which can now be done by the computer. Students are led to believe that being able to complete multitudes of exercises and problems is what calculus is all about. Our book includes only a fraction of this amount. We develop and ask different types of questions—some exercises, some conceptual problems, and some essay questions. Many of our exercises and problems are unlike any example in the text, thus encouraging students to think about what they are doing, not to simply plug numbers into familiar equations.

As we mentioned, one of the motivating factors behind the calculus reform movement is the appearance of computers and calculators which can serve to take the drudgery out of doing calculus. The benefit of this increased use of technology is that it allows instructors to emphasize concepts rather than just the computations. Our book does not require any specific technology, although there are many places where the classroom presentation of a topic will be enhanced through use of a computer or graphing calculator. Some of the exercises, problems, and projects require or are made easier through technology. We offer some strategies for incorporating technology into the calculus course in our instructor's manual.

Finally, we'd like to hear your reactions to this text. While we've been encouraged by our colleagues at Franklin and Marshall and by reviewers, we realize that there are many ways of looking at the philosophical and pedagogical problems we've addressed. Please feel free to share your insights with us.

TABLE OF CONTENTS

ACKNOWLEDGEMENTS

Many individuals and institutions have helped and supported us throughout the development of this book.

The Howard Hughes Medical Institute provided Franklin and Marshall College with a grant that supported the development of this text for several years. We are grateful that we have been part of this effort to improve science education at the college.

Brad Rathbone has been a part of this project since the beginning. He created many of the graphs in the text and suggested numerous exercises and problems. By serving as a teaching assistant for the first two years in which we class-tested this book, he was able to observe and report student reactions from a student's perspective. As a result, he was able to suggest many areas of the book that needed clarification. He and Beth Rosenstein are preparing the solution manual for the book.

The students at Franklin and Marshall College who were taught from earlier versions of this book deserve thanks for their tolerance. Their responses to the book, not always positive, have encouraged us and pointed us in better directions.

The individual and collective support of our departmental colleagues has been invaluable. They allowed us to undertake this project, and then agreed to teach from the text during the 1991-92 and 1992-93 school years. Each one of them has contributed to the text.

We'd like to thank our Arnold Feldman and Gene Johnson for being brave enough to try teaching from this text during the 1990-91 school year. Their suggestions have been most valuable. William Tyndall has proven to be a proof reader without peer. His eagle eyes have saved us from any number of gaffes and inconsistencies. Timothy Hesterberg has also been a careful and helpful reader. Bernard Jacobson has contributed the wisdom of his years of experience teaching calculus to an accurate and even-handed appraisal of our work. Robert Gethner's enthusiasm for the project, his many helpful suggestions and his thoughtful reflections on teaching have strongly influenced this book. Robert Lubarsky suggested the term "direction" as a collective noun for "increasing or decreasing".

Ali Salahuddin is responsible for proofreading this version of the text and preparing the index.

We'd like to acknowledge the many reviews we received from unnamed colleagues at other institutions. This project certainly would not have come to this point without their support. We have gloried in their praise and have acknowledged ruefully the validity of their criticisms. Their comments have been most helpful as we prepared this revision.

Many of the historical comments are the result of conversations with historians of mathematics, particularly V. Frederick Rickey of Bowling Green State University.

Finally, we would like to thank the McGraw-Hill Publishing Company and in particular, our current editor, Jack Shira, and our former editor, Richard Wallis, for believing enough in this project to offer us a contract to publish it.

Alan Levine
George M. Rosenstein, Jr.

PREFACE TO THE STUDENT

"What is mathematics?"

Ponder that question for a moment. You've taken something called "math" throughout most of your elementary and high school careers, so you ought to have a pretty good idea of what mathematics is, right? Maybe. You can list subjects--arithmetic, algebra, geometry, trigonometry--that you covered in your math courses, but can you identify some unifying theme, some reason that they are all called "math"?

What do these courses have in common? Think about the kinds of tasks you had to perform in these courses. Certainly, a major activity in all math courses--either in class, on exams or homework--is solving problems. The problems may be routine exercises involving nothing more than straightforward calculations. They may be more complicated, multi-step problems. They may involve applications or they may be proofs, as in geometry. Since learning to solve problems is a desired outcome of all math courses, then maybe mathematics is problem solving.

That's not a bad answer but it's a bit too simple. Why is problem solving important? Certainly, the application of mathematics to other disciplines has led to many important discoveries and theories, but there's more to it. Problem solving is the process by which mathematics itself is created!

Perhaps you've never thought about mathematics being "created" or "discovered". Maybe you thought that it just appeared on earth one day (a sort of Big Bang theory of mathematics) or that it is part of the Old Testament (in the Book of Numbers?). In fact, new mathematics is constantly being discovered, just like any science, through experimentation, through conjecture, through problem solving.

It is this idea of discovery that we emphasize throughout this book; hence, we've chosen the title, "Discovering Calculus". We want to take you on a journey, starting with some very simple numerical and geometrical concepts and building upon them until we develop the subject of calculus. Along the way, we'll stop to see some interesting applications. And we'll give you the opportunity to explore some things on your own. Of course, in order to enjoy the trip, you have to want to enjoy it. We realize that you may have found mathematics in the past to be difficult, boring or generally not a pleasant experience. While there may be many reasons for this, we hope you can put the past behind you and approach calculus with a fresh attitude.

In order to truly appreciate this journey, you have to be an active participant. You may be accustomed to learning mathematics as a spectator, with an instructor lecturing and you practicing what the instructor shows you how to do. If you use this approach, you are really missing a lot of the discovery. It's like getting a guided tour of a foreign country without ever stopping to meet the people or sample the local food or see the sights up close. Years later, you may vaguely remember being there but the memories will be far more intense and lasting if you actually have "hands-on" experience.

Perhaps you also have discovered clever ways to avoid the "sights" that your teacher has wanted you to see. One way all of us (including the authors of this book) have done this is, when faced with a problem, looked back in the text for an example like the problem that we've been assigned. When we can find such an example (and in most texts, that's not too difficult) we simply follow the steps, applying them to our problem. That way, we don't have to think too carefully about what we're doing and we miss the attraction that our instructor wanted us to see.

If you've used this technique and others like it frequently, you may have learned that you didn't have to read the text in order to do your assignments. In fact, you may have discovered that, if your teacher was helpful, you could get good grades without ever reading the text. Perhaps that's fine as far as it goes, but you will not always have a teacher available and — surprise! — you may have to learn some mathematics on your own.

We've written a book for you to read. We suggest that you read the book before your instructor covers the material in class. That way, it will seem familiar and you will have some idea what to expect. This, in turn, makes the class easier to follow and makes you a better prepared participant in the discussion. Even if you don't understand everything that you read, at least you'll recognize some of the words and basic concepts. It's somewhat like reading a travel guide before going on vacation--you know what to look for when you get there. At the very least, you should read the book shortly after the lecture (not the night before the exam) to reinforce the ideas and give you a different perspective. It's much easier to understand something when you see it from several points of view.

Here are a few pointers for reading our book. First, reading a math book is not like reading a novel. Mathematics is much more structured and much denser (and, quite honestly, despite our efforts to use picturesque language, a bit blander) than ordinary prose. There are not many extra words thrown in for color. You cannot try to scan one paragraph at a time; you must read each sentence and equation and make sure you understand it before you go on to the next. While we've tried to provide as much detail as possible, we occasionally skip some algebraic steps. Keep a paper and pencil handy to fill in details if you cannot follow what we've done.

A section of the book probably contains several different ideas. It's often difficult to see a new idea coming, so we've put a marker, ¤, at the beginning of the development of a new subsection. When really big changes in direction are made, we introduce subsections with their own titles. Of course, definitions and theorems are important, so we've used bold-faced type to make them stand out. So, you have a variety of clues as to when something important has happened or will happen.

To help you decide whether you really understand a concept, we've interspersed questions, called Test Your Understanding (TYU for short), throughout the text. When you reach one, stop and do it to make sure you understand the concept before going on. The answers to the TYU's are found at the end of the section but you must resist the temptation to look at the answers before you really try the question. If you are stuck, try reading the preceding paragraphs again. Only as a last resort should you look at the answers. The key to understanding mathematics is being able to do a problem from start to finish, not watching someone else do it or working backwards from the answers. This point cannot be emphasized too strongly.

There is an analogy to foreign languages: It is much easier to learn to read a language or understand when someone else speaks it than to actually speak or write the language coherently yourself. We want you speaking and writing mathematics. Only in this way will calculus become a useful tool for you.

At the end of each section is a set of Exercises and a set of Problems. The Exercises are fairly routine and mechanical, much like the TYU's. We don't have as many exercises as some other books. We believe it is better to concentrate on a few exercises and really understand the underlying concepts than to practice superficially. Again resist the temptation to work backwards. You will discover that often the exercises are not merely examples from the text with new numbers. We'd like you to understand the ideas of the section and we hope the exercises help that understanding.

The Problems are not as straightforward as the Exercises and will require even more thought. You may find them frustrating at first but if you persevere, we think you'll find them easier as you get further into the course. Perhaps your instructor can teach you some problem solving strategies if you find that you have difficulty getting started.

Finally, at the end of each chapter is a set of questions called Questions to Think About. These review the main points of the chapter and ask you to discuss the concepts.

Well, that's enough advice from the authors. Just sit back, relax and begin "Discovering Calculus".

CHAPTER 11

INFINITE SERIES

11.1 FUNCTION APPROXIMATION AND TAYLOR POLYNOMIALS

In the first ten chapters of this book, we have learned many techniques for solving calculus problems. We can find derivatives of all algebraic and some important transcendental functions, we can find some antiderivatives, we can solve some differential equations and, most importantly, we can apply these techniques to many interesting problems. That's the good news.

The bad news is that there are an awful lot of interesting, important problems that we cannot solve, at least not in closed form. (The phrase "solving in closed form" means to be able to express the solution in terms of functions that can be evaluated easily on a calculator.) For instance, at this point, we have a very limited ability to solve differential equations. Essentially we can solve only two types of equations:

1. First-order separable equations--i.e, those which can be expressed in the form $h(y)\, dy = g(x)\, dx$, where h and g have antiderivatives that can be written in closed form.

2. Second-order equations of the form $\dfrac{d^2 y}{dx^2} + a\dfrac{dy}{dx} + by = 0$, where a and b are constants.

The methods we learned for solving these equations always yield exact, closed-form solutions. Furthermore, given appropriate initial conditions, the solution is unique.

There are many applications which give rise to differential equations which are not of either of these types. For example, the equation

$$x^2\frac{d^2 y}{dx^2} + x\frac{dy}{dx} + (x^2 - p^2)y = 0$$

occurs very frequently in physics. (It is known as **Bessel's equation of order p.**) This is certainly not a separable first-order equation and does not match the form of the second-order equations since, even after dividing by x^2 to make the coefficient of $\dfrac{d^2y}{dx^2}$ equal to 1, the coefficients of $\dfrac{dy}{dx}$ and y would not be constants.

The question we face then is how to solve such equations. The first thing we must realize is that, although the solutions of differential equations are functions, they may not be "nice" in the sense that they are expressible in terms of the polynomials, exponential, logarithmic and trigonometric functions with which we've dealt before. There are hordes of functions that cannot be defined by a simple formula, yet they are perfectly valid functions. Indeed, any graph with the property that no x-value has two different y-values associated with it represents a function, whether or not that graph came from a formula. This suggests that it would likely be fruitless to try to "cook up" a solution (perhaps by an organized trial-and-error approach) in terms of well-known functions. Rather, we'll relax the requirement that we find an exact solution and settle for an approximate solution.

¤   The idea of approximating functions is one we've seen before. In Chapters 2 and 3, we learned how to write an equation of the line tangent to the graph of a function at $x = c$. This line has the property that it passes through the point $(c, f(c))$ with slope $f'(c)$. Therefore, its equation is

$$y = f(c) + f'(c)(x - c).$$

Furthermore, if we pick an x-value near c, then the y-value on the tangent line will be close to y-value on the graph of f. So, the tangent line serves as a first-degree polynomial approximation to the function. Of course, the approximation is a bit crude since tangent lines are straight while the graph of the function is likely to be curved. Thus, straying too far from the point of tangency will probably produce bad approximations.

To get better approximations, we might try a polynomial of higher degree. Look at Figure 11.1 which shows the graph of $y = \sin(x)$ for $-\pi \le x \le \pi$. If we didn't know that this was the graph of the sine function, we might be inclined to think it was the graph of a polynomial of, perhaps, degree 3 or 5 or 7. Indeed, cubic polynomials of the form $p(x) := x^3 + bx$, where $b < 0$, look very much like Figure 11.1, especially for x near 0.

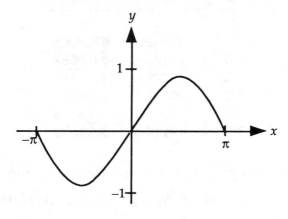

Fig. 11.1

In Figure 11.2, we see the graphs of $f(x) := \sin(x)$ and the polynomial $p(x) := x - \dfrac{x^3}{6} + \dfrac{x^5}{120} - \dfrac{x^7}{5040}$. (Don't worry where this polynomial comes from--we'll figure that out later.) For x-values between -2 and 2, the graphs are virtually indistinguishable. As we get further from $x = 0$, however, the differences between the graphs become more pronounced.

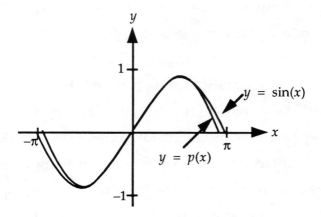

Fig. 11.2

The table of values below reinforces this observation numerically. As you can see, there are at least 2 correct digits for all x except $x = 3$. The precision increases as we get closer to 0. Beyond $x = 3$, the approximation gets rapidly worse. For example, $f(4) = -.7568$ while $p(4) = -1.384$.

x	$f(x)$	$p(x)$
0	0	0
.5	.4794255	.4794255
1.0	.8414710	.8414682
1.5	.9974951	.9973912
2.0	.9092975	.9079365
2.5	.5984721	.5885338
3.0	.1411200	.0091072

Our plan then is to approximate the solution of a differential equation by finding (if possible) a polynomial whose values are "close" to the desired solution, at least within some range of x-values. The choice to use polynomials as approximations is not the only one we could have made. We picked them because they are, in some sense, "easy to evaluate" (involving just addition and multiplication) and we know a lot about their behavior. There are situations in which it might be more prudent to use a different type of function (perhaps sine and cosine) as an approximation. We'll see that in Chapter 13.

The next question we must answer is what degree polynomial should we use. A first-degree polynomial (i.e. tangent line) is easy to compute but does not give very accurate approximations if we stray too far from the point of tangency. A second-degree polynomial can be "bent" to match the curve and ought to give better approximations. It shouldn't be hard to believe that the higher the degree of the polynomial, the better the approximations should be, at least for x-values near the point of tangency. The tradeoff is that more work is required to determine the coefficients of a high-degree polynomial and evaluating them requires more calculations. Our approach will be to derive a sequence of polynomials $\{p_1(x), p_2(x), ...\}$, where $p_n(x)$ is a polynomial of degree n. Later in this section, we'll show how to pick n so that the approximations are within some prespecified tolerance of the actual function values. (For instance, if we want approximations accurate to 10^{-3}, we might need a 5th degree polynomial, while if we want them accurate to 10^{-5}, we might need a 9th degree polynomial.)

◻ Let's begin by looking at the first-order equation

$$\text{(1)} \qquad \frac{dy}{dx} = y$$

subject to the initial condition $y(0) = 1$. This is a separable equation whose unique solution is $y = e^x$. (Re-read Chapter 4 if you don't remember how to get this solution.)

Suppose, for now, that we don't know the solution of Eq.(1). We might assume that the solution is an nth degree polynomial of the form

$$\text{(2)} \qquad p_n(x) := a_0 + a_1 x + a_2 x^2 + \ldots + a_n x^n,$$

for some constants $a_0, a_1, \ldots, a_n$ and positive integer n.

Note: Some of you may already be thinking that the polynomial in Eq. (2) could not possibly be the solution of Eq. (1) since if y is a polynomial of degree n, then $\frac{dy}{dx}$ is a polynomial of degree $n - 1$ and it is impossible for a polynomial of degree n to be identically equal to a polynomial of degree $n - 1$ for all values of x. Of course, you are correct but remember we are not trying to get an exact solution, just an approximation.

It follows by differentiating both sides of Eq. (1) repeatedly that

$$y = y' = y'' = y''' = y^{(4)} = \ldots;$$

that is, all the derivatives of y are equal to y. Also, since $y(0) = 1$, then

$$\text{(3)} \qquad y(0) = y'(0) = y''(0) = y'''(0) = \ldots = 1.$$

Let $p_1(x) := a_0 + a_1 x$ be the first polynomial in the sequence of approximations. Our goal is to determine the coefficients a_0 and a_1. What properties would we like the polynomial to have? Since the initial condition is specified for $x = 0$, we want p_1 to agree exactly with y at $x = 0$; that is,

$p_1(0)$ should be equal to $y(0)$. Since $p_1(0) = a_0$, then $a_0 = y(0) = 1$. Next, it seems desirable that y and p_1 should have the same slope at $x = 0$; that is, $y'(0) = p_1'(0)$. Since $p_1'(x) = a_1$, then $p_1'(0) = a_1$ and we should take $a_1 = y'(0) = 1$. Thus,

$$p_1(x) := 1 + x,$$

which is an equation of the line tangent to the graph of f at $x = 0$.

Now let $p_2(x) := a_0 + a_1x + a_2x^2$ be the second-degree polynomial approximation. In addition to having $p_2(0) = y(0)$ and $p_2'(0) = y'(0)$, we can now get the second derivatives to agree; that is, $p_2''(0) = y''(0)$. Since $p_2'(x) := a_1 + 2a_2x$, then $p_2''(x) := 2a_2$. Thus, $y''(0) = 2a_2 = 1$ from which $a_2 = \frac{1}{2}$. Furthermore, $p_2(0) = a_0$ and $p_2'(0) = a_1$, the same equations we solved for $p_1(x)$, so the coefficients a_0 and a_1 are the same for $p_2(x)$ and $p_1(x)$. Thus,

$$p_2(x) := 1 + x + \frac{1}{2}x^2.$$

It seems reasonable that the 3rd degree polynomial $p_3(x) := a_0 + a_1x + a_2x^2 + a_3x^3$ should satisfy the additional condition $p_3'''(0) = y'''(0) = 1$. Since $p_3'''(x) := 6a_3$, then $a_3 = \frac{1}{6}$ and

$$p_3(x) := 1 + x + \frac{1}{2}x^2 + \frac{1}{6}x^3.$$

(Again, the coefficients a_0, a_1 and a_2 for $p_3(x)$ are the same as for $p_2(x)$.)

TEST YOUR UNDERSTANDING

1. Find the fourth degree polynomial approximation for $y = e^x$.

This process can be generalized to obtain an nth degree polynomial $p_n(x)$ such that the first n derivatives of y and p_n are equal to each other at $x = 0$.

Upon substituting $x = 0$ into Eq. (2), we have $p_n(0) = a_0$; hence, $a_0 = 1$. Differentiating Eq. (2) gives

$$p_n'(x) := a_1 + 2a_2x + 3a_3x^2 + 4a_4x^3 + \ldots + na_nx^{n-1},$$

from which $p_n'(0) = a_1$. Thus, $a_1 = 1$.

Continuing in this fashion, we have:

$$p_n''(x) := 2a_2 + 6a_3x + 12a_4x^2 + \ldots + n(n-1)a_nx^{n-2},$$

$$p_n'''(x) := 6a_3 + 24a_4x + \ldots + n(n-1)(n-2)a_nx^{n-3},$$

$$p_n^{(4)}(x) := 24a_4 + \ldots + n(n-1)(n-2)(n-3)a_nx^{n-4}, \text{ etc.}$$

from which $p_n''(0) = 2a_2$, $p_n'''(0) = 6a_3$, $p_n^{(4)}(0) = 24a_4$, etc. Thus, $a_2 = \frac{1}{2}$, $a_3 = \frac{1}{6}$, $a_4 = \frac{1}{24}$, etc. In general, $a_j = \frac{1}{j!}$ where $j!$ (read "j factorial") is the product of the first j positive integers--that is, $j! = j(j-1)(j-2)\ldots(2)(1)$. Putting it all together, it appears that we have:

$$(4) \qquad p_n(x) := 1 + x + \frac{1}{2}x^2 + \frac{1}{6}x^3 + \frac{1}{24}x^4 + \ldots + \frac{1}{n!}x^n$$

as the nth degree polynomial approximation to the solution of the differential equation (1).

Let us emphasize once again that the polynomial in Eq.(4) is not an exact solution of Eq.(1). To see why, note that if n is a (finite) positive integer, then upon differentiating Eq.(4) $n + 1$ times, we have:

$$p_n^{(n+1)}(x) = 0.$$

But Eq.(3) tells us that all the derivatives of y have to equal 1 when evaluated at $x = 0$. Hence, we have a contradiction.

Figure 11.3 shows the graphs of the first four polynomials in the sequence compared to the graph of $y = e^x$. Note that, as the degree increases, the polynomial "fits" the curve better.

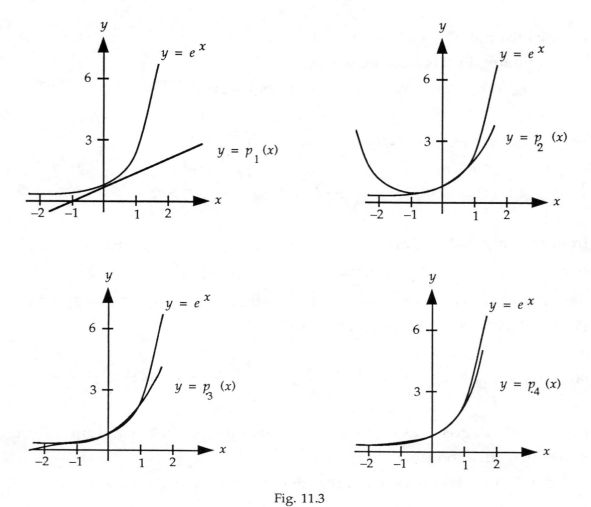

Fig. 11.3

The table below supports numerically what the graphs seem to indicate.

x	$p_1(x)$	$p_2(x)$	$p_3(x)$	$p_4(x)$	e^x
−2	−1	1	−.333	.333	.135
−1.5	−.5	.625	.0625	.273	.233
−1	0	.5	.333	.375	.368
−.5	.5	.625	.604	.607	.607
0	1	1	1	1	1
.5	1.5	1.625	1.646	1.648	1.649
1	2	2.5	2.667	2.708	2.718
1.5	2.5	3.625	4.188	4.398	4.482
2	3	5	6.333	7	7.389

TAYLOR POLYNOMIALS

This process of using polynomials to approximate a function can be applied to any "suitably well-behaved" (a term we'll clarify later) function, whether or not the function is a solution of a given differential equation. Let $p_n(x)$ be the nth degree polynomial used to approximate some function f near $x = 0$. It seems reasonable that $p_n(x)$ should have the property that the first n derivatives of f are equal respectively to the first n derivatives of p_n at $x = 0$. The polynomial so obtained is called the **Taylor polynomial of degree n centered at 0**. (We'll investigate later how to get Taylor polynomials centered at some other x-value.)

Let

$$p_n(x) := a_0 + a_1 x + a_2 x^2 + a_3 x^3 + \cdots + a_n x^n .$$

Since $p_n(0) = a_0$, then we should take $a_0 = f(0)$. Differentiate p_n to get

$$p_n'(x) := a_1 + 2a_2 x + 3a_3 x^2 + \cdots + na_n x^{n-1}.$$

Since $p_n'(0) = a_1$, then setting $p_n'(0) = f'(0)$ gives $a_1 = f'(0)$. Similarly,

$$p_n''(x) := 2a_2 + 6a_3 x + \cdots + n(n-1)a_n x^{n-2}$$

from which $p_n''(0) = 2a_2$. Therefore, $a_2 = \dfrac{f''(0)}{2}$. Continuing in the same manner gives $a_3 = \dfrac{f'''(0)}{6}, a_4 = \dfrac{f^{(4)}(0)}{24}, a_5 = \dfrac{f^{(5)}(0)}{120}$, etc. In general, we have the following:

THEOREM 11.1: The Taylor polynomial of degree n centered at $x = 0$ for a function f is given by $p_n(x) := a_0 + a_1 x + a_2 x^2 + a_3 x^3 + \cdots + a_n x^n$, where $a_k = \dfrac{f^{(k)}(0)}{k!}$ and $f^{(k)}(0)$ is the kth derivative of f evaluated at $x = 0$.

Note: In order to make the formula for a_k, as well as other formulas, work for the special case $k = 0$, we agree that the 0th derivative of f is f itself and $0! = 1$. Thus, $a_0 = f(0)$ as we noted earlier.

Using this theorem requires us to find the values of f and its first n derivatives at $x = 0$. There are two ways of doing this. One way is to start with the function, take the derivatives and evaluate them at 0. The other way to get these values is from a differential equation, with appropriate initial conditions.

To illustrate the first approach, suppose we wanted to find the 3rd degree Taylor polynomial centered at $x = 0$ for $f(x) := e^x$. We've already done this calculation starting with a differential equation for which this function happens to be the solution. Here we'll start with the function itself.

Since all derivatives of e^x are e^x, then $f^{(k)}(0) = 1$ for all k. Hence, $a_0 = 1, a_1 = 1, a_2 = \frac{1}{2!} = \frac{1}{2}$ and $a_3 = \frac{1}{3!} = \frac{1}{6}$. Thus, $p_3(x) := 1 + x + \frac{x^2}{2} + \frac{x^3}{6}$, as we found before.

EXAMPLE 11.1:

Find the 7th degree Taylor polynomial for $f(x) := \sin(x)$, centered at 0.
The first 7 derivatives of f are:

$f'(x) := \cos(x), f''(x) := -\sin(x), f'''(x) := -\cos(x), f^{(4)}(x) := \sin(x), f^{(5)}(x) := \cos(x), f^{(6)}(x) := -\sin(x)$ and $f^{(7)}(x) := -\cos(x)$.

Hence, $f'(0) = 1, f''(0) = 0, f'''(0) = -1, f^{(4)}(0) = 0, f^{(5)}(0) = 1, f^{(6)}(0) = 0$, and $f^{(7)}(0) = -1$. Thus, $a_0 = 0, a_1 = 1, a_2 = 0, a_3 = \frac{-1}{3!} = \frac{-1}{6}, a_4 = 0, a_5 = \frac{1}{5!} = \frac{1}{120}, a_6 = 0$ and $a_7 = \frac{-1}{7!} = \frac{-1}{5040}$. Therefore, the 7th degree Taylor polynomial is:

$$p_7(x) := x - \frac{x^3}{6} + \frac{x^5}{120} - \frac{x^7}{5040}.$$

Note that this is the polynomial we had investigated earlier in Figure 11.2. ◆

- -

TEST YOUR UNDERSTANDING

2. Determine the 8th and 9th degree Taylor polynomials centered at 0 for $f(x) := \sin(x)$.

- -

As a general rule, higher degree polynomials give better approximations. For instance, the first degree Taylor polynomial for $f(x) := \sin(x)$ is $p_1(x)$ $:= x$. This polynomial gives good approximations for x very near 0. For example, $\sin(.1) = .0998334$ which is very close to $p_1(.1) = .1$. On the other hand, $\sin(.5) = .4794255$ which is not as close to $p_1(.5) = .5$. The further from 0 we go, the worse the results. If we use the third degree polynomial $p_3(x)$ $:= x - \dfrac{x^3}{6}$, then $p_3(.5) = .4791667$ which is much closer to $\sin(.5)$.

Figure 11.4 shows a graph of $f(x) := \sin(x)$ and its Taylor polynomials of degree 1, 3, 5 and 7. (Note that since f is odd, the even degree Taylor polynomials are the same as the odd ones of one less degree; e.g., $p_8(x) = p_7(x)$.) We should expect that the higher the degree of the polynomial, the wider the range of x-values over which it matches f closely.

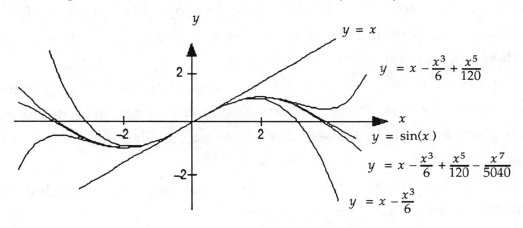

Fig. 11.4

TEST YOUR UNDERSTANDING

3. (a) Determine the 6th degree Taylor polynomial centered at 0 for $f(x) := \cos(x)$.

   (b) Use the result of (a) to approximate $\cos(.5)$.

4. Suppose $f(0) = 3, f(0) = -4, f''(0) = 6$ and $f'''(0) = 12$.

    (a) Write the 3rd degree Taylor polynomial for f, centered at $x = 0$.

    (b) Use the result of (a) to approximate $f(.3)$.

    At this point you might be thinking: If we have a formula for the function, why do we need to approximate it with a polynomial? Why not just evaluate it with a calculator?

    Granted, a calculator or computer will get the answer but think about how it does so. A calculator is much like a human being--it can inherently only add, subtract, multiply and divide. Using these operations, the only functions it can evaluate are rational functions. So how does it evaluate non-rational functions such as $\sin(x)$, or e^x, or $\sqrt{x}$?

    The answer is that the calculator uses something like Taylor polynomials (which it can evaluate using ordinary arithmetic) to approximate the values of the given function. It knows what degree polynomial to use to get answers accurate to as many digits it can handle.

¤ Now we'll look at some more examples of how to derive Taylor polynomials from a differential equation.

EXAMPLE 11.2:

    Determine an 8th degree Taylor polynomial approximation to the solution of the second-order equation $y'' + y = 0$, subject to the initial conditions $y(0) = 1, y'(0) = 0$.

    Since $y'' + y = 0$, then $y'' = -y$. Differentiating the equation repeatedly gives $y''' = -y', y^{(4)} = -y'' = y, y^{(5)} = -y''' = y', y^{(6)} = -y^{(4)} = -y$, etc. Similarly, $y^{(7)} = -y'$ and $y^{(8)} = y$. Therefore, $y''(0) = -1, y'''(0) = 0, y^{(4)}(0) = 1, y^{(5)}(0) = 0, y^{(6)}(0) = -1, y^{(7)}(0) = 0, y^{(8)}(0) = 1$, from which $a_0 = 1, a_1 = 0, a_2 = -\frac{1}{2}, a_3 = 0, a_4 = \frac{1}{4!}, a_5 = 0, a_6 = -\frac{1}{6!}$,

$a_7 = 0, a_8 = \frac{1}{8!}$.

The Taylor polynomial is $p_8(x) := 1 - \frac{x^2}{2!} + \frac{x^4}{4!} - \frac{x^6}{6!} + \frac{x^8}{8!}$.

Note that this differential equation is one we can solve by methods of Chapter 7. The solution is $y = \cos(x)$. So, the polynomial $p_8(x)$ ought to give good approximations to the values of $\cos(x)$, at least for x near 0.   ◆

EXAMPLE 11.3:

Find a 6th degreee Taylor polynomial approximation to the solution of the equation $y'' - xy = 0$, subject to the initial conditions $y(0) = 1, y'(0) = 2$.

First note that this is an equation which we cannot solve by any other means. It is not first-order separable and it does not fit the format of the second-order equations we studied in Chapter 7. (The coefficient of y is x, which is not a constant.)

Since the differential equation can be rewritten as $y'' = xy$, then upon differentiating repeatedly (invoking the product rule in the process since y is a function of x) and substituting $x = 0$, we have $y''(0) = 0$ and:

$$y''' = xy' + y \qquad\qquad y'''(0) = 1$$
$$y^{(4)} = xy'' + y' + y' = xy'' + 2y' \qquad\qquad y^{(4)}(0) = 4$$
$$y^{(5)} = xy''' + y'' + 2y'' = xy''' + 3y'' \qquad\qquad y^{(5)}(0) = 0$$
$$y^{(6)} = xy^{(4)} + y''' + 3y''' = xy^{(4)} + 4y''' \qquad\qquad y^{(6)}(0) = 4,$$

etc. The coefficients of the power series are $a_0 = 1, a_1 = 2, a_2 = 0, a_3 = \frac{1}{3!}$ $= \frac{1}{6}, a_4 = \frac{4}{4!} = \frac{1}{6}, a_5 = 0, a_6 = \frac{4}{6!} = \frac{1}{180}$, etc. Therefore, the 6th degree Taylor polynomial is:

$$p_6(x) := 1 + 2x + \frac{x^3}{6} + \frac{x^4}{6} + \frac{x^6}{180}.$$ ◆

TEST YOUR UNDERSTANDING

5. Find a fifth-degree Taylor polynomial for the solution of the equation $y'' + y = 0$ subject to the conditions $y(0) = 0, y'(0) = 1$.

6. Find a fourth-degree Taylor polynomial for the solution of the equation

$y'' - y = 0$ subject to the conditions $y(0) = 2, y'(0) = 0.$

7. Redo Example 11.3, using initial conditions $y(0) = 2, y'(0) = -1.$

□ There are some shortcuts we can take. For instance, we can use the Taylor polynomial for f to create the Taylor polynomial of a function "related to" f, as the next example illustrates.

EXAMPLE 11.4:

Determine the third degree Taylor polynomial for $f(x) := e^{2x}$.

We could start from "square one"--that is, take the derivatives of f and evaluate them.

$f'(x) := 2e^{2x}, f''(x) := 4e^{2x}, f'''(x) := 8e^{2x}$ so $a_0 = f(0) = 1, a_1 = f'(0) = 2, a_2 = \dfrac{f''(0)}{2} = 2, a_3 = \dfrac{f'''(0)}{6} = \dfrac{4}{3}$. Hence,

$$p_3(x) := 1 + 2x + 2x^2 + \frac{4}{3}x^3.$$

On the other hand, we could have simply replaced x by $2x$ in the Taylor polynomial for e^x, obtaining

$$p_3(x) := 1 + 2x + \frac{(2x)^2}{2} + \frac{(2x)^3}{6} = 1 + 2x + 2x^2 + \frac{4}{3}x^3. \qquad \blacklozenge$$

More specifically, if $g(x) := ax^m$, where m is a positive integer, then the Taylor polynomial for $f(g(x))$ can be obtained by replacing x by $g(x)$ in the Taylor polynomial for f. (In the example above, we have $g(x) := 2x$.) Note, however, that if $g(x)$ is of degree m, then the nth degree Taylor polynomial for $f(x)$ is transformed into the mn^{th} degree Taylor polynomial for $f(g(x))$. For example, if we replace x by x^2 in the 3rd degree polynomial in Example 11.1, we get the 6th degree polynomial for e^{x^2}.

It is also true that the $(n-1)^{\text{st}}$ degree Taylor polynomial for $f'(x)$ can be obtained by differentiating the nth degree Taylor polynomial for $f(x)$ and that the $(n+1)^{\text{st}}$ degree Taylor polynomial for any antiderivative of f can be obtained by antidifferentiating the nth degree Taylor polynomial for $f(x)$ and choosing the proper constant of integration. For example, in TYU #3, we found that $p_6(x) := 1 - \dfrac{x^2}{2!} + \dfrac{x^4}{4!} - \dfrac{x^6}{6!}$ is the 6th degree Taylor polynomial for $\cos(x)$. Note, however, that this is the derivative of $p_7(x) :=$ $x - \dfrac{x^3}{6} + \dfrac{x^5}{120} - \dfrac{x^7}{5040}$, the 7th degree Taylor polynomial for $\sin(x)$.

TEST YOUR UNDERSTANDING

8. Write the 5th degree Taylor polynomial for $f(x) := \sin(4x)$.

9. Write the 8th degree Taylor polynomial for $f(x) := \cos(x^2)$.

◻   We have used the phrase "centered at 0" to describe the Taylor polynomials generated so far. (Sometimes the term **Maclaurin polynomial** is used to describe Taylor polynomials centered at 0.) This means that the approximations obtained by using the polynomials are most precise for x in some interval centered around $x = 0$. In some cases, it is more desirable to center the polynomials at some other x value, say $x = c$. This is easily accomplished. The **Taylor polynomial of degree n centered at $x = c$** is:

$$p_n(x) := a_0 + a_1(x - c) + a_2(x - c)^2 + \cdots + a_n(x - c)^n$$

where $a_k = \dfrac{f^{(k)}(c)}{k!}$.

The only differences are that this polynomial is expressed as powers of $(x - c)$, rather than x, and the coefficients are obtained by evaluating the derivatives at $x = c$, rather than at $x = 0$.

EXAMPLE 11.5:

Determine the 3rd degree Taylor polynomial for $f(x) := \ln(x)$ centered at $x = 1$.

[Note: Since $f(0)$ does not exist, we cannot center the polynomial at $x = 0$.]

The derivatives of f are $f'(x) := \dfrac{1}{x}$, $f''(x) := \dfrac{-1}{x^2}$, $f'''(x) := \dfrac{2}{x^3}$. Evaluating at $x = 1$ gives $f'(1) = 1, f''(1) = -1, f'''(1) = 2$. Therefore, since $f(1) = 0$, we have $a_0 = 0, a_1 = 1, a_2 = \dfrac{-1}{2}$ and $a_3 = \dfrac{2}{6} = \dfrac{1}{3}$. The desired polynomial is:

$$p_3(x) := (x - 1) - \frac{(x - 1)^2}{2} + \frac{(x - 1)^3}{3}$$

whose graph, along with that of f, is given in Figure 11.5. Note the similarity in the vicinity of $x = 1$.

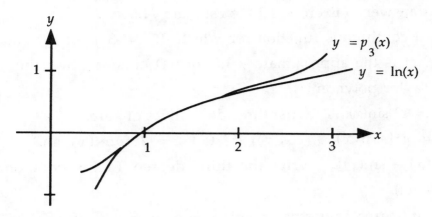

Fig. 11.5

It appears that, for $f(x) := \ln(x)$, $f^{(k)}(1) = (-1)^k (k-1)!$. Therefore, the coefficients are $a_k = \dfrac{(-1)^k (k-1)!}{k!} = \dfrac{(-1)^k}{k}$. So, the 4th degree polynomial is

$$p_4(x) := (x-1) - \frac{(x-1)^2}{2} + \frac{(x-1)^3}{3} - \frac{(x-1)^4}{4}$$, the 5th degree polynomial is

$$p_5(x) := (x-1) - \frac{(x-1)^2}{2} + \frac{(x-1)^3}{3} - \frac{(x-1)^4}{4} + \frac{(x-1)^5}{5}$$, etc.

TEST YOUR UNDERSTANDING

10. Write the 3rd degree Taylor polynomial for $f(x) := \sin(x)$ centered at $x = \pi$.

EXERCISES FOR SECTION 11.1:

1. Determine the Taylor polynomial of specified n and c for each function below:

  (a) $f(x) := \sin(2x)$, $n = 5$, $c = 0$ (b) $f(x) := \tan(x)$, $n = 3$, $c = 0$

  (c) $f(x) := \frac{1}{x}$, $n = 4$, $c = 1$ (d) $f(x) := \ln(1 + x^2)$, $n = 4$, $c = 0$

  (e) $f(x) := e^{-x^2}$, $n = 6$, $c = 0$ (f) $f(x) := \cos(x)$, $n = 4$, $c = \pi/2$

  (g) $f(x) := e^x + e^{-2x}$, $n = 3$, $c = 0$ (h) $f(x) := \sqrt{1 + x}$, $n = 3$, $c = 0$

2. Use your answer to Exercise 1(h) to estimate $\sqrt{1.5}$.

3. Let f be a continuous function for which $f(0) = 3$, $f'(0) = 6$ and $f''(0) = -12$. What is the approximate value of $f(1)$ obtained by using a second degree Taylor polynomial?

4. Let $f(x) := e^x \sin(x)$. The first three derivatives of f are:
$f'(x) := e^x[\sin(x) + \cos(x)]$, $f''(x) := 2e^x\cos(x)$ and $f'''(x) := 2e^x[\cos(x) - \sin(x)]$. Write the third degree Taylor polynomial for f centered at 0.

5. The fourth degree Taylor polynomial centered at $x = 0$ for $f(x)$ is
$$p_4(x) := 1 - x - 2x^2 + 6x^3 - 12x^4.$$
   (a) What is $f^{(4)}(0)$? Explain.

   (b) If $f^{(5)}(0) = 480$, what is $p_5(x)$?

6. Starting with the fourth degree Taylor polynomial for $f(x) := e^x$, derive the third degree Taylor polynomial for $g(x) := \dfrac{e^x - 1}{x}$.

7. Derive a second-degree Taylor polynomial for the solution of the differential equation $\dfrac{dy}{dx} = y \sin(x)$, $y(0) = 1$.

8. Derive a second-degree Taylor polynomial for the solution of the equation $\dfrac{dy}{dx} = y^2(x + 1)$, $y(0) = 2$.

9. Derive a fourth-degree Taylor polynomial for the solution of the equation $y'' + y = x$, $y(0) = 1$, $y'(0) = 0$.

PROBLEMS FOR SECTION 11.1:

1. (a) Use the methods of Chapter 7 to solve $y'' - 4y' + 3y = 0$, subject to $y(0) = 5$, $y'(0) = 11$.

   (b) Write the fourth degree Taylor polynomial for the function in (a).

   (c) Use the methods of this chapter to find a fourth degree Taylor polynomial approximation for the solution of the equation in (a).

   (d) Show that the answer to (c) agrees with the answer to (b).

2. (a) Show that $y = \tan(x)$ is a solution of the equation $y' = 1 + y^2$, subject to $y(0) = 0$.

   (b) Apply the methods of this chapter to the differential equation in (a), thus obtaining a fifth degree Taylor polynomial for $f(x) := \tan(x)$.

3. Use the methods of this chapter to find a third degree Taylor polynomial approximation for the solution of $y' + xy = e^x$, subject to $y(0) = 0$.

4. (a) By replacing x with $\sqrt{x}$ in the 6th degree Taylor polynomial for $f(x) := \cos(x)$, obtain a 3rd degree Taylor polynomial for $g(x) := \cos(\sqrt{x})$.

   (b) Can you replace x with $\sqrt{x}$ in a Taylor polynomial for $\sin(x)$ to obtain one for $\sin(\sqrt{x})$? Explain.

5. Prove that the derivative of the $(n + 1)^{\text{st}}$ degree Taylor polynomial for $f(x)$ is the nth degree Taylor polynomial for $f'(x)$.

TYU Answers for Section 11.1

1. $p_4(x) := 1 + x + \frac{1}{2}x^2 + \frac{1}{6}x^3 + \frac{1}{24}x^4$

2. $p_8(x) = p_7(x);\ p_9(x) := x - \frac{x^3}{3!} + \frac{x^5}{5!} - \frac{x^7}{7!} + \frac{x^9}{9!} = p_7(x) + \frac{x^9}{9!}$

3. (a) $p_6(x) := 1 - \frac{x^2}{2!} + \frac{x^4}{4!} - \frac{x^6}{6!}$ (b) $\cos(.5) \approx p_6(.5) = .8776$

4. (a) $p_3(x) := 3 - 4x + 3x^2 + 2x^3$ (b) $p_3(.3) = 2.124$ 5. $p_5(x) := x - \frac{x^3}{3!} + \frac{x^5}{5!}$

6. $p_4(x) := 2 + x^2 + \frac{x^4}{12}$ 7. $p_6(x) := 2 - x + \frac{x^3}{3} - \frac{x^4}{12} + \frac{x^6}{90}$

8. $p_5(x) := 4x - \frac{32x^3}{3} + \frac{128x^5}{15}$ 9. $p_8(x) := 1 - \frac{x^4}{2} + \frac{x^8}{24}$ 10. $p_3(x) := -(x - \pi) + \frac{(x - \pi)^3}{6}$

11.2 POWER SERIES

In the last section, we used Taylor polynomials to approximate functions. It appears that, in all cases, the accuracy of the approximation improves as the degree of the polynomial increases, at least for values of x near 0 (or wherever the polynomials are centered). This raises an interesting question: Can we get exact values of the function by taking a polynomial of "infinite degree"? That is, can we actually define (not approximate) a function by an infinite-degree polynomial?

Surely, you may be thinking, the authors need a vacation; how could you have infinitely many terms in a polynomial? How would you evaluate such a thing, since doing so would require adding up infinitely many numbers?

The idea is not as strange as it seems; in fact, we've hinted at it as far back as Chapter 2. Consider the infinite repeating decimal 0.3333333... which we all agree is "equal" to $\frac{1}{3}$. However, $0.33333... = 0.3 + 0.03 + 0.003 + 0.0003 + ...$ which is the sum of an infinite number of terms. Moreover, if we define an "infinite-degree polynomial"

$$p(x) := 3x + 3x^2 + 3x^3 + ... \text{, then}$$

$$p(.1) = 0.3 + 0.03 + 0.003 + 0.0003 + ... = \frac{1}{3}.$$

So, in this case, it is possible to define an "infinite-degree polynomial" which has a finite, precise value, at least for $x = .1$. Note, however, that $p(x)$ is not finite for every x since $p(1) = 3 + 3 + 3 +...$ which is not a finite number.

Admittedly, we are waving our hands a bit. We still have not defined precisely what we mean by "adding up infinitely many terms", even though we agree that, in some cases, it makes sense to do so. We'll clean this up later in the chapter.

A polynomial with infinitely many terms is called a **power series**. The remaining sections of this chapter are devoted to defining what we mean when we say a power series "gives a finite value" and to determining the conditions under which it does so. If the power series gives a finite value when $x = c$, we say the series **converges** at $x = c$. Otherwise, it **diverges**.

❑ For the remainder of this section, assume that power series are well-defined entities of the form $a_0 + a_1 x + a_2 x^2 + a_3 x^3 + a_4 x^4 +... = \sum_{j=0}^{\infty} a_j x^j$

Assume that a function f can be defined as a power series; that is,

$$(5) \qquad f(x) := a_0 + a_1 x + a_2 x^2 + a_3 x^3 + a_4 x^4 +... = \sum_{j=0}^{\infty} a_j x^j.$$

The first task is to determine the coefficients in the power series.

Assuming we can find derivatives of infinite-degree polynomials in exactly the same way we find them for finite-degree polynomials, it follows that

$$f'(x) := a_1 + 2a_2x + 3a_3x^2 + 4a_4x^3 + \ldots = \sum_{j=0}^{\infty} ja_j x^{j-1},$$

$$f''(x) := 2a_2 + 6a_3x + 12a_4x^2 + \ldots = \sum_{j=1}^{\infty} j(j-1)a_j x^{j-2},$$

$$f'''(x) := 6a_3 + 24a_4x + \ldots = \sum_{j=2}^{\infty} j(j-1)(j-2)a_j x^{j-3}, \text{ etc.}$$

Upon substituting $x = 0$, we have $f(0) = a_0, f'(0) = a_1, f''(0) = 2a_2,$ $f'''(0) = 6a_3$, etc. In general, $f^{(k)}(0) = k!a_k$, from which we have:

THEOREM 11.2: If $f(x) := \sum_{j=0}^{\infty} a_j x^j$, then $a_k = \dfrac{f^{(k)}(0)}{k!}$ for all k.

Note the similarity to the result obtained in Section 11.1 for the coefficients in the Taylor polynomials. The only difference here is that we have infinitely many terms. Not surprisingly, we shall call the power series obtained in this fashion a **Taylor series**.

Now, if f is any infinitely differentiable function, it is possible to write down a power series, the coefficients of which are derived from f by using the formula in Theorem 11.2. In other words, if f can be equal to a power series, then the series derived by Theorem 11.2 must be that series.

EXAMPLE 11.6:

Derive the Taylor series for $f(x) := \ln(1 + x)$.

Successive derivatives of f are:

$$f'(x) := \frac{1}{1+x}, \ f''(x) := \frac{-1}{(1+x)^2}, \ f'''(x) := \frac{2}{(1+x)^3}, \ f^{(4)}(x) := \frac{-6}{(1+x)^4}, \text{ etc.}$$

Therefore, $f(0) = 0, f'(0) = 1, f''(0) = -1, f'''(0) = 2, f^{(4)}(0) = -6,$ etc. Thus, $a_0 = 0, a_1 = 1, a_2 = -\frac{1}{2!}, a_3 = \frac{2}{3!} = \frac{1}{3}, a_4 = -\frac{6}{4!} = -\frac{1}{4}, \ldots$ from which we get the Taylor series $x - \frac{x^2}{2} + \frac{x^3}{3} - \frac{x^4}{4} + \ldots = \sum_{j=1}^{\infty} \frac{(-1)^{j+1} x^j}{j}.$ $\blacklozenge$

TEST YOUR UNDERSTANDING

1. Derive the Taylor series for $f(x) := \sin(x)$.

It will be helpful to remember the Taylor series for some well-known functions since we will use them throughout the remainder of this chapter. For instance:

$$\sin(x): \quad x - \frac{x^3}{3!} + \frac{x^5}{5!} - \frac{x^7}{7!} + \ldots = \sum_{j=0}^{\infty} (-1)^j \frac{x^{2j+1}}{(2j+1)!}$$

$$\cos(x): \quad 1 - \frac{x^2}{2!} + \frac{x^4}{4!} - \frac{x^6}{6!} + \ldots = \sum_{j=0}^{\infty} (-1)^j \frac{x^{2j}}{(2j)!}$$

$$e^x: \quad 1 + x + \frac{x^2}{2!} + \frac{x^3}{3!} + \frac{x^4}{4!} + \frac{x^5}{5!} + \frac{x^6}{6!} + \ldots = \sum_{j=0}^{\infty} \frac{x^j}{j!}$$

$$\ln(1+x): \quad x - \frac{x^2}{2} + \frac{x^3}{3} - \frac{x^4}{4} + \ldots = \sum_{j=1}^{\infty} \frac{(-1)^{j+1} x^j}{j}$$

These are just "extensions" of the Taylor polynomials obtained in Section 1.

◻ Note that we have *not* written $\ln(1+x) = \sum_{j=1}^{\infty} \frac{(-1)^{j+1} x^j}{j}$. There are two reasons for this. One is that the power series may not converge for all x. If so, then it can't be equal to $\ln(1+x)$ at any x at which the series diverges. We have not yet developed methods for determining the values of x for which the series converges (we shall do so in Section 11.4). However, upon substituting $x = 3$ into the series above, we get $3 - 9/2 + 27/3 - 81/4 + 243/5 - 729/6 + \ldots$ which does not appear to be converging (since we're adding and subtracting bigger and bigger numbers) in which case it certainly can't be equal to $\ln(1 + 3) = \ln(4) \approx 1.386$.

On the other hand, we'll show that the series $\sum\limits_{j=0}^{\infty} \frac{x^j}{j!}$, which is the Taylor series for e^x, does indeed converge for all x. All this means is that $\sum\limits_{j=0}^{\infty} \frac{x^j}{j!}$ yields a finite value for every x. It does not say that this value is the same as e^x. In other words, it is possible that a Taylor series derived from a function f will converge when $x = c$ but won't converge to $f(c)$. To understand how this might happen, recall that the Taylor series is created using information about f and its derivatives at $x = 0$. There may be another function g such that $g^{(k)}(0) = f^{(k)}(0)$ for all $k \geq 0$. Thus, f and g will have the same Taylor series but they may not have the same value at x-values other than 0. Hence, the Taylor series for g may converge at $x = c$ but it might converge to $f(c)$, not $g(c)$. So the function may not be equal to its Taylor series for all x in the domain of the function even though the series converges there.

◻ It is usually not possible to write Taylor series in compact "sigma notation", as we could in the examples above. Finding a formula that generates the coefficients of the Taylor series is impossible except in very simple cases. For example, the Taylor series for $f(x) := e^{\sin(x)}$ is $1 + x + \frac{x^2}{2!} - \frac{3x^4}{4!} - \frac{8x^5}{5!} - \frac{3x^6}{6!} + \frac{56x^7}{7!} + ...$ A formula for the coefficients is not readily apparent. Nonetheless, the Taylor series is still correct, albeit a bit harder to deal with algebraically.

The same shortcuts we used to get Taylor polynomials for functions related to one of these functions can be used to derive Taylor series. For example, the Taylor series for $\sin(2x)$ can be obtained by replacing x by $2x$ in the Taylor series for $\sin(x)$ obtaining $\sum\limits_{j=0}^{\infty} (-1)^j \frac{(2x)^{2j+1}}{(2j+1)!}$.

---

2. Determine the Taylor series for:

(a) $f(x) := e^{2x}$ (b) $g(x) := \ln(1-x)$ (c) $f(x) := \sin(x^2)$

REMAINDERS

One way to determine whether the Taylor series derived from a function f actually converges to f (at any x-value for which the series converges) is to look at the **remainders**. Let $p_n(x)$ be the value of the nth degree Taylor polynomial for f and let $r_n(x) := f(x) - p_n(x)$ be the remainder --that is, the difference between the function value and the Taylor polynomial. The sequence of Taylor polynomials may converge for some values of x and diverge for others. Let $p(x) := \lim_{n \to \infty} p_n(x)$, for any x for which the limit exists. In other words, $p(x)$ is the number which the sequence of numbers $\{p_1(x), p_2(x), p_3(x),...\}$ approaches if, in fact, such a number exists. We'll say that $p(x)$ is the value of the Taylor series; that is, $p(x) = \sum_{j=0}^{\infty} a_j x^j$. By definition, the Taylor series derived from f will converge to f if and only if $f(x) = p(x)$ for all x for which $p(x)$ exists. This will happen if and only if the remainders approach 0 as n increases. More formally,

$$f(x) = p(x) \text{ if and only if } \lim_{n \to \infty} r_n(x) = 0.$$

For example, let $f(x) := e^x$. We have seen that the third-degree Taylor polynomial for f is $p_3(x) := 1 + x + \frac{1}{2}x^2 + \frac{1}{6}x^3$. So, $r_3(2) = e^2 - p_3(2) = 7.389 - 6.333 = 1.056$. The table below gives the remainders incurred by using Taylor polynomials of degree 1, 2, 3 and 4 to approximate e^x, at several different values of x.

x	$r_1(x)$	$r_2(x)$	$r_3(x)$	$r_4(x)$
-2	1.135	-.865	.468	-.198
-1.5	.723	-.402	.161	-.050
-1	.368	-.132	.035	-.007
-.5	.107	-.018	.002	-.0002
0	0	0	0	0
.5	.149	.024	.003	.0003
1	.718	.218	.052	.001
1.5	1.981	.857	.294	.083
2	4.389	2.389	1.056	.389

Note that at $x = 0$, all the remainders are 0 (why?). For each polynomial, the remainders increase in absolute value as we move away from $x = 0$. For each x-value, the remainders decrease in absolute value as the degree of the polynomial increases. All of this suggests that the Taylor series created from $f(x) := e^x$ does converge to e^x, at least for x near 0.

¤ At this point, you may be thinking something fishy is going on here. In order to compute the remainders, we need to know the function values. But the reason for computing the Taylor polynomials is to approximate the function values, presuming they are unknown or not easily calculated. We seem to be going in circles.

What we need is a way of *predicting* what the remainder will be (or, more precisely, how big it could *possibly* be) if we use the nth degree Taylor polynomial to approximate $f(x)$ without actually calculating the remainders themselves. The following theorem, called **Taylor's Theorem** (surprise!) gives us one method for estimating the magnitude of $r_n(x)$.

THEOREM 11.3: Suppose f and its first $n + 1$ derivatives are continuous on some interval I containing 0. Let $p_n(x) := \displaystyle\sum_{k=0}^{n} \frac{f^{(k)}(0)}{k!} x^k$ be the nth degree Taylor polynomial and let $r_n(x) = f(x) - p_n(x)$ be the remainder. Then, for every x on I, there exists some z between 0 and x such that

$$r_n(x) := \frac{f^{(n+1)}(z)}{(n+1)!} x^{n+1}.$$

Note: The form in which the remainder is expressed in this theorem is due to the 18th century French mathematician Joseph Louis Lagrange. It is not the only form in which the remainder can be expressed.

Admittedly, this theorem is hard to understand and even harder to use. It is a classic example of what are called "existence theorems" in mathematics. We won't prove it here (but its proof uses the Mean Value Theorem). However, we can illustrate it by looking at the special case where $n = 1$. Figure 11.6 shows the graph of $f(x)$ and its first-degree Taylor polynomial $p_1(x)$ in the vicinity of $c = 0$. For some x_0, the remainder $r_1(x_0)$ is also indicated. Theorem 11.3 says that there is some z between 0 and x_0 such that $r_1(x_0) = \dfrac{f''(z)}{2} x_0^2$. Unfortunately, it doesn't tell us how to find z, except that it is somewhere on the interval $[0, x_0]$.

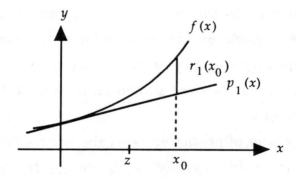

Fig. 11.6

Rather than try to compute the remainder exactly, we shall settle for determining an upper bound; that is, some number which is surely bigger than the absolute value of the remainder. Suppose that there is some number B_n such that $|f^{(n+1)}(x)| \le B_n$ for all x in I. Then, $|f^{(n+1)}(z)| \le B_n$ and we have the following:

COROLLARY: If there is some number B_n such that $|f^{(n+1)}(x)| \le B_n$ for all x in some interval I, then $|r_n(x)| \le \dfrac{B_n}{(n+1)!} |x|^{n+1}$.

To illustrate this corollary, suppose we estimate $f(x) := e^x$ for $-1 \le x \le 1$ by its fourth degree Taylor polynomial $p_4(x) := 1 + x + \dfrac{x^2}{2} + \dfrac{x^3}{6} + \dfrac{x^4}{24}$. The remainder is $r_4(x) := e^x - p_4(x) = e^x - (1 + x + \dfrac{x^2}{2} + \dfrac{x^3}{6} + \dfrac{x^4}{24})$. The corollary says to find a number B_4 such that $|f^{(5)}(x)| \le B_4$, for all x. Here, $f^{(5)}(x) := e^x$ which is less than or equal to 3 if $-1 \le x \le 1$. (It is actually less than e on that interval, but we're only interested in rough estimates, so 3 is close enough.) Thus, $|r_4(x)| \le \dfrac{3}{5!}|x|^5$.

The graph in Figure 11.7 shows $y = |r_4(x)|$ and $y = \dfrac{3}{5!}|x|^5 = \dfrac{|x|^5}{40}$. Notice that, wherever we can see a difference, $|r_4(x)| \le \dfrac{|x|^5}{40}$.

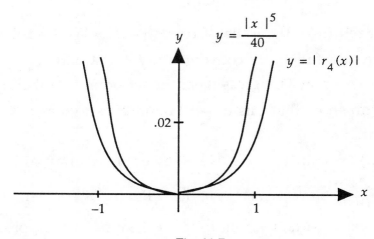

Fig. 11.7

If we wanted to use this polynomial to estimate $e = f(1)$, the corollary says the absolute value of the remainder $|r_4(1)| \le \dfrac{3}{5!} = .025$. This agrees with our table of values which lists the actual remainder (assuming we could compute the function itself) as .001.

EXAMPLE 11.7:

What is the maximum possible error incurred when using the third degree Taylor polynomial to estimate sin(1)?

The third degree Taylor polynomial for the function $f(x) := \sin(x)$ is

$p_3(x) := x - \dfrac{x^3}{6}$. The fourth derivative of f is $f^{(4)}(x) = \sin(x)$ which is always less than or equal to 1 in absolute value. Hence, take $B_3 = 1$. Thus, $|r_3(x)| \le \dfrac{1}{4!}|x|^4$.

So, if we use this polynomial to estimate $\sin(1)$, the remainder should be less than $\dfrac{1}{24}$. In fact, $\sin(1) = .841471$ and $p_3(1) = .833333$, so $r_3(1) = .008137$ which is considerably less than $\dfrac{1}{24} = .0416667$.

More generally, note that all the derivatives of $\sin(x)$ are either $\pm \sin(x)$ or $\pm \cos(x)$ and, hence, less than or equal to 1 in absolute value. Thus, we can set $B_n = 1$ for all n. Therefore, $|r_n(x)| \le \dfrac{|x|^{n+1}}{(n+1)!}$ from which $|r_n(1)| \le \dfrac{1}{(n+1)!}$. $\blacklozenge$

◻ Now we can return to the issue of convergence. We said that the Taylor series derived from a function f converges to f if and only if $\lim\limits_{n \to \infty} r_n(x) = 0$. The corollary to Theorem 11.3 gives us an upper bound on the absolute value of $r_n(x)$. If we can show that this upper bound goes to 0 as n approaches ∞, then we are done.

Suppose $f(x) := \sin(x)$. As we showed in Example 11.7, we have $|r_n(x)| \le \dfrac{|x|^{n+1}}{(n+1)!}$. Since $|r_n(x)| \ge 0$, then $\lim\limits_{n \to \infty} r_n(x) = 0$ if $\lim\limits_{n \to \infty} \dfrac{|x|^{n+1}}{(n+1)!} = 0$ for all x. This is certainly true if $|x| < 1$ since $|x|^n$ approaches 0 as n increases and $(n+1)!$ grows without bound as n increases. Thus, the numerator gets smaller and the denominator gets bigger so the ratio goes to 0. If $|x| = 1$, then the numerator is always 1, but the denominator gets bigger, so the ratio goes to 0. It is a bit harder to show that $\lim\limits_{n \to \infty} \dfrac{|x|^{n+1}}{(n+1)!} = 0$ even if $|x| > 1$ since, now, both the numerator and denominator increase without bound as n increases. Let's try a specific case, say $x = 2$. The sequence $\left\{ \dfrac{2^{n+1}}{(n+1)!} \right\} = \left\{ 2, \dfrac{4}{3}, \dfrac{2}{3}, \dfrac{4}{15}, \dfrac{4}{45}, ... \right\}$ which appears to approach 0. This is not a proof that this works for every x, but at least it is evidence. For more evidence, you might try another x-value, say $x = 5$ or $x = 10$.

We shall show in Section 11.4 that the Taylor series $\sum\limits_{j=0}^{\infty} (-1)^j \dfrac{x^{2j+1}}{(2j+1)!}$ created from $\sin(x)$ converges for all x. Given that fact and what we've just asserted about the remainders, we can now say that $\sin(x) = \sum\limits_{j=0}^{\infty} (-1)^j \dfrac{x^{2j+1}}{(2j+1)!}$ for all x.

¤ We can also use the corollary to Theorem 11.3 to tell us what degree Taylor polynomial we'd need to estimate $f(c)$ to some specified accuracy. For example, suppose we wanted to estimate e within .005 of its actual value. Let $f(x) := e^x$ so we want to find the smallest n for which $|r_n(1)| \leq .005$. Since $f^{(n)}(x) := e^x$, for all n, and $e^x \leq 3$ for $-1 \leq x \leq 1$, then we can take B_n = 3 for all n. Thus, $|r_n(x)| \leq \dfrac{3\,|x|^{n+1}}{(n+1)!}$. In particular, $|r_n(1)| \leq \dfrac{3}{(n+1)!}$. To make $\dfrac{3}{(n+1)!} \leq .005$, we need to have $(n+1)! \geq \dfrac{3}{.005} = 6000$ which happens if $n \geq 7$. (We found this by trial and error.) So, at least in principle, we need to use the 7th degree polynomial to ensure the desired accuracy. (In practice, we may be able to get away with a lower degree polynomial since the bounds given by the corollary are usually quite liberal in the sense that the actual remainder is often much less than the one predicted by the corollary. There is, however, no way of knowing how much lower we can go.)

TEST YOUR UNDERSTANDING

3. For the example above, what degree polynomial would we need to compute e with an accuracy of .0001?

4. What degree polynomial would we need to estimate e^2 with an accuracy of .0001? (Assume $e^2 < 8$.)

EXERCISES FOR SECTION 11.2:

1. Write the Taylor series for each of the following functions:

   (a) $f(x) := e^{-x}$ (b) $f(x) := \sin(3x)$ (c) $f(x) := \ln(1 + x^2)$

   (d) $g(x) := \sqrt{1 + x}$ (e) $g(x) = \sinh(x) := \dfrac{e^x - e^{-x}}{2}$ (f) $f(x) := e^{-2x} + e^{3x}$

2. (a) Differentiate the power series for $f(x) := \ln(1 + x)$ from Example 11.6
   to obtain a power series for $g(x) = f'(x) := \dfrac{1}{1+x}$.

   (b) Use your answer to (a) to show that $\dfrac{2}{3} = 1 - \dfrac{1}{2} + \dfrac{1}{4} - \dfrac{1}{8} + \dfrac{1}{16} - \dfrac{1}{32} + \dots$,
   assuming the series on the right actually converges.

3. Use the fact that $\dfrac{x}{1 + 3x + 2x^2} = \dfrac{1}{1 + x} - \dfrac{1}{1 + 2x}$ and the result of Exercise
   2(a) to write a Taylor series for $f(x) := \dfrac{x}{1 + 3x + 2x^2}$.

4. Use Taylor's theorem to approximate the error incurred by using the
   third degree polynomial for the function in Exercise 1(d) to estimate $\sqrt{1.5}$.

5. Suppose f has the property that $|f^{(4)}(x)| \le 2$ for all x. What is the
   maximum possible error incurred when using the third degree Taylor
   polynomial for f to estimate $f(.5)$?

6. Suppose we could show that for some function f, the remainder incurred
   by using an nth degree Taylor polynomial satisfies the condition $|r_n(x)|$
   $\le \dfrac{1}{n(n+1)} |x|^{n+1}$. How large must n be to estimate $f(.5)$ with a
   remainder less than .001?

PROBLEMS FOR SECTION 11.2:

1. Let $f(x) := \dfrac{1}{1 + x}$.

   (a) Show that the Taylor series for f is $1 - x + x^2 - \dots + x^n + \dots$.
       (cf. Exercise 2a)

   (b) Use (a) to show that the Taylor series for $g(x) := \dfrac{1}{1 + x^2}$ is
       $1 - x^2 + x^4 - \dots + x^{2n} + \dots$.

   (c) Integrate both sides of the result in (b) from 0 to 1 to show that
       $\dfrac{\pi}{4} \approx \left(1 - \dfrac{1}{3} + \dfrac{1}{5} - \dots + \dfrac{1}{2n + 1} + \dots\right)$, assuming everything converges.

2. (a) Determine the Taylor series for $f(x) := \dfrac{1}{\sqrt{1-x^2}}$. Hint: Begin by finding a Taylor series for $g(x) := \dfrac{1}{\sqrt{1+x}}$.

   (b) Use the result of (a) to find a Taylor series for $h(x) := \arcsin(x)$.

   (c) Use (b) to derive an infinite series expression for π, assuming everything converges.

   [Hint: Evaluate at $x = 1/2$.]

3. (a) Use the fact that $\dfrac{d}{dx}[\sin^2(x)] = 2\sin(x)\cos(x) = \sin(2x)$ to find the Taylor series for $f(x) := \sin^2(x)$.

   (b) Use (a) and a well-known identity to find the Taylor series for $g(x) := \cos^2(x)$.

4. Determine a Taylor series for $f(x) = \dfrac{\sin(x)}{x}$ and use it to conclude that $\displaystyle\lim_{x \to 0}\dfrac{\sin(x)}{x} = 1$. (This is a result we proved numerically in Chapter 7.)

5. (a) Determine the Taylor series for $f(x) := \ln(1-x)$.

   (b) Find the Taylor series for $g(x) := \ln\!\left(\dfrac{1+x}{1-x}\right)$.

   [Hint: $\ln\!\left(\dfrac{1+x}{1-x}\right) = \ln(1+x) - \ln(1-x)$.]

   (c) It can be shown by methods beyond the scope of this book that $\displaystyle\int_0^1 \dfrac{1}{x}\ln\!\left(\dfrac{1+x}{1-x}\right) dx = \dfrac{\pi^2}{4}$. Use this result and your answer to (b) to show

   that $1 + \dfrac{1}{9} + \dfrac{1}{25} + \dfrac{1}{49} + \dfrac{1}{81} + \cdots = \dfrac{\pi^2}{8}$, assuming everything converges.

6. In Chapter 3, we showed that, in the absence of air resistance, the height of an object which is dropped from initial height h is given by $y(t) := -\dfrac{1}{2}gt^2 + h$. In Chapter 8, we showed that if we took air resistance into account, the height is given by $y_r(t) := -\dfrac{g}{b^2}(bt + e^{-bt} - 1) + h$, where b is a measure of the friction. By writing a Taylor polynomial for $y_r(t)$, show that $y(t) \approx y_r(t)$, for small t.

7. (a) Determine the Taylor series for $f(x) := e^{-x^2}$ and use it to show that $\displaystyle\int_0^1 e^{-x^2}\,dx = \sum_{j=0}^{\infty}\dfrac{(-1)^j}{j!\,(2j+1)}$, assuming everything converges.

(b) Add the first 5 terms of the series to get an approximate value of
$$\int_0^1 e^{-x^2} dx .$$

8. Let $f(x) := e^x$ and let $g(x) := \begin{cases} e^x, -1 \le x \le 1 \\ x \quad elsewhere \end{cases}$.

(a) Show that f and g have the same Taylor series.

(b) The Taylor series in (a) converges at $x = 2$. Does it converge to $f(2)$ or $g(2)$?

TYU Answers for Section 11.2

1. $x - \dfrac{x^3}{3!} + \dfrac{x^5}{5!} - \dfrac{x^7}{7!} + ... = \displaystyle\sum_{j=0}^{\infty} (-1)^j \dfrac{x^{2j+1}}{(2j+1)!}$

2. (a) $\displaystyle\sum_{j=0}^{\infty} \dfrac{(2x)^j}{j!}$ (b) $-\displaystyle\sum_{j=1}^{\infty} \dfrac{x^j}{j}$ (c) $\displaystyle\sum_{j=0}^{\infty} \dfrac{(-1)^j x^{4j+2}}{(2j+1)!}$ 3. $n = 7$ 4. $n = 11$

11.3 INFINITE SERIES OF NUMBERS

In this section, we'll look at the question of convergence, which initially arose in the discussion of power series, in a more general setting. In the process, we'll clean up the loose ends of the last section. Recall that a power series is a polynomial with infinitely many terms; hence, evaluating a power series at some specific value of x involves adding up infinitely many numbers. For example, consider the power series $1 + x + x^2 + ... = \displaystyle\sum_{j=0}^{\infty} x^j$. Determining whether this converges at $x = 0.1$ involves computing the "sum" $1 + .1 + .01 + .001 + ...$.

One way to think about this calculation is as follows: Add the first two numbers, obtaining 1.1. Then add the third number to the sum of the first two, obtaining 1.11. Then add the fourth number to the sum of the first three, obtaining 1.111. Then add the fifth number to the sum of the first four, etc. Along the way, we get a sequence of **partial sums** {1.1, 1.11, 1.111,...}; the nth partial sum is the sum of the first n terms of the series. Here, it appears that the sequence of partial sums "settles down" after a while; in fact, it approaches the repeating decimal 1.111..., which is equivalent to the rational number 10/9. Hence, this power series converges to 10/9 when $x = 0.1$.

On the other hand, consider what happens when $x = 1$. Now, we get the "sum" $1 + 1 + 1 + ...$. The sequence of partial sums is $\{1, 2, 3,...\}$ which does not converge. Therefore, this power series diverges when $x = 1$. (Note that the partial sums obtained along the way are nothing more than values of the Taylor polynomials; e.g., $1.11 = p_2(.1)$, where $p_2(x) = 1 + x + x^2$ is the corresponding Taylor polynomial of degree 2.) More generally, the Taylor series converges at $x = c$ if the "sum" $1 + c + c^2 + ... = \sum\limits_{j=0}^{\infty} c^j$ is finite--that is, if the sequence $\{1, 1 + c, 1 + c + c^2, ...\}$ of partial sums converges.

So, we will consider the more general problem of determining when the sum of an infinite number of real numbers (which may or may not arise from a power series) converges. First, we need a few definitions:

DEFINITION: A **sequence** is a list of real numbers, $\{u_1, u_2, u_3,...\}$.

We often denote the sequence by $\{u_n\}$. We may have a formula that generates the terms in the sequence. For example, the sequence $\{1, 1/2, 1/3, 1/4,...\}$ is generated by the formula $u_n := 1/n$. In other cases, we may just have a list of numbers, such as $\{1, 3, -2, 7, 9, -11, 19, 14,...\}$, with no apparent underlying formula.

Note: We use the := sign when defining a sequence by a formula, much as we did for functions. Sequences can be thought of as a special type of function, one whose domain is the set of positive integers. We could write $u(n)$ rather than u_n.

DEFINITION: The summation $\sum\limits_{j=1}^{\infty} u_j = u_1 + u_2 + u_3 + ... +$ is called an **infinite series**.

Every sequence $\{u_n\}$ has a corresponding series $\sum_{j=1}^{\infty} u_j$. For example, if $\{u_n\}$ is the sequence $\{.3, .03, .003, .0003,...\}$, then the corresponding infinite series is $\sum_{j=1}^{\infty} u_j = .3 + .03 + .003 + .0003 + ... = .3333... = 1/3$; that is, the series converges to 1/3. On the other hand, if $\{u_n\}$ is the sequence $\{1, 1, 1,...\}$, then $\sum_{j=1}^{\infty} u_j = 1 + 1 + 1 + 1 +...$ which clearly diverges.

It is possible to talk about the **convergence of a sequence**. We say that a sequence $\{u_n\}$ converges if $\lim_{n \to \infty} u_n$ exists. In both examples above, the sequence converges; in the first case, $\lim_{n \to \infty} u_n = 0$, in the second case, $\lim_{n \to \infty} u_n = 1$. However, the series corresponding to the first sequence converges, while the series corresponding to the second sequence diverges. It is important not to confuse the convergence of a sequence with the convergence of its corresponding infinite series. A sequence converges if the terms themselves "settle down" after a while; the corresponding infinite series converges if the *sum* of the terms is finite.

TEST YOUR UNDERSTANDING

1. Let $u_n = n^2 + 1$. Write the first 4 terms of the sequence. Does $\{u_n\}$ converge? Do you think the corresponding infinite series will converge?

2. Repeat TYU #1 for the sequence $u_n = \dfrac{n}{n+1}$.

◻ We are now prepared to state precisely what we mean by the convergence of an infinite series.

DEFINITION: Let $\{u_n\}$ be a sequence of real numbers. Define the sequence of partial sums by $s_1 = u_1, s_2 = u_1 + u_2, s_3 = u_1 + u_2 + u_3$, etc. In general, $s_n = \sum_{j=1}^{n} u_j$. Then, the infinite series $\sum_{j=1}^{\infty} u_j$ converges if $\lim_{n \to \infty} s_n$ exists. If $\lim_{n \to \infty} s_n = L$, we say $\sum_{j=1}^{\infty} u_j = L$; if $\lim_{n \to \infty} s_n$ does not exist, then we say $\sum_{j=1}^{\infty} u_j$ diverges.

In other words, the infinite series $\sum_{j=1}^{\infty} u_j$ converges if and only if the corresponding sequence of partial sums approaches a (finite) limit. This agrees with our previous notion about convergence. For instance, if $\{u_n\} = \{.3, .03, .003, .0003, \ldots\}$, then $\{s_n\} = \{.3, .33, .333, .3333, \ldots\}$ which converges to $1/3$. On the other hand, if $\{u_n\} = \{1, 1, 1, \ldots\}$, then $\{s_n\} = \{1, 2, 3, 4, \ldots\}$ which diverges.

TEST YOUR UNDERSTANDING

3. Let $\{u_n\} = \{1, 4, -2, 7, 3, -1, \ldots\}$. Compute the first 5 partial sums of $\{u_n\}$.

4. Let $u_n = 1/n$. Compute the first 3 partial sums of $\{u_n\}$.

We can use this definition to actually determine whether a sequence converges in one of two ways. The first is to try to come up with a formula for s_n in terms of n and then evaluate $\lim_{n \to \infty} s_n$ analytically. For example, let $u_n = \dfrac{1}{n(n+1)}$. The terms of $\{u_n\}$ are $\left\{\dfrac{1}{2}, \dfrac{1}{6}, \dfrac{1}{12}, \dfrac{1}{20}, \ldots\right\}$. The corresponding partial sums are $s_1 = \dfrac{1}{2}$, $s_2 = \dfrac{1}{2} + \dfrac{1}{6} = \dfrac{2}{3}$, $s_3 = \dfrac{1}{2} + \dfrac{1}{6} + \dfrac{1}{12} = \dfrac{3}{4}$, etc. After a bit of thought, we might surmise that $s_n = \dfrac{n}{n+1}$. (In the Problems, we'll ask you to prove this.) Then $\lim_{n \to \infty} s_n = 1$, so the infinite series $\displaystyle\sum_{n=1}^{\infty} \dfrac{1}{n(n+1)}$ converges to 1.

Another approach is to compute some terms of $\{s_n\}$ and determine whether $\lim_{n \to \infty} s_n$ exists based on numerical evidence. For example, suppose $u_n = \dfrac{1}{n^3}$. The first few partial sums are $s_1 = 1$, $s_2 = 1 + \dfrac{1}{8} = 1.125$, $s_3 = 1 + \dfrac{1}{8} + \dfrac{1}{27} = 1.162, \ldots$, $s_{10} = 1.198, \ldots$, $s_{20} = 1.201, \ldots$, $s_{30} = 1.202$, etc. It appears that the series is converging to a number near 1.202.

There are problems with both these approaches. Consider the sequence $u_n = \dfrac{1}{n}$. As we saw in TYU #4, the first few partial sums are $s_1 = 1$, $s_2 = 1 + \dfrac{1}{2} = \dfrac{3}{2}$, $s_3 = 1 + \dfrac{1}{2} + \dfrac{1}{3} = \dfrac{11}{6}$, $s_4 = 1 + \dfrac{1}{2} + \dfrac{1}{3} + \dfrac{1}{4} = \dfrac{25}{12}$, etc. There is no "obvious" formula for s_n in terms of n and, hence, it will be impossible to determine whether this series converges by analytically evaluating $\lim_{n \to \infty} s_n$. On the other hand, using a computer, we can show that $s_{10} = 2.928968$, $s_{100} = 5.187378$, $s_{1000} = 7.485478$, $s_{10000} = 9.787613$, and $s_{100000} = 12.09085$. The partial sums do not appear to be settling but we really can't be sure what's happening.

What we need are methods for determining whether an infinite series converges that circumvent the use of the definition (much like we developed rules for finding derivatives and evaluating definite integrals that avoided their definitions). Here's one such method.

The partial sums for $\{u_n\}$ are defined by $s_n = s_{n-1} + u_n$ or, equivalently, $s_n - s_{n-1} = u_n$. If the infinite series converges, then $\lim_{n \to \infty} s_n$ exists. But, $\lim_{n \to \infty} s_n = \lim_{n \to \infty} s_{n-1}$, so $\lim_{n \to \infty} s_n - \lim_{n \to \infty} s_{n-1} = 0$. Therefore, in order for the infinite series $\sum\limits_{n=1}^{\infty} u_n$ to converge, the terms of the sequence $\{u_n\}$ must approach 0. Equivalently, if the terms of the sequence $\{u_n\}$ do not approach 0, then the infinite series $\sum\limits_{n=1}^{\infty} u_n$ diverges. We state this as:

THEOREM 11.3 (DIVERGENCE TEST): If $\lim\limits_{n \to \infty} u_n \neq 0$, then $\sum\limits_{n=1}^{\infty} u_n$ must diverge.

Please do not misunderstand this theorem. It does <u>not</u> say that if terms of the sequence approach 0, then the series converges. This is <u>absolutely incorrect</u>. While it is true that if the terms of the sequence do not approach 0 then the series diverges, the converse is false. The fact that the terms of the sequence approach 0 <u>does not guarantee convergence</u> of the series. Indeed, consider the series $\sum\limits_{n=1}^{\infty} \frac{1}{n}$ which we have seen before. The terms of the sequence $\{\frac{1}{n}\}$ do approach 0 but the numerical evidence we gathered about the series $\sum\limits_{n=1}^{\infty} \frac{1}{n}$ is inconclusive. (We'll show later that this series diverges.) What matters is not just that the terms of the sequence approach 0, but that they approach 0 "fast enough" to make the series converge. We'll explore this in more detail later in this section.

TEST YOUR UNDERSTANDING

5. What does Theorem 11.3 tell you about each of the following series?

(a) $\sum\limits_{n=1}^{\infty} \dfrac{n+1}{2n}$ (b) $\sum\limits_{n=1}^{\infty} e^{-n}$

An approach that is sometimes useful for determining whether a given series converges is to compare the series to one about which we already know something. For instance, suppose $\{u_n\}$ and $\{v_n\}$ are sequences such that $0 \le u_n \le v_n$, for all n. Let $\{s_n\}$ be the sequence of partial sums for $\{u_n\}$ and $\{t_n\}$ be the partial sums for $\{v_n\}$. Since u_n and v_n are both positive for all n, then $\{s_n\}$ and $\{t_n\}$ are increasing sequences. Furthermore, since $v_n \ge u_n$ for all n, then $t_n \ge s_n$ for all n. Now suppose $\{t_n\}$ converges to a finite limit t. Then $\{s_n\}$ must also converge to a finite limit which is less than or equal to t. Conversely, if $\{s_n\}$ diverges, then $\{t_n\}$ must also diverge. Put differently, we have:

THEOREM 11.4 (COMPARISON TEST): Let $\{u_n\}$ and $\{v_n\}$ be sequences such that $0 \le u_n \le v_n$, for all n.

(a) If $\displaystyle\sum_{n=1}^{\infty} u_n$ diverges, then $\displaystyle\sum_{n=1}^{\infty} v_n$ must diverge.

(b) If $\displaystyle\sum_{n=1}^{\infty} v_n$ converges, then $\displaystyle\sum_{n=1}^{\infty} u_n$ must converge.

Note that if $\displaystyle\sum_{n=1}^{\infty} v_n$ diverges or if $\displaystyle\sum_{n=1}^{\infty} u_n$ converges, we cannot draw any conclusions.

EXAMPLE 11.8:

Given that $\displaystyle\sum_{n=1}^{\infty} \frac{1}{n^3}$ converges, what conclusions can we draw from Theorem 11.4 about (a) $\displaystyle\sum_{n=1}^{\infty} \frac{1}{n^4}$ (b) $\displaystyle\sum_{n=1}^{\infty} \frac{1}{n^2}$?

(a) Since $\dfrac{1}{n^4} < \dfrac{1}{n^3}$ for all n and $\displaystyle\sum_{n=1}^{\infty} \frac{1}{n^3}$ converges, then $\displaystyle\sum_{n=1}^{\infty} \frac{1}{n^4}$ must converge.

(b) Since $\frac{1}{n^2} > \frac{1}{n^3}$ for all n, we can't draw any conclusions about $\sum\limits_{n=1}^{\infty} \frac{1}{n^2}$ from this theorem despite the fact that $\sum\limits_{n=1}^{\infty} \frac{1}{n^3}$ converges. (We'll show later that $\sum\limits_{n=1}^{\infty} \frac{1}{n^2}$ indeed converges). ♦

TEST YOUR UNDERSTANDING

6. Given that $\sum\limits_{n=1}^{\infty} \frac{1}{n^2}$ converges, what does Theorem 11.4 tell you about:

(a) $\sum\limits_{n=1}^{\infty} \frac{1}{n^2+1}$ (b) $\sum\limits_{n=1}^{\infty} \frac{2^n}{n^2}$

We can actually relax the hypotheses of Theorem 11.4. It is not necessary that $u_n \le v_n$ for all n. The convergence of a series hinges on what happens "at the far end" and, thus, should be unaffected by the terms at the beginning. Hence, we really only need to have $u_n \le v_n$ for all $n > N$, where N is a positive integer. In other words, the first few (million) terms don't count. As an example, consider the series $\sum\limits_{n=1}^{\infty} \frac{\ln(n)}{n}$. Since $\ln(n) > 1$ when $n \ge 3$, then $\frac{\ln(n)}{n} > \frac{1}{n}$, for $n \ge 3$. Since $\sum\limits_{n=1}^{\infty} \frac{1}{n}$ diverges, then by Theorem 11.4, $\sum\limits_{n=1}^{\infty} \frac{\ln(n)}{n}$ diverges.

In order to effectively use Theorem 11.4, we need to build up a "database" of series whose convergence has been determined so that we compare a given series to them. That's the subject of the remainder of this section.

GEOMETRIC SERIES AND P-SERIES

A **geometric sequence** is one in which each term is a constant r times the preceding term. In other words, if $u_1 = a$, then $u_2 = ar, u_3 = ar^2, u_4 = ar^3$, etc. In general, $u_n = ar^{n-1}$. The corresponding series is:

$$S = \sum_{j=1}^{\infty} a r^{j-1} = a + ar + ar^2 + ar^3 + \dots .$$

If $r \geq 1$ or $r \leq -1$, then the terms of the sequence increase in absolute value (or remain the same) and, by Theorem 11.3, the corresponding series must diverge. Earlier in this section, we looked at the example $\{u_n\} = \{.3, .03, .003, \dots\}$, a geometric sequence with $a = .3$ and $r = .1$. The nth partial sum of the corresponding series is $s_n = .3 + .03 + .003 + \dots + .00\dots03$ (n digits) $=$ .333...3 (n threes) which converges to $\frac{1}{3}$. The question is: Under what conditions does a geometric series converge? It certainly must be true that, in order for the series to converge, the terms of the sequence must approach 0 (in absolute value). This happens if $-1 < r < 1$. However, the fact that the terms of the sequence approach 0 does not guarantee convergence of the series. So, what we really want to know is whether every geometric series with $-1 < r < 1$ converges.

Let's invoke the definition of convergence of a series. The nth partial sum for the geometric sequence is given by:

(6) $\qquad s_n = \sum_{j=1}^{n} a r^{j-1} = a + ar + ar^2 + ar^3 + \dots + ar^{n-1}.$

In order for us to determine whether the sequence of partial sums has a limit, we will need to express s_n in terms of n. Doing so in this case requires a little trick.

Multiply Eq.(6) by r, obtaining:

(7) $\qquad rs_n = ar + ar^2 + ar^3 + \dots + ar^n.$

Now subtract Eq.(7) from Eq.(6), noting that all but the first term on the right of (6) and the last term on the right of (7) cancel:

$$s_n - rs_n = a - ar^n = a(1 - r^n)$$

from which

(8) $\qquad s_n = \dfrac{a(1-r^n)}{1-r}$, if $r \neq 1$.

In order to determine whether $\lim\limits_{n \to \infty} s_n$ exists, consider several cases. If $r > 1$ or $r < -1$, then r^n gets infinitely large (in absolute value) as n increases without bound. Therefore, $\lim\limits_{n \to \infty} s_n$ does not exist. If $-1 < r < 1$, then $r^n \to 0$, as n increases. Therefore, $\lim\limits_{n \to \infty} s_n = \dfrac{a(1-0)}{1-r} = \dfrac{a}{1-r}$ and the series converges. If $r = -1$, then $\{u_n\} = \{a, -a, a, -a, ...\}$ and the corresponding sequence of partial sums is $\{s_n\} = \{a, 0, a, 0, ...\}$ which does not converge. Finally, if $r = 1$, then $\{u_n\} = \{a, a, a, a, ...\}$ and $\{s_n\} = \{a, 2a, 3a, 4a, ...\}$ which also does not converge. Putting this all together, we have:

THEOREM 11.5: The geometric series $\sum\limits_{j=1}^{\infty} ar^{j-1}$ converges to $\dfrac{a}{1-r}$ if and only if $-1 < r < 1$. Otherwise, it diverges.

For the sequence $\{u_n\} = \{.3, .03, .003, ...\}$, Theorem 11.5 tells us the corresponding series converges to $\dfrac{.3}{1-.1} = \dfrac{.3}{.9} = \dfrac{1}{3}$, as we expect.

TEST YOUR UNDERSTANDING

7. For each geometric sequence below, determine whether the corresponding series converges and, if so, to what does it converge?

   (a) $\{u_n\} = \{1, -1/2, 1/4, -1/8, ...\}$ (b) $\{u_n\} = \{2, 6, 18, 54, ...\}$

   (c) $u_n := 3(.2)^{n-1}$

◻ Now consider the series $\sum_{n=1}^{\infty} \dfrac{1}{n^p}$, where p is a positive number. A series of this type is called a **p-series**. We have surmised that if $p = 3$, the series converges while if $p = 1$, the series diverges. Our conclusions at the time were based on numerical evidence. Now we would like to prove these results and make a general statement about the convergence of p-series.

Consider the case $p = 1$--that is, the series $\sum_{n=1}^{\infty} \dfrac{1}{n} = 1 + \dfrac{1}{2} + \dfrac{1}{3} + \dfrac{1}{4} + \dots$. This special case of the p-series is known as the **harmonic series**.

Let's write out a bunch of terms in the series and group them in a special way:

$$\sum_{n=1}^{\infty} \frac{1}{n} = 1 + \frac{1}{2} + \left(\frac{1}{3} + \frac{1}{4}\right) + \left(\frac{1}{5} + \frac{1}{6} + \frac{1}{7} + \frac{1}{8}\right) + \left(\frac{1}{9} + \dots + \frac{1}{16}\right) + \left(\frac{1}{17} + \dots + \frac{1}{32}\right) + \dots .$$

Since $\dfrac{1}{3} > \dfrac{1}{4}$, then $\dfrac{1}{3} + \dfrac{1}{4} > \dfrac{1}{4} + \dfrac{1}{4} = \dfrac{1}{2}$. Since $\dfrac{1}{5} > \dfrac{1}{6} > \dfrac{1}{7} > \dfrac{1}{8}$, then $\dfrac{1}{5} + \dfrac{1}{6} + \dfrac{1}{7} + \dfrac{1}{8} >$ $\dfrac{1}{8} + \dfrac{1}{8} + \dfrac{1}{8} + \dfrac{1}{8} = \dfrac{1}{2}$. Similarly, $\dfrac{1}{9} + \dots + \dfrac{1}{16} > \dfrac{1}{2}$, $\dfrac{1}{17} + \dots + \dfrac{1}{32} > \dfrac{1}{2}$, etc. Therefore,

(9) $$\sum_{n=1}^{\infty} \frac{1}{n} > 1 + \frac{1}{2} + \frac{1}{2} + \frac{1}{2} + \dots .$$

The right hand side of (9) clearly increases without bound. Hence, the harmonic series must diverge.

Now consider the case $p = 2$--that is, the series $\sum_{n=1}^{\infty} \dfrac{1}{n^2} = 1 + \dfrac{1}{4} + \dfrac{1}{9} + \dots$. Again, we'll group the terms in a special way:

$$\sum_{n=1}^{\infty} \frac{1}{n^2} = 1 + \left(\frac{1}{4} + \frac{1}{9}\right) + \left(\frac{1}{16} + \frac{1}{25} + \frac{1}{36} + \frac{1}{49}\right) + \left(\frac{1}{64} + \dots + \frac{1}{225}\right) + \dots$$

Certainly, $\frac{1}{4} + \frac{1}{9} < \frac{1}{4} + \frac{1}{4} = \frac{1}{2}$.   Similarly, $\frac{1}{16} + \frac{1}{25} + \frac{1}{36} + \frac{1}{49} < \frac{4}{16} = \frac{1}{4}$, and

$\frac{1}{64} + \ldots + \frac{1}{225} < \frac{8}{64} = \frac{1}{8}$.

So,

(10) $$\sum_{n=1}^{\infty} \frac{1}{n^2} < 1 + \frac{1}{2} + \frac{1}{4} + \frac{1}{8} + \ldots.$$

But the expression on the right of Eq.(10) is a geometric series with $a = 1$ and

$r = \frac{1}{2}$ and, by Theorem 11.5, converges to 2. Hence, $\sum_{n=1}^{\infty} \frac{1}{n^2}$ must converge

to a number less than 2. (It can be shown that this series converges to

$\frac{\pi^2}{6} \approx 1.645$.)

We can now use arguments similar to those in Example 11.8 to claim that p-series converge if $p \geq 2$ and diverge if $p \leq 1$. We still don't know what happens for p between 1 and 2 although it turns out that those p-series converge also. We'll prove this in Section 11.5. For now, we'll accept it and state:

THEOREM 11.6: The p-series $\sum_{n=1}^{\infty} \frac{1}{n^p}$ diverges if $p \leq 1$ and converges if

$p > 1$.

TEST YOUR UNDERSTANDING

8. Determine whether each of the following p-series converges or diverges.

(a) $\sum_{n=1}^{\infty} \frac{1}{n^{5/2}}$ (b) $\sum_{n=1}^{\infty} \frac{1}{\sqrt{n}}$ (c) $\sum_{n=1}^{\infty} \frac{1}{\sqrt[4]{n^3}}$

◻ Recall that in order for a series to converge, the terms of the sequence must go to 0 "fast enough". The reason p-series are important is that it allows us to give one interpretation to the phrase "fast enough". Theorem 11.6 tells us roughly that a series of decreasing positive numbers will converge if the terms of the sequence go to 0 faster than $\frac{1}{n}$.

It also seems plausible that if the terms in two different series approach 0 at the same rate, the series ought to behave the same way--that is, they should either both diverge or both converge. Let's give a precise interpretation to what we mean by a series "behaving like" another. When computing the limit of a sequence, essentially one of three things can happen. The sequence either approaches 0, or approaches some finite non-zero limit, or the limit does not exist. In particular, if $w_n = \frac{u_n}{v_n}$, then $\lim_{n \to \infty} w_n = 0$ if $\{v_n\}$ "grows faster" than $\{u_n\}$; $\lim_{n \to \infty} w_n = \infty$ if $\{u_n\}$ "grows faster" than $\{v_n\}$. If $\{u_n\}$ and $\{v_n\}$ "grow at the same rate", then $\lim_{n \to \infty} w_n = L$, where L is non-zero and finite. For example, if $\{u_n\}$ is defined by a 3rd degree polynomial and $\{v_n\}$ is defined by a 5th degree polynomial, then $\{v_n\}$ grows faster than $\{u_n\}$ and $\lim_{n \to \infty} w_n = 0$. On the other hand, if $\{u_n\}$ is defined by a 3rd degree polynomial and $\{v_n\}$ by a 2nd degree polynomial, then $\{u_n\}$ grows faster than $\{v_n\}$ and $\lim_{n \to \infty} w_n = \infty$. Finally, if both $\{u_n\}$ and $\{v_n\}$ are defined by 3rd degree polynomials, then $\{u_n\}$ and $\{v_n\}$ grow at the same rate and $\lim_{n \to \infty} w_n = L \neq 0$.

It is this last case which exemplifies what we mean by "behaving alike". Thus, we have the following:

THEOREM 11.7 (LIMIT COMPARISON TEST): Let $\{u_n\}$ and $\{v_n\}$ be sequences of positive terms such that $\lim_{n \to \infty} \frac{u_n}{v_n} = L$, where L is a (finite), *non-zero* number. Then the infinite series $\sum_{n=1}^{\infty} u_n$ and $\sum_{n=1}^{\infty} v_n$ either both converge or both diverge.

Note that the reason we take the limit as n approaches infinity is that, as we said earlier, the first few (million) terms don't count; the interesting behavior occurs at the far end.

EXAMPLE 11.9:

Use Theorem 11.7 to determine whether the series $\displaystyle\sum_{n=1}^{\infty} \frac{\sqrt{n}}{n^2+4}$ converges.

Let $u_n := \dfrac{\sqrt{n}}{n^2+4}$. Since, for large n, the 4 in the denominator is negligible, then we think this sequence might grow at the same rate as $v_n :=$ $\dfrac{\sqrt{n}}{n^2} = \dfrac{1}{n^{3/2}}$. To check, note that $\displaystyle\lim_{n \to \infty} \frac{u_n}{v_n} = \lim_{n \to \infty} \frac{\sqrt{n}/(n^2+4)}{1/n^{3/2}} = \lim_{n \to \infty} \frac{n^2}{n^2+4}$

$= 1$. Hence, $\displaystyle\sum_{n=1}^{\infty} \frac{\sqrt{n}}{n^2+4}$ behaves in the same way as $\displaystyle\sum_{n=1}^{\infty} \frac{1}{n^{3/2}}$. Since $\displaystyle\sum_{n=1}^{\infty} \frac{1}{n^{3/2}}$

converges by Theorem 11.5, then $\displaystyle\sum_{n=1}^{\infty} \frac{\sqrt{n}}{n^2+4}$ must also converge. ◆

TEST YOUR UNDERSTANDING

9. Use Theorem 11.7 to determine the convergence of:

(a) $\displaystyle\sum_{n=1}^{\infty} \frac{n^2}{n^4+9n^2+5}$ (b) $\displaystyle\sum_{n=1}^{\infty} \frac{1}{n+6}$ (c) $\displaystyle\sum_{n=1}^{\infty} \frac{\sqrt{n}}{n+1}$

EXERCISES FOR SECTION 11.3:

1. Let $\{u_n\} = \{1, 3, 5, 7, \ldots\}$. Write a formula for the nth partial sum of $\{u_n\}$.

Does $\displaystyle\sum_{n=1}^{\infty} u_n$ converge?

2. Determine the sum $1 - 1/3 + 1/9 - 1/27 + \ldots$.

3. The nth partial sum for a sequence is given by $s_n = \dfrac{n^2 + n}{3n^2 + 2n + 1}$. Does the corresponding infinite series converge and, if so, to what number?

4. Repeat Exercise 3 if $s_n = \dfrac{n^3 + n}{3n^2 + 2n + 1}$.

5. Express the repeating decimal .68686868... as the quotient of positive integers.

6. Suppose that $\displaystyle\sum_{j=1}^{\infty} u_j = 3$. What is $\displaystyle\lim_{j \to \infty} u_j$?

7. For each series below, state whether it converges or diverges and explain how you know.

   (a) $\displaystyle\sum_{n=1}^{\infty} \frac{1}{n\sqrt{n}}$
   (b) $\displaystyle\sum_{n=1}^{\infty} \frac{n}{n^2 + 1}$
   (c) $\displaystyle\sum_{n=0}^{\infty} \frac{3^n}{4^n}$
   (d) $\displaystyle\sum_{n=1}^{\infty} (-1)^n \, n^2$

   (e) $\displaystyle\sum_{n=1}^{\infty} \frac{e^{-n^2}}{n^4}$
   (f) $\displaystyle\sum_{n=1}^{\infty} \frac{1}{1 + \sin(n)}$
   (g) $\displaystyle\sum_{n=1}^{\infty} \frac{\sin(n)}{n^2}$
   (h) $\displaystyle\sum_{n=1}^{\infty} \frac{2^n}{3^n + 1}$

8. Draw triangle $A_1 B_1 C_1$. Construct triangle $A_2 B_2 C_2$ by joining the midpoints of the sides of triangle $A_1 B_1 C_1$. Construct triangle $A_3 B_3 C_3$ by joining the midpoints of the sides of triangle $A_2 B_2 C_2$. Continue in this fashion indefinitely. What is the sum of the areas of all the triangles if the area of triangle $A_1 B_1 C_1$ is 10? (Hint: The area of each triangle is 1/4 the area of the triangle in which it is inscribed.)

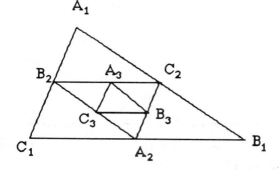

PROBLEMS FOR SECTION 11.3:

1. Consider the series $\displaystyle\sum_{j=1}^{\infty} \frac{1}{j(j+1)}$. Let $s_n = \displaystyle\sum_{j=1}^{n} \frac{1}{j(j+1)}$ be the corresponding partial sum.

(a) Show that $\dfrac{1}{j(j+1)} = \dfrac{1}{j} - \dfrac{1}{j+1}$.

(b) Use (a) to show that $s_2 = 1 - \dfrac{1}{3} = \dfrac{2}{3}, s_3 = 1 - \dfrac{1}{4} = \dfrac{3}{4}, s_4 = 1 - \dfrac{1}{5} = \dfrac{4}{5}$.

(c) Generalize to show $s_n = \dfrac{n}{n+1}$ and conclude that this series converges to 1.

(d) Using the fact that $\dfrac{1}{j(j+2)} = \dfrac{1}{2}\left(\dfrac{1}{j} - \dfrac{1}{j+2}\right)$, show that the partial sums of the series $\displaystyle\sum_{j=1}^{n} \dfrac{1}{j(j+2)}$ are given by $s_n = \dfrac{1}{2}\left(\dfrac{3}{2} - \dfrac{1}{n+1} - \dfrac{1}{n+2}\right)$. What can you conclude about the convergence of $\displaystyle\sum_{j=1}^{n} \dfrac{1}{j(j+2)}$?

2. Determine the sum $1 + 1/3 - 1/9 - 1/27 + 1/81 + 1/243 - 1/729 - \ldots$, where two positive terms alternate with two negative terms.

3. Consider the series $\displaystyle\sum_{n=2}^{\infty} \dfrac{1}{n \ln(n)}$.

(a) Show that $\dfrac{1}{n^2} < \dfrac{1}{n \ln(n)} < \dfrac{1}{n}$ for $n > 3$.

(b) Show that neither the comparison test nor the limit comparison test leads to any conclusion about the convergence of this series.

4. Assuming p_n and q_n are polynomials, state precisely under what conditions the series $\displaystyle\sum_{n=1}^{\infty} \dfrac{p_n}{q_n}$ converges.

TYU Answers for Section 11.3

1. {2, 5, 10, 17}, no, no   2. {1/2, 2/3, 3/4, 4/5}, yes it converges to 1, no

3. $\{s_n\}$ = {1, 5, 3, 10, 13,...}   4. $\{s_n\}$ = {1, 3/2, 11/6,...}

5. (a) $\displaystyle\lim_{n \to \infty} \dfrac{n+1}{2n} = \dfrac{1}{2}$, series diverges   (b) $\displaystyle\lim_{n \to \infty} e^{-n} = 0$, no conclusion

6. (a) series converges (b) no conclusion   7. (a) $r = -1/2$, series converges to 2/3

   (b) $r = 3$, series diverges (c) $r = .2$, series converges to 15/4

8. (a) converges (b) diverges (c) diverges   9. (a) converges (b) diverges (c) diverges

11.4 POWER SERIES REVISITED

We now return to the problem we first raised in Section 2: For what values of x does the power series $\sum\limits_{n=0}^{\infty} a_n x^n$ converge?

Let's begin by looking at a special case when $a_n = 1$ for all n--that is, the power series $\sum\limits_{n=0}^{\infty} x^n = 1 + x + x^2 + x^3 + \dots$. This is nothing more than a geometric series with first term $a = 1$ and common ratio $r = x$ and, by Theorem 11.5, converges if $|x| < 1$. The key idea of this section is that a series converges if the ratio between the absolute value of consecutive terms is eventually less than 1.

The more general power series $\sum\limits_{n=0}^{\infty} a_n x^n$ is, in some sense, a "modified geometric series". Of course, unless a_n is constant, the ratio between the absolute value of consecutive terms in the series will depend on n. The idea is the same, however: The series will converge if that ratio is ultimately less than 1. By "ultimately", we mean "as n increases without bound".

In fact, there is nothing special about power series, as far as this idea is concerned. We claim that any infinite series will converge if the ratio between the absolute value of consecutive terms is ultimately less than 1. We state this as:

THEOREM 11.8 (THE RATIO TEST): Let $\{u_n\}$ be a sequence and let $r = \lim\limits_{n \to \infty} \left| \dfrac{u_{n+1}}{u_n} \right|$.

(a) If $r < 1$, then $\sum\limits_{n=1}^{\infty} u_n$ converges.

(b) If $r > 1$, then $\sum\limits_{n=1}^{\infty} u_n$ diverges.

(c) If $r = 1$, then there is no conclusion.

Note that, unlike some of our previous tests, which apply only to series of positive terms, the ratio test applies to any series of real numbers.

EXAMPLE 11.10:

Use the ratio test to determine the convergence of $\displaystyle\sum_{n=1}^{\infty} \frac{1}{n!}$.

$$\frac{u_{n+1}}{u_n} = \frac{1/(n+1)!}{1/n!} = \frac{n!}{(n+1)!} = \frac{1}{n+1} \quad . \quad \text{Therefore,}$$

$$r = \lim_{n \to \infty}\left|\frac{u_{n+1}}{u_n}\right| = \lim_{n \to \infty}\frac{1}{n+1} = 0.$$

Since $r < 1$, the series must converge. ♦

EXAMPLE 11.11:

Use the ratio test to determine the convergence of $\displaystyle\sum_{n=1}^{\infty} \frac{1}{n}\left(\frac{3}{2}\right)^n$.

$$\frac{u_{n+1}}{u_n} = \frac{\frac{1}{n+1}\left(\frac{3}{2}\right)^{n+1}}{\frac{1}{n}\left(\frac{3}{2}\right)^n} = \frac{3}{2}\left(\frac{n}{n+1}\right) \quad . \quad \text{Therefore,}$$

$$r = \lim_{n \to \infty}\left|\frac{u_{n+1}}{u_n}\right| = \lim_{n \to \infty}\frac{3}{2}\left(\frac{n}{n+1}\right) = \frac{3}{2} \quad .$$

Since $r > 1$, the series diverges. ♦

EXAMPLE 11.12:

Use the ratio test to determine the convergence of $\displaystyle\sum_{n=1}^{\infty} \frac{1}{n^2}$.

$$\frac{u_{n+1}}{u_n} = \frac{1/(n+1)^2}{1/n^2} = \frac{n^2}{(n+1)^2} \quad . \quad \text{Therefore,}$$

$$r = \lim_{n \to \infty}\left|\frac{u_{n+1}}{u_n}\right| = \lim_{n \to \infty}\frac{n^2}{(n+1)^2} = 1.$$

Since $r = 1$, no conclusion can be drawn. (However, we do know from our earlier discussion of p-series that this series converges.) ♦

Note: Typically, if u_n is a quotient of polynomials, the ratio test leads to no conclusion.

TEST YOUR UNDERSTANDING

1. Use Theorem 11.8 to determine whether each of the following series converges or diverges:

(a) $\displaystyle\sum_{n=1}^{\infty} \frac{n}{3^n}$ 　　　　(b) $\displaystyle\sum_{n=1}^{\infty} \frac{2^n}{n!}$ 　　　(c) $\displaystyle\sum_{n=1}^{\infty} \frac{n}{n^2-2}$

¤ Now let's go back to power series. We showed that the geometric series $\displaystyle\sum_{n=0}^{\infty} x^n$ converges if $|x| < 1$--that is, for $-1 < x < 1$. Note that this is an interval centered at $x = 0$. Let's see what happens in general for power series of the form $\displaystyle\sum_{n=0}^{\infty} a_n x^n$. Invoking the Ratio Test, let $u_n := a_n x^n$ and let

$$r = \lim_{n \to \infty}\left|\frac{u_{n+1}}{u_n}\right| = \lim_{n \to \infty}\left|\frac{a_{n+1} x^{n+1}}{a_n x^n}\right| = \lim_{n \to \infty}\left|\frac{a_{n+1}}{a_n}\right| |x|.$$ We have three cases:

Suppose $\displaystyle\lim_{n \to \infty}\left|\frac{a_{n+1}}{a_n}\right| = L$, a finite, non-zero number. Then $r = L|x| < 1$, and the series converges, if and only if $|x| < \frac{1}{L}$ or, equivalently, $-\frac{1}{L} < x < \frac{1}{L}$. This is an interval centered at 0. If $L = 0$, then $r = 0$ for all x, in which case the series converges for all x. If L is not finite, then r can never be less than 1 for any $x \neq 0$; hence, the series converges only for $x = 0$. In all three cases, however, we can claim that the set of values for which the power series converges is an interval centered at $x = 0$. We state this as:

THEOREM 11.9: The power series $\displaystyle\sum_{n=0}^{\infty} a_n x^n$ converges either:

 (a) for all x 　　or (b) for $x = 0$ only 　　or (c) for $-R < x < R$, for some R.

In this third case, it is possible that the series will converge at $x = R$ or $x = -R$ or neither or both as well. These endpoints will have to be considered separately.

The set of values for which the series converges is called the **interval of convergence** for the power series. The number R is called the **radius of convergence**. If $R = \infty$, then we have (a). If $R = 0$, then we have (b). If $0 < R < \infty$, then we have (c).

This theorem tells us a lot about the interval of convergence for a series. For instance, it is not possible for the series to converge only for $-2 < x < 4$ or just for $x = 1, 2$ and 3. The set of values for which the series converges must be an interval centered at 0.

TEST YOUR UNDERSTANDING

2. A power series of the form $\displaystyle\sum_{n=0}^{\infty} a_n x^n$ is known to converge at $x = 3$. At which of the following x-values are we sure that the series must also converge? (There may be more than one correct answer.)

   (a) $x = 4$ (b) $x = 2$ (c) $x = -2$ (d) $x = -3$

Power series centered at an x-value other than 0 converge for all x in an interval symmetric about the center. Specifically, $\displaystyle\sum_{n=0}^{\infty} a_n (x - c)^n$ converges for $c - R < x < c + R$, an interval of length R centered at $x = c$.

EXAMPLE 11.13:

Determine the interval of convergence for the power series $\displaystyle\sum_{n=0}^{\infty} \frac{x^n}{n!}$.

Here we have $a_n = \dfrac{1}{n!}$ so that

$$r = \lim_{n \to \infty} \left| \frac{x^{n+1}/(n+1)!}{x^n/n!} \right| = \lim_{n \to \infty} \frac{n!}{(n+1)!} |x| = \lim_{n \to \infty} \frac{1}{n+1} |x| = 0.$$

Hence, $R = \infty$ and the series converges for all x.   ◆

Note that the series in Example 11.13 is the Taylor series for the function $f(x) := e^x$. However, as we said in Section 11.2, the fact that the Taylor series for e^x converges for all x does not mean it converges to e^x (although in this case it actually does).

EXAMPLE 11.14:

Determine the interval of convergence for the power series $\sum\limits_{n=0}^{\infty} n^2 x^n$.

Here, $r = \lim\limits_{n \to \infty} \left| \dfrac{(n+1)^2 x^{n+1}}{n^2 x^n} \right| = \lim\limits_{n \to \infty} \dfrac{(n+1)^2}{n^2} |x| = |x|$. Thus the series converges for when $|x| < 1$ (or, equivalently, $-1 < x < 1$) which implies the radius of convergence is $R = 1$.

Now we must check what happens for $x = 1$ and -1. When $x = 1$, the series becomes $\sum\limits_{n=0}^{\infty} n^2$ which clearly diverges (the terms don't go to 0). When $x = -1$, the series becomes $\sum\limits_{n=0}^{\infty} (-1)^n n^2$ which also diverges (for the same reason). Hence, the power series converges *only* for $-1 < x < 1$. ◆

EXAMPLE 11.15:

Determine the interval of convergence of $\sum\limits_{n=0}^{\infty} \dfrac{x^{2n}}{2^n}$.

This is not quite of the form covered by Theorem 11.9 because of the presence of the $2n$ in the exponent. However, the basic result that the series converges on an interval centered at 0 still holds. Again we use the ratio test.

Let $u_n = \dfrac{x^{2n}}{2^n}$. Then $\dfrac{u_{n+1}}{u_n} = \dfrac{x^{2(n+1)}/2^{n+1}}{x^{2n}/2^n} = \dfrac{x^2}{2}$. Thus, $r = \lim\limits_{n \to \infty} \dfrac{u_{n+1}}{u_n}$ $= \lim\limits_{n \to \infty} \dfrac{x^2}{2} = \dfrac{x^2}{2}$.

$|r| < 1$ whenever $x^2 < 2$ or, equivalently, $-\sqrt{2} < x < \sqrt{2}$.

Now, let's check the endpoints. When $x = \sqrt{2}$, the series becomes $\displaystyle\sum_{n=0}^{\infty} \frac{(\sqrt{2})^{2n}}{2^n} = \sum_{n=0}^{\infty} \frac{2^n}{2^n} = \sum_{n=0}^{\infty} 1$. When $x = -\sqrt{2}$, the series becomes $\displaystyle\sum_{n=0}^{\infty} \frac{(-\sqrt{2})^{2n}}{2^n} = \sum_{n=0}^{\infty} \frac{2^n}{2^n} = \sum_{n=0}^{\infty} 1$. Since $\displaystyle\sum_{n=0}^{\infty} 1 = 1 + 1 + 1 + \dots$ clearly diverges, then the power series diverges at both endpoints. Hence, the interval of convergence is $-\sqrt{2} < x < \sqrt{2}$. ◆

¤ Sometimes checking the endpoints requires some work. Consider the power series $\displaystyle\sum_{n=1}^{\infty} \frac{x^n}{n}$. Here, $r = \displaystyle\lim_{n \to \infty} \left| \frac{x^{n+1}/(n+1)}{x^n/n} \right| = \lim_{n \to \infty} \frac{n}{n+1} |x| = |x|$. As in Example 11.14, this implies that the series converges on the interval $-1 < x < 1$.

Now we must check what happens for $x = 1$ and -1. When $x = 1$, the series becomes $\displaystyle\sum_{n=1}^{\infty} \frac{1}{n}$ which diverges, as we saw in the last section. On the other hand, when $x = -1$, the series becomes $\displaystyle\sum_{n=1}^{\infty} \frac{(-1)^n}{n} = -1 + \frac{1}{2} - \frac{1}{3} + \frac{1}{4} - \dots$ about which we can draw no conclusions at this point. (The comparison tests apply only to sequences of positive terms and the ratio test will lead to no conclusion.)

Note that the signs of the terms in the series $\displaystyle\sum_{n=1}^{\infty} \frac{(-1)^n}{n}$ alternate (due to the presence of the $(-1)^n$ factor. Any series with this property is called an **alternating series** and a special test can sometimes be used to determine its convergence.

THEOREM 11.10 (ALTERNATING SERIES TEST): Let $\{u_n\}$ be a sequence of positive terms such that $\displaystyle\lim_{n \to \infty} u_n = 0$ and $u_{n+1} \le u_n$ for all n. Then the alternating series $\displaystyle\sum_{n=1}^{\infty} (-1)^n u_n$ and $\displaystyle\sum_{n=1}^{\infty} (-1)^{n+1} u_n$ converge.

In other words, the only conditions necessary for an alternating series to converge are that the absolute value of the terms be non-increasing and approach 0 as $n \to \infty$.

The alternating series $\sum_{n=1}^{\infty} \frac{(-1)^n}{n}$ satisfies these conditions and, hence, converges. Therefore, the power series $\sum_{n=1}^{\infty} \frac{x^n}{n}$ converges for $-1 \le x < 1$.

To see why the alternating series test works, look at the first few partial sums for the series $\sum_{n=1}^{\infty} \frac{(-1)^n}{n}$:

$s_1 = -1, s_2 = -1/2, s_3 = -5/6, s_4 = -7/12, s_5 = -47/60, s_6 = -37/60$. Note that the odd-numbered partial sums are increasing ($s_1 < s_3 < s_5 < ...$), while the even-numbered partial sums are decreasing ($s_2 > s_4 > s_6 > ...$). Furthermore, all of the odd-numbered sums are smaller than all of the even-numbered sums ($s_1 < s_3 < s_5 < ... < s_6 < s_4 < s_2$). Thus, $|s_{n+1} - s_n|$ approaches 0 as n increases. This means that the sequence of partial sums gets "squeezed" towards a limit as n approaches infinity, implying that the series converges. So, what we are saying here is that even though the harmonic series diverges, the alternating harmonic series converges. This often happens: A series of positive terms might diverge, but the series obtained by alternating the signs converges.

In general, if $\{u_n\}$ is a decreasing sequence that converges to 0, then it can be shown that the partial sums of the alternating series $\sum_{n=1}^{\infty} (-1)^n u_n$ will satisfy the inequality $s_1 < s_3 < s_5 < ... < s_6 < s_4 < s_2$, as we saw above with the alternating harmonic series.

If $\{u_n\}$ is a sequence of positive terms such that $\displaystyle\sum_{n=1}^{\infty} (-1)^n u_n$ converges but $\displaystyle\sum_{n=1}^{\infty} u_n$ diverges, then we say that $\displaystyle\sum_{n=1}^{\infty} (-1)^n u_n$ converges **conditionally**. If, on the other hand, $\displaystyle\sum_{n=1}^{\infty} u_n$ converges, we say that $\displaystyle\sum_{n=1}^{\infty} (-1)^n u_n$ converges **absolutely**. An absolutely convergent sequence must converge conditionally; however, a series (such as the alternating harmonic series) may converge conditionally, but not absolutely.

TEST YOUR UNDERSTANDING

3. Determine whether each of the following converges or diverges:

(a) $\displaystyle\sum_{n=1}^{\infty} \frac{(-1)^n}{n^2}$

(b) $\displaystyle\sum_{n=1}^{\infty} \frac{(-1)^n n^2}{n^2+1}$

4. Determine the interval of convergence of each of the following power series. Make sure to check the endpoints.

(a) $\displaystyle\sum_{n=1}^{\infty} \frac{x^n}{n^2}$

(b) $\displaystyle\sum_{n=1}^{\infty} \frac{(3x)^n}{n}$

(c) $\displaystyle\sum_{n=0}^{\infty} (4x)^n$

(d) $\displaystyle\sum_{n=0}^{\infty} n! \, x^n$

¤   The next theorem tells us that we can find the derivative of f by differentiating each term of the power series and, furthermore, the power series for $f'(x)$ has the same radius of convergence as the power series for $f(x)$.

THEOREM 11.11: If $f(x) := \sum\limits_{n=0}^{\infty} a_n x^n$, then $f'(x) := \sum\limits_{n=1}^{\infty} na_n x^{n-1}$.

Moreover, the power series for $f(x)$ and the power series for $f'(x)$ have the same radius of convergence.

NOTE: Although the two series have the same radius of convergence, they may not have exactly the same interval of convergence since they may behave differently at the endpoints.

EXAMPLE 11.16:

Starting the with the fact that $f(x) := \dfrac{1}{1-x} = 1 + x + x^2 + \ldots = \sum\limits_{n=0}^{\infty} x^n$,

find a power series representation for $f'(x) := \dfrac{1}{(1-x)^2}$.

We invoke Theorem 11.11 and differentiate the power series for $f(x)$

term by term, obtaining $\dfrac{1}{(1-x)^2} = 1 + 2x + 3x^2 + \ldots = \sum\limits_{n=1}^{\infty} nx^{n-1}$. Moreover,

since the power series for $f(x)$ converges for $-1 < x < 1$, then the power series for $f'(x)$ also converges for $-1 < x < 1$ and, possibly at $x = 1$ or $x = -1$ also. Convince yourself that neither of these values should be included in the interval of convergence. $\qquad\qquad\blacklozenge$

A result similar to Theorem 11.11 holds for antiderivatives also; that is, given a power series for $f(x)$, we can get a power series for $\int f(x)\,dx$ by integrating term by term. The new power series will have the same radius of convergence as the series for $f(x)$.

EXAMPLE 11.17:

Derive a power series for $\ln(1-x)$.

Since $\dfrac{d}{dx}(\ln(1-x)) = \dfrac{-1}{1-x}$, then $\int \dfrac{1}{1-x}\,dx = -\ln(1-x) + c$. As in

Example 11.16, $\dfrac{1}{1-x} = 1 + x + x^2 + \ldots = \sum\limits_{n=0}^{\infty} x^n$.

Thus, $\int \frac{1}{1-x}\,dx \;=\; x + \frac{x^2}{2} + \frac{x^3}{3} + \ldots \;=\; -\ln(1-x) + c.$ Substituting $x = 0$

implies $c = 0$. Therefore, $\ln(1-x) = -x - \frac{x^2}{2} - \frac{x^3}{3} - \ldots = -\sum_{n=1}^{\infty} \frac{x^n}{n}$.

When $x = 1$, we get the harmonic series, which diverges. When $x = -1$, we get the alternating harmonic series, which converges. Thus, the power series for $\ln(1 - x)$ converges for $-1 \le x < 1$.

Note that if we substitute $x = -1$, we get (assuming the series converges to the function)

$$\ln(2) \;=\; 1 - \frac{1}{2} + \frac{1}{3} - \frac{1}{4} + \ldots \;.$$ ◆

A LAST LOOK AT DIFFERENTIAL EQUATIONS

Recall that we began this chapter by developing a method for approximating the solution to a differential equation by using a Taylor polynomial. We argued that, under certain conditions, the accuracy of the approximation improves as the degree of the polynomial increases. Another way of saying this is that we can represent (not approximate) the solution of the differential equation as a Taylor series.

Of course, this raises the issue of convergence. All our tests for convergence of power series require that the terms of the series be written in closed form--that is, we need to have the coefficients a_n expressed explicitly in terms of n. Unfortunately, for differential equations, this is rarely possible.

Consider, for example, the equation $y'' - xy = 0, y(0) = 1, y'(0) = 2$ from Example 11.2. We showed that the 6th degree Taylor polynomial for the solution is $p_6(x) := 1 + 2x + \frac{x^3}{6} + \frac{x^4}{6} + \frac{x^6}{180}$. We could continue the solution process and generate as many terms of the Taylor series as we like. The problem is that there appears to be no recognizable pattern to the coefficients. Hence, invoking the Ratio Test to determine the interval of convergence is impossible.

There are some theorems that can help us. For instance, consider the second-order differential equation $y'' + P(x)y' + Q(x)y = 0$, a generalization of the type of equation we solved in Chapter 7. (The coefficients of y and y' are not necessarily constants.) It can be shown that if P and Q have power series that converge for $-R < x < R$, then y has a power series that converges at least for $-R < x < R$. We won't prove this theorem; you'll have to take a course in differential equations to see the proof and other theorems like it. For example, consider the differential equation $y'' + \frac{1}{x+1}y' - y = 0$, subject to the initial conditions $y(0) = 1$, $y'(0) = 1$. The coefficient of y' is $P(x) := \frac{1}{x+1}$ which has a power series that converges for $-1 < x < 1$. Hence, the power series solution of the differential equation will converge at least for $-1 < x < 1$.

EXERCISES FOR SECTION 11.4:

1. For each series below, state whether it converges or diverges and explain how you know.

   (a) $\sum\limits_{n=1}^{\infty} \frac{3^n}{n!}$ (b) $\sum\limits_{n=1}^{\infty} \frac{n}{5^n}$ (c) $\sum\limits_{n=1}^{\infty} \cos(n\pi)$ (d) $\sum\limits_{n=1}^{\infty} \frac{(-1)^{n+1}}{\sqrt{n}}$

2. Determine the intervals on which each of the following power series converges. Make sure to check the endpoints.

   (a) $\sum\limits_{n=1}^{\infty} \frac{x^n}{n^3}$ (b) $\sum\limits_{n=1}^{\infty} (n+1)x^n$ (c) $\sum\limits_{n=1}^{\infty} \frac{x^n}{\sqrt{n}}$

   (d) $\sum\limits_{n=1}^{\infty} \left(\frac{x}{5}\right)^n$ (e) $\sum\limits_{n=1}^{\infty} (-1)^n \left(\frac{x}{9}\right)^{2n}$ (f) $\sum\limits_{n=1}^{\infty} \frac{2^n x^{n+1}}{n!}$

PROBLEMS FOR SECTION 11.4:

1. Find the Taylor series for $f(x) := xe^x$ about $x = 0$. Integrate term-by-term to show that $\sum\limits_{n=0}^{\infty} \frac{1}{n!(n+2)} = 1$.

2. Consider the differential equation $y' - y = e^x$, subject to $y(0) = 1$.

   (a) Derive the power series solution for this equation.

   (b) Use the ratio test to show that it converges for all x.

   (c) Show that $y = xe^x + e^x$ is a solution of the differential equation.

   (d) Derive the Taylor series for $y = xe^x + e^x$ and show that it is the same as your answer to (a).

3. Prove that the alternating p-series $\sum_{n=1}^{\infty} \frac{(-1)^n}{n^p}$ always converges if $p > 0$.

4. (a) Substitute $x = \frac{1}{2}$ in the result of Example 11.16 to show that

$$\sum_{n=0}^{\infty} \frac{n}{2^n} = 2.$$

(b) More generally, show that $\sum_{n=0}^{\infty} \frac{n}{q^n} = \frac{q}{(1-q)^2}$, where $-1 < q < 1$.

(c) Differentiate the result of Example 11.16 again and derive a value for

$$\sum_{n=0}^{\infty} \frac{n^2}{2^n}.$$

5. Show that $\sum_{n=0}^{\infty} a_n x^n$ and $\sum_{n=1}^{\infty} n a_n x^{n-1}$ have the same radius of convergence. [Note: This is part of the conclusion of Theorem 11.11. The other part, that the second series is actually the derivative of the first, is harder to prove.]

6. Is it possible for a series of positive terms to converge, while the series obtained by alternating signs diverges? Explain.

TYU Answers for Section 11.4

1. (a) converges (b) converges (c) no conclusion from ratio test, but series diverges

2. Converges at $x = 2$ and $x = -2$, cannot tell about the others.   3. (a) converges (b) diverges   4. (a) $-1 \leq x \leq 1$ (b) $-1/3 \leq x < 1/3$ (c) $-1/4 < x < 1/4$ (d) $x = 0$

11.5 INFINITE SERIES AND IMPROPER INTEGRALS

By definition, the infinite series $\sum_{j=1}^{\infty} u_j = \lim_{n \to \infty} \sum_{j=1}^{n} u_j$, if the limit exists. The expression on the right is reminiscent of the definiton of the definite integral in terms of Riemann sums that we studied in Chapter 6:

$$\int_a^b f(x)\, dx = \lim_{n \to \infty} \sum_{j=1}^{n} f(x_j)\, \Delta x, \text{ where } \Delta x = \frac{b-a}{n} \text{ and } x_j = a + j\Delta x, j = 1, 2, 3,\ldots, n.$$ This suggests a connection between infinite series and integration.

Suppose $\{u_n\}$ is a strictly decreasing sequence of positive numbers. Plot $\{u_n\}$ and draw rectangles, as shown in Figure 11.8 .

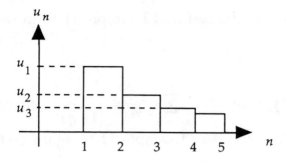

Fig. 11.8

Since the rectangles are all one unit wide, then u_j represents the area of the jth rectangle, $\displaystyle\sum_{j=1}^{n} u_j$ represents the total area of the first n rectangles, and by logical extension, $\displaystyle\sum_{j=1}^{\infty} u_j$ represents the total area enclosed by all of the rectangles.

Let f be any decreasing function such that $f(n) = u_n$ for all n; that is, f passes through the points on the graph of the sequence, as in Figure 11.9. If u_n is defined by a formula, then one way to construct f is to define it by the same formula that defines $\{u_n\}$; e.g., if $u_n := \frac{1}{n}$, then $f(x) = \frac{1}{x}$. (There are many other functions with the required properties but this one will serve our purposes.) The graph of $y = f(x)$, the x-axis and the line $x = 1$ enclose an infinitely long region.

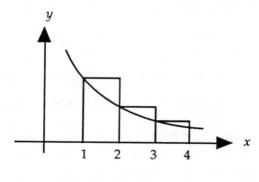

Fig 11.9

At first glance, we might think that the "area" of such a region must be infinite. By extending our definition of "area", we shall show that, in fact, this need not be the case--the area of an infinitely long region may be finite.

The area of this region can be represented by the definite integral $\int_1^\infty f(x)\,dx$. Note that this is slightly different from our usual definite integral since the upper limit is ∞, not a finite number. If we try to adapt the definition of the integral, we run into an immediate problem. The first step in that definition says to partition the interval of integration into a finite number of subintervals, each of finite length Δx. This is not possible if the interval of integration is infinitely long.

More generally, integrals of the form $\int_a^\infty f(x)\,dx$ or $\int_{-\infty}^b f(x)\,dx$ are said to be **improper** and require a special definition. Assume that f is bounded for $x \geq a$ and let $g(t) := \int_a^t f(x)\,dx$, which is well-defined and finite for any finite number $t > a$. The function $g(t)$ is analogous to the partial sum s_n for infinite series. Moreover, if $g(t)$ approaches a finite limit as t increases without bound, then this limit seems like a reasonable definition for $\int_a^\infty f(x)\,dx$. Thus, we have:

DEFINITION: $\displaystyle \int_a^\infty f(x)\,dx \;=\; \lim_{t\,\to\,\infty}\int_a^t f(x)\,dx \; .$

A similar definition holds for integrals of the form $\int_{-\infty}^b f(x)\,dx$.

If the limit exist, we say that the improper integral converges. Otherwise, it diverges. Note the similarity to the definition of infinite series: The infinite series $\displaystyle\sum_{j=1}^{\infty} u_j$ is defined by the limit of a sequence of partial sums $\displaystyle\sum_{j=1}^{n} u_j$; the improper integral $\int_a^\infty f(x)\,dx$ is defined by the limit of "partial integrals" $\int_a^t f(x)\,dx$.

EXAMPLE 11.18:

Determine the area bounded by $y = 0, x = 0$ and the graph of $y = e^{-x}$, as shown in Figure 11.10.

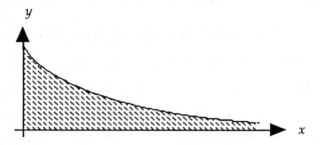

Fig. 11.10

The area can be found by evaluating the integral $\int_0^\infty e^{-x}\, dx$.

By definition, $\int_0^\infty e^{-x}\, dx = \lim_{t \to \infty} \int_0^t e^{-x}\, dx = \lim_{t \to \infty} -e^{-x}\Big|_{x=0}^{x=t} = \lim_{t \to \infty} \left(1 - e^{-t}\right) = 1$ since $e^{-t} \to 0$ as $t \to \infty$. In other words, the integral converges to 1, implying that the area of this region is a finite number 1, even though the region is infinitely long. ◆

EXAMPLE 11.19:

Evaluate $\int_1^\infty \frac{1}{\sqrt{x}}\, dx$.

By definition, $\int_1^\infty \frac{1}{\sqrt{x}}\, dx = \lim_{t \to \infty} \int_1^t \frac{1}{\sqrt{x}}\, dx = \lim_{t \to \infty} 2\sqrt{x}\Big|_{x=1}^{x=t} = \lim_{t \to \infty} \left(2\sqrt{t} - 2\right)$ $= \infty$. Therefore, the integral diverges. ◆

□ Now let's return to the relationship between the infinite series $\sum_{n=1}^{\infty} u_n$ and the improper integral $\int_1^\infty f(x)\, dx$. Assuming f has a "nice" antiderivative, then we should be able to tell if the improper integral $\int_1^\infty f(x)\, dx$ converges by invoking the Fundamental Theorem of Calculus. We claim that if $\int_1^\infty f(x)\, dx$

converges, then $\sum\limits_{n=1}^{\infty} u_n$ converges and if $\int_1^{\infty} f(x)\,dx$ diverges, then $\sum\limits_{n=1}^{\infty} u_n$ diverges.

To see why, look again at Figure 11.9. As we said before, since $\Delta x = 1$, the area of the first rectangle is $f(1)\Delta x = u_1$; the area of the second rectangle is $f(2)\Delta x = u_2$, etc. The total area of all the rectangles is given by:

$$S = \sum_{j=1}^{\infty} u_j .$$

Notice that $s_n = \sum\limits_{j=1}^{n} u_j > \int_1^{n} f(x)\,dx$. If the integral diverges, then

$\lim\limits_{n \to \infty} \int_1^{n} f(x)\,dx = +\infty$ in which case the sequence of partial sums must grow without bound also. (Think about it: Any quantity bigger than infinity must be infinite.)

To prove the converse statement, draw rectangles with heights at the right side of each subinterval, as shown in Figure 11.11.

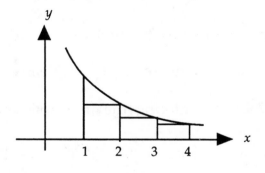

Fig. 11.11

Now the area of the first rectangle is $f(2)\Delta x = u_2$; the area of the second rectangle is $f(3)\Delta x = u_3$, etc. The total area of all the rectangles is given by:

$$s = \sum_{j=2}^{\infty} u_j .$$

Now $s_n - u_1 < \int_1^{n} f(x)\,dx \le \int_1^{\infty} f(x)\,dx$. Since we are assuming the integral converges, then this last integral represents a finite number. Thus, as n gets larger, s_n gets larger but it can never exceed $\int_1^{\infty} f(x)\,dx + u_1$. Hence, the sequence of partial sums converges.

We restate this result as:

THEOREM 11.12 (INTEGRAL TEST FOR INFINITE SERIES): Let $\{u_n\}$ be a decreasing sequence of positive numbers and let f be a decreasing function such that $f(n) = u_n$ for all n. Then $\displaystyle\sum_{n=1}^{\infty} u_n$ converges if and only if $\displaystyle\int_1^{\infty} f(x)\,dx$ converges.

This theorem, while a nice theoretical result, is not very useful in practice. First, it only applies to decreasing sequences of positive numbers. More importantly, it requires us to evaluate the improper integral, not an easy task if f does not have a nice antiderivative. Nevertheless, it illustrates a nice connection between integrals and infinite series.

EXAMPLE 11.20:

Use the integral test to show that the harmonic series $\displaystyle\sum_{n=1}^{\infty} \frac{1}{n}$ diverges.

Since $u_n := \frac{1}{n}$ is a decreasing sequence of positive terms, then we can invoke Theorem 11.12 by considering the improper integral $\displaystyle\int_1^{\infty} \frac{1}{x}\,dx$. By definition, $\displaystyle\int_1^{\infty} \frac{1}{x}\,dx = \lim_{t \to \infty} \int_1^t \frac{1}{x}\,dx = \lim_{t \to \infty} \ln(x)\big|_{x=1}^{x=t} = \lim_{t \to \infty} \ln(t) = \infty$. Since the integral diverges, then the series diverges. $\blacklozenge$

EXAMPLE 11.21:

Determine whether the series $\displaystyle\sum_{n=1}^{\infty} \frac{1}{n^2+1}$ converges or diverges.

The sequence $u_n := \dfrac{1}{n^2+1}$ is decreasing and positive, so we can apply the integral test with $f(x) := \dfrac{1}{x^2+1}$.

$$\int_1^\infty \frac{1}{x^2+1}\,dx \;=\; \lim_{t\to\infty}\int_1^t \frac{1}{x^2+1}\,dx \;=\; \lim_{t\to\infty}\arctan(x)\big|_{x=1}^{x=t}$$

$$=\; \lim_{t\to\infty}\big(\arctan(t)-\arctan(1)\big) \;=\; \frac{\pi}{2}-\frac{\pi}{4} \;=\; \frac{\pi}{4}$$

Since the integral converges, the series converges.   ♦

IMPORTANT: Theorem 11.12 does NOT say that the series converges to the value of the integral. Hence, all we can say about the series in Example 11.21 is that it converges, but we don't know to what number it converges.

EXAMPLE 11.22:

Determine whether the series $\displaystyle\sum_{n=1}^{\infty} \frac{1}{n!}$ converges or diverges.

Again the integral test applies with $f(x) := \dfrac{1}{x!}$. However, we cannot easily evaluate $\displaystyle\int_1^\infty \frac{1}{x!}\,dx$ since we don't know any antiderivatives of $\dfrac{1}{x!}$. (In fact, we don't even know what $\dfrac{1}{x!}$ means if x is not a positive integer.) Hence, we cannot come to any conclusion about this series.   ♦

- -

TEST YOUR UNDERSTANDING

1. Use the integral test to determine whether each of the following series converges or diverges.

   (a) $\displaystyle\sum_{n=1}^{\infty} \frac{1}{n^3}$ (b) $\displaystyle\sum_{n=1}^{\infty} e^{-n}$ (c) $\displaystyle\sum_{n=1}^{\infty} \frac{n}{n^2+4}$

- -

◻ Recall in Section 3 we considered infinite series of the form $\sum\limits_{n=1}^{\infty} \dfrac{1}{n^p}$, the so-called p-series. We showed that p-series diverge if $p \le 1$ and converge if $p \ge 2$. We claimed, but did not prove, that the converge if $1 < p < 2$, also. We can now prove this.

The sequence $\{\dfrac{1}{n^p}\}$ is positive and since p is a positive number, the sequence is decreasing; hence, the integral test applies by letting $f(x) := \dfrac{1}{x^p}$. Then, if $p \ne 1$,

$$\int_1^{\infty} \dfrac{1}{x^p} \, dx \ = \ \lim_{t \to \infty} \int_1^t \dfrac{1}{x^p} \, dx \ = \ \lim_{t \to \infty} \dfrac{x^{-p+1}}{-p+1} \Big|_{x=1}^{x=t} \ = \ \lim_{t \to \infty} \dfrac{t^{-p+1}-1}{-p+1} \ .$$

If $p > 1$, then the exponent on t will be negative and t^{-p+1} will approach 0 as $t \to \infty$. Thus, the integral converges. On the other hand, if $p < 1$, then the exponent on t will be positive and t^{-p+1} will increase without bound as $t \to \infty$. Thus, the integral diverges. Since we have already shown that the integral diverges when $p = 1$, we have the complete result.

EXERCISES FOR SECTION 11.5:

1. Evaluate each of the improper integrals below or state that it diverges:

(a) $\displaystyle\int_1^{\infty} \dfrac{1}{x} \, dx$

(b) $\displaystyle\int_0^{\infty} \dfrac{1}{1+x^2} \, dx$

(c) $\displaystyle\int_{-\infty}^{0} \dfrac{1}{x-1} \, dx$

(d) $\displaystyle\int_0^{\infty} \sin(x) \, dx$

(e) $\displaystyle\int_1^{\infty} \dfrac{1}{\sqrt[3]{x}} \, dx$

(f) $\displaystyle\int_0^{\infty} e^{-x} \sin(x) \, dx$

2. Determine the area in the first quadrant bounded by $y = xe^{-x}$ and the x-axis.

3. Determine whether each of the following infinite series converges or diverges:

(a) $\displaystyle\sum_{n=0}^{\infty} n \, e^{-n^2}$

(b) $\displaystyle\sum_{n=2}^{\infty} \dfrac{1}{n \, \ln(n)}$

(c) $\displaystyle\sum_{n=1}^{\infty} \dfrac{\ln(n)}{n}$

(d) $\displaystyle\sum_{n=1}^{\infty} \dfrac{n}{\sqrt{n^2+1}}$

4. Consider the integral $I(p) := \int_1^\infty \frac{1}{x^p}\,dx$, where p is a positive number.

   We have seen that $I(p)$ converges for $p < 1$. Express the value of $I(p)$ in terms of p.

PROBLEMS FOR SECTION 11.5:

1. Suppose f and g are functions such that $0 \le f(x) \le g(x)$ for all $x \ge 0$.

   (a) If $\int_0^\infty f(x)\,dx$ diverges, what can we say about $\int_0^\infty g(x)\,dx$? Explain.

   (b) If $\int_0^\infty f(x)\,dx$ converges, what can we say about $\int_0^\infty g(x)\,dx$? Explain.

   (c) If $\int_0^\infty g(x)\,dx$ converges, what can we say about $\int_0^\infty f(x)\,dx$? Explain.

2. We showed that $\int_0^\infty e^{-x}\,dx = 1$. Use problem 1(c) to argue that $\int_0^\infty e^{-x^2}\,dx$ converges.

TYU Answers for Section 11.5

   1. (a) converges (b) converges (c) diverges

QUESTIONS TO THINK ABOUT

1. Describe the process of approximating functions by Taylor polynomials. What properties do the polynomials have?

2. Define what is meant by the convergence of an infinite series of numbers. Your definition should include terms such as "partial sum" and "limit".

3. Explain why the comparison test works and why the limit comparison test works.

4. Explain why the alternating series test works. What does it mean for a series to converge absolutely? conditionally? Give examples.

5. Explain the connection between infinite series and improper integrals.

PROJECT 11.1

THE GAMMA FUNCTION

OBJECTIVE: Let $\Gamma(p) := \int_0^\infty e^{-x} x^{p-1}\, dx$, where p is a positive number. This function is very common in many areas of mathematics and is known as the **Gamma function**. In this project, we will investigate some of its properties.

PROCEDURE:

Part 1: Some preliminaries

Let $f_p(x) := e^{-x}x^{p-1}$.

   a. Use a computer of graphing calculator to graph $f_p(x)$ for $0 < x < 5$ for the cases $p = 1, p = 2, p = 3$ and $p = 4$.
   b. Describe the direction of each graph in 1a.
   c. Show that $f_p(x)$ has a local maximum at $x = p - 1$, if $p \geq 1$.
   d. Based on your graphs, would you expect $\Gamma(p)$ to be an increasing or decreasing function of p?

Part 2: Calculating $\Gamma(p)$ when p is an integer

   a. Determine $\Gamma(1)$, $\Gamma(2)$ and $\Gamma(3)$ by direct evaluation of the integral. (You may use integration by parts or the integration tables for $\Gamma(2)$ and $\Gamma(3)$.)
   b. Use integration by parts to show that $\Gamma(p) = (p - 1)\, \Gamma(p - 1)$ for all p.
   c. Use 2a and 2b to evaluate $\Gamma(4)$, $\Gamma(5)$ and $\Gamma(6)$.
   d. Generalize to obtain the value of $\Gamma(p)$, when p is an integer.

Part 3: The case where $p = n + 1/2$, where n is a positive integer

   a. Write an integral representing $\Gamma(1/2)$.
   b. By letting $x = u^2$, express $\Gamma(1/2)$ as an integral in terms of u.
   c. It can be shown by methods beyond the scope of this book that

$$\int_0^\infty e^{-u^2}\, du = \frac{\sqrt{\pi}}{2}.$$ Use this to find $\Gamma(1/2)$.

   d. Use 2b to find $\Gamma(3/2)$ and $\Gamma(5/2)$.

PROJECT 11.2

LEGENDRE'S EQUATION

OBJECTIVE: A differential equation that arises often in mathematical physics is $(1 - x^2)y'' - 2xy' + n(n + 1)y = 0$, where n is a positive number. This equation is called **Legendre's equation of order n**. In the special case where n is an integer, then one of the solutions of this equation is a polynomial of degree n, called a **Legendre polynomial**. In this project we will derive the Legendre polynomials and investigate some of their properties.

PROCEDURE:

Part 1: The special case $n = 0$

In this case, Legendre's equation reduces to $(1 - x^2)y'' - 2xy' = 0$.

a. By making the substitution $v = y'$, rewrite this equation as a first-order differential equation in v.

b. Solve the equation in 1a by separation of variables.

c. Integrate your answer to b to get $y = c_0 + c_1 \ln\left(\dfrac{1+x}{1-x}\right)$.

Notice that the general solution in 1c consists of a polynomial part (in this case, a constant polynomial c_0) and a non-polynomial part. This always happens for Legendre's equation, when n is a positive integer.

Part 2: The cases $n = 1$ and $n = 2$

If $n \neq 0$, then the technique used in Part 1 does not work since there will be a y-term in the equation. Hence, we must resort to power series techniques to solve the differential equation.

a. Let $n = 1$ and assume that $y(0) = c_0$ and $y'(0) = c_1$. By repeated differentiation, show that $y''(0) = -2c_0$, $y'''(0) = 0$, $y^{iv}(0) = -8c_0$ and $y^{v}(0) = 0$.

b. It is not hard to believe that the kth derivative of y satisfies the relationship

$$(1 - x^2)\, y^{(k)} = a_k x y^{(k-1)} + b_k y^{(k-2)},$$

for some numbers a_k and b_k. Use this and the results of 2a to show that $y^{(k)}(0) = 0$ if k is an odd number > 1 and $y^{(k)}(0) \neq 0$ if k is even, unless $c_0 = 0$.

c. Conclude from 2a and b that the general solution to Legendre's equation for the case $n = 1$ is $y = c_0\left(1 - x^2 - \frac{x^4}{3} + ...\right) + c_1 x$. Note, again, that the general solution consists of a polynomial part, $c_1 x$, and a non-polynomial part (in this case, written as a power series).

d. Now let $n = 2$. Show that $y''(0) = -6c_0$, $y'''(0) = -4c_1$, $y^{iv}(0) = 0$ and $y^v(0) = -24c_1$.

e. Show that $y^{(k)}(0) = 0$ if k is an even number > 2 and $y^{(k)}(0) \neq 0$ if k is odd, unless $c_1 = 0$. Thus, conclude that the general solution in this case is $y = c_0\left(1 - 3x^2\right) + c_1\left(x - \frac{x^5}{5} + ...\right)$, again the sum of a polynomial and a non-polynomial part.

Part 3: The Legendre polynomials

We could generalize the calculations in Part 2 to show that, indeed, the general solution of Legendre's equation always consists of a polynomial and a power series provided n is a positive integer. Moreover, the polynomial is of degree n. We will call it the nth Legendre polynomial, denoted $P_n(x)$. So far, we have shown that $P_0(x) := c$, $P_1(x) := cx$, $P_2(x) := c(1 - 3x^2)$.

a. It is usually agreed that the arbitrary constant c should be chosen such that the graph of the Legendre polynomials pass through $(1, 1)$. For each of the three cases above, determine c so that the polynomial has this property.

b. The third and fourth Legendre polynomials are $P_3(x) := \frac{1}{2}\left(5x^3 - 3x\right)$ and $P_4(x) := \frac{1}{8}\left(35x^4 - 30x^2 + 3\right)$. Show by substitution that these satisfy Legendre's equation of order 3 and 4, respectively, and that their graphs pass through $(1, 1)$.

c. It is quite tedious to use Legendre's equation to actually derive Legendre polynomials. An alternative method is to use the following formula, known as **Rodrigues' formula**: $P_n(x) = \frac{1}{2^n n!} \frac{d^n}{dx^n}\left[(x^2 - 1)^n\right]$. (This says to find $P_n(x)$, find the nth derivative of $(x^2 - 1)^n$, and multiply by $\frac{1}{2^n n!}$.) Use Rodrigues' formula to verify $P_n(x)$, for $n = 1, 2$ and 3.

Part 4: Orthogonality of Legendre polynomials

Let $p(x)$ and $q(x)$ be polynomials. We say that p and q are **orthogonal** on the interval $[a, b]$ if $\int_a^b p(x)q(x)\,dx = 0$. In this part, we will show that any two distinct Legendre polynomials are orthogonal on $[-1, 1]$; that is, $\int_{-1}^1 P_m(x)P_n(x)\,dx = 0$, if $m \neq n$.

a. Show that P_1 and P_2 are orthogonal but P_1 is not orthogonal to itself.

b. More generally, since P_n and P_m satisfy Legendre's equation of orders n and m, respectively, then

  (1) $\quad (1 - x^2)P_n'' - 2xP_n' + n(n + 1)P_n = 0 \quad$ and

  (2) $\quad (1 - x^2)P_m'' - 2xP_m' + m(m + 1)P_m = 0$.

c. Multiply (1) by P_m and (2) by P_n and subtract. Rearrange terms to get

  (3) $\quad (1 - x^2)(P_n''P_m - P_nP_m'') - 2x(P_n'P_m - P_nP_m') =$
  $$[m(m + 1) - n(n + 1)]P_nP_m.$$

d. Let $u(x) := (1 - x^2)(P_n'P_m - P_nP_m')$.

  Show that $u'(x) := (1 - x^2)(P_n''P_m - P_nP_m'') - 2x(P_n'P_m - P_nP_m')$ and, hence, (3) can be rewritten as:

  (4) $\quad u'(x) := [m(m + 1) - n(n + 1)]P_nP_m$

e. Integrate both sides of (4) from -1 to 1, noting that $u(-1) = u(1) = 0$,

  to obtain $[m(m + 1) - n(n + 1)]\int_{-1}^1 P_m(x)P_n(x)\,dx = 0$.

f. Conclude that if $m \neq n$, then P_m and P_n are orthogonal on $[-1, 1]$.

CHAPTER 12

THREE-DIMENSIONAL VECTORS AND FUNCTIONS OF TWO VARIABLES

12.1 THREE-DIMENSIONAL SPACE AND VECTOR-VALUED FUNCTIONS

When we discussed the trajectory of a thrown ball in Chapter 9, we assumed the motion was confined to a plane (no curve balls). As a result, we could use two-dimensional vectors to describe the motion. Now imagine what happens when the wind blows across the field or a batter hits the ball not quite squarely. Clearly, the path of the ball is no longer just confined to a plane. Recall also the problem on radioactive decay in the same chapter in which over time one substance decayed into another which in turn decayed. We used a set of two parametric equations to keep track of how much of each substance is present as a function of time. It is possible that this substance could be decaying too, so that over time we would have three (or even more) quantities to track. In this section, we will extend our discussion of vector-valued functions and parametric equations to three dimensions.

Let's begin by extending our familiar coordinate system to three dimensions. Unfortunately, we are confined to a two-dimensional page, so we'll have to use some artistic tricks like perspective and shading to give the illusion of three dimensions. Also, you'll have to use your imagination and perhaps build some models to see the objects we're talking about.

Figure 12.1 shows a three-dimensional coordinate system. We will generally draw the axes so that the horizontal axis on the page is labelled y, the vertical axis is labelled z and the axis "coming out of the page" is labelled x. The system has 3 coordinate planes: if you were looking at a room, the yz-plane would be the front wall, the xy-plane would be the floor and the xz-plane would be the left wall. This creates 8 **octants**, 4 above the xy-plane and

4 below the xy-plane. Unlike the 4 quadrants of the standard xy-plane (in a two-dimensional coordinate system), there is no universally agreed-upon numbering of the 8 octants, although most would agree that the octant in which x, y and z are all positive is the "first octant".

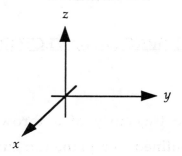

Fig.12.1

There may be occasions in which we may rotate the axes for clarity. For example, we may rotate the system so that the x-axis points to the right and the y-axis points into the page. Or we may rotate it so that both the x- and y-axes stick out from the page at 45° angles. The only requirement is that if you stand at the origin with your head in the direction of the positive z-axis and looking out along the positive part of the x-axis, then the positive part of the y-axis is reached by turning 90° to the left (counterclockwise).

Points in a three-dimensional system have coordinates which are ordered triplets of the form (x, y, z). Figure 12.2 shows the location of the point $(1, 2, 3)$; this point is in the first octant.

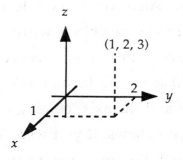

Fig. 12.2

Many results from two dimensions can be extended to three. For example, the distance between the points (x_1, y_1, z_1) and (x_2, y_2, z_2) is given by:

$$D = \sqrt{(x_1 - x_2)^2 + (y_1 - y_2)^2 + (z_1 - z_2)^2} \ .$$

TEST YOUR UNDERSTANDING

1. Determine the distance between $(1, 3, 5)$ and $(-2, 4, 0)$.

2. Write an equation of all the points whose distance from the origin is 2. What does this set of points look like?

◻ Now let's extend the concept of a **vector** and vector operations to three dimensions. Again, we can think of a vector as a quantity characterized by **magnitude** and **direction**. We simply allow ourselves the freedom to point the arrows in any direction without confining them to a plane.

We can define vector operations exactly as we did in Chapter 9. **Scalar multiplication** is an operation that changes the magnitude but not the direction of a vector; that is, kv is in the same direction as v but is $|k|$ times as long. **Vector addition** again works using the same parallelogram definition; that is, $u + v$ is the diagonal of a parallelogram whose sides are u and v. Note that $u + v$ is in the plane determined by u and v.

We can decompose a three-dimensional vector into **components**, much like we did in two dimensions. Now we need three unit vectors, $i = \langle 1, 0, 0 \rangle$ which points in the positive x-direction, $j = \langle 0, 1, 0 \rangle$ which points in the positive y-direction and $k = \langle 0, 0, 1 \rangle$ which points in the positive z-direction. Any vector v can be expressed in the form $v = ai + bj + ck$, where a, b and c are real numbers (called the **coordinates** of v) and we'll write, as before, $v = \langle a, b, c \rangle$.

Once again, vector operations can be expressed in terms of coordinates.

The results are analogous to those in Theorem 9.1, with one additional coordinate.

THEOREM 12.1: Suppose $u = \langle u_1, u_2, u_3 \rangle$ and $v = \langle v_1, v_2, v_3 \rangle$. For any real number k, $ku = \langle k u_1, k u_2, k u_3 \rangle$ and $u + v = \langle u_1 + v_1, u_2 + v_2, u_3 + v_3 \rangle$.

Furthermore, if we "extend" the definition of the dot product in a natural way, then Theorem 9.2 still holds, although part (e) is slightly more difficult to prove.

DEFINITION: Let $u = \langle u_1, u_2, u_3 \rangle$ and $v = \langle v_1, v_2, v_3 \rangle$. be vectors. The **dot product of u and v** is defined by $u \cdot v = u_1 v_1 + u_2 v_2 + u_3 v_3$.

THEOREM 12.2: For all vectors u, v and w:

(a) $u \cdot v = v \cdot u$.

(b) $k u \cdot v = u \cdot k v = k (u \cdot v)$, where k is a scalar.

(c) $u \cdot (v + w) = u \cdot v + u \cdot w$.

(d) $u \cdot u = \| u \|^2$

(e) The angle θ between u and v is determined by $\cos(\theta) = \dfrac{u \cdot v}{\| u \| \| v \|}$.

(f) Non-zero vectors u and v are perpendicular if and only if $u \cdot v = 0$.

TEST YOUR UNDERSTANDING

3. Let $u = \langle 2, 4, -3 \rangle$ and $v = \langle -1, 3, 6 \rangle$. Determine:

   (a) $u + v$ (b) $5u - 3v$ (c) $u \cdot v$ (d) the length of u

4. Let $u = \langle 3, 2t, 2 - t \rangle$ and $v = \langle t, -3, 2 + t \rangle$. For what values of t are u and v perpendicular?

◻ Now let's talk about vector functions in three dimensions. Let $r(t) :=$ $\langle f(t), g(t), h(t) \rangle$, where f, g, and h are scalar functions of t. If all vectors have their tails at the origin, then the head of the vector for a given t is at the point whose coordinates are $(f(t), g(t), h(t))$; in other words, the vector function r traces in three-dimensional space a curve defined by the parametric equations $x = f(t)$, $y = g(t)$ and $z = h(t)$.

EXAMPLE 12.1:

Describe the path traced by $r(t) := \langle \sin(t), \cos(t), t \rangle$.

We begin by looking at a slightly different problem first. Suppose the third component were 0, not t. Then, as we saw in Chapter 9, the path traced would be a circle in the xy-plane traversed clockwise as t increases. The fact that third component is t means that, as the path circles around, it also moves up the z-axis in such a way that at time t, the z-coordinate is t. Thus, the path traced is a **helix** (or spiral, as it is sometimes called). The graph in Figure 12.3 shows the curve for $t \geq 0$.

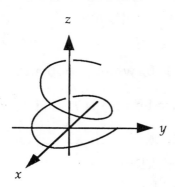

Fig. 12.3

◻ Given a vector function $r(t)$, it makes sense to talk about its derivative $r'(t)$, using the definition from Chapter 9. Geometrically, $r'(t)$ is still a vector tangent to the curve traced by $r(t)$. The next theorem tells us how to compute $r'(t)$.

THEOREM 12.3: If $r(t) = \langle x(t), y(t), z(t) \rangle$, then $r(t) = \langle x'(t), y'(t), z'(t) \rangle$.

If $r(t)$ represents the position of an object at time t, then we have the following:

THEOREM 12.4:

    (a) The velocity function $v(t)$ is $r(t)$ and the acceleration function $a(t)$ is $r'(t)$.

    (b) The speed is given by $v(t) := \sqrt{\left(\frac{dx}{dt}\right)^2 + \left(\frac{dy}{dt}\right)^2 + \left(\frac{dz}{dt}\right)^2}$.

    (c) The distance travelled by the object during the time interval $[a, b]$ is given by $L = \int_a^b v(t)\, dt$.

EXAMPLE 12.2:

Determine the speed of a particle moving along the helix in Example 12.1 and the length of the helix from the point $(0, 1, 0)$ to $(1, 0, \pi/2)$.

Since $\frac{dx}{dt} = \cos(t)$, $\frac{dy}{dt} = -\sin(t)$ and $\frac{dz}{dt} = 1$, the speed is given by $v(t) := \sqrt{(\cos(t))^2 + (\sin(t))^2 + (1)^2} = \sqrt{2}$.

Since the particle is at $(0, 1, 0)$ when $t = 0$ and at $(1, 0, \pi/2)$ when $t = \pi/2$, then the distance travelled (arc length) is $L = \int_0^{\pi/2} \sqrt{2}\, dt = \frac{\sqrt{2}\,\pi}{2}$.   ◆

TEST YOUR UNDERSTANDING

    5. Let $r(t) := \langle t, t^2, 3 \rangle$. Determine:

        (a) the velocity vector $v(t)$ (b) the speed $v(t)$

        (c) the length of the curve from $t = 0$ to $t = 1$

◻ Now let's return to a problem we mentioned at the beginning of this section. How can we describe the path of a thrown ball when there is a wind blowing? After we make some assumptions about what the wind will do the ball, this problem is not much harder than the two-dimensional problem that we discussed in Chapter 9.

EXAMPLE 12.3:

Suppose a ball is thrown with initial velocity $v = \langle v_1, v_2, v_3 \rangle$ and that the wind imparts a constant velocity $w = \langle w_1, w_2, w_3 \rangle$. Find parametric equations for the path of the ball.

As in the solution of the ball problem in Chapter 9, assume that the only acceleration is in the vertical direction; that is, $a(t) := \langle 0, 0, -g \rangle$.
Integrating both sides gives:

$$v(t) := \langle 0, 0, -gt \rangle + c$$

where c is a constant vector. Letting $t = 0$, we see that c describes the initial velocity of the ball. This is composed of two parts, the velocity imposed by the thrower, v_0, and the part imposed by the wind , $w = \langle w_1, w_2, w_3 \rangle$. Assume that when the ball is first thrown, it moves in the xz-plane at an angle of θ_0 with the horizontal. Then, adapting the results of Chapter 9, we have $v_0 = \langle v_0 \cos(\theta_0), 0, v_0 \sin(\theta_0) \rangle$. Note that the second component is 0 since initially there is no movement in the y-direction. Since $c = v_0 + w$, then $v(t) := \langle v_0 \cos(\theta_0) + w_1, w_2, -gt + v_0 \sin(\theta_0) + w_3 \rangle$.
Integrating once more gives

$$r(t) := \langle (v_0 \cos(\theta_0) + w_1)t, w_2 t, -\tfrac{1}{2}g t^2 + (v_0 \sin(\theta_0) + w_3)t \rangle + c$$

where c is the initial position. If we assume that the thrower stands at the origin and releases the ball h feet above the ground, then $c = \langle 0, 0, h \rangle$ and

$$r(t) := \langle (v_0 \cos(\theta_0) + w_1)t, w_2 t, -\tfrac{1}{2}g t^2 + (v_0 \sin(\theta_0) + w_3)t + h \rangle. \quad \blacklozenge$$

There are many other possible assumptions we could make about the wind velocity and the forces acting on the ball. This is a topic for future investigation.

⌀ Remember that in Chapter 9 we said that it was useful to write the acceleration as the sum of two components, one parallel to the velocity (the tangential component) and one perpendicular to the velocity (the normal component). Specifically, we wrote:

$$a(t) = a_T T(t) + a_N N(t),$$

where $T(t)$ is a unit vector in the direction of $v(t)$ and $N(t)$ is (one of) the unit vectors perpendicular to $v(t)$. We saw that a_T and a_N were useful in discussing the rate of change of speed and the curvature. We can do the same thing in three dimensions, but, because of the extra dimension, we must be even more careful. First, if we want again to write $a(t) = a_T T(t) + a_N N(t)$, then $a(t)$, $T(t)$ and $N(t)$ must lie in the same plane. (Remember that the sum of two vectors lies in the plane determined by those vectors.) Hence, we must pick $N(t)$ so that it is perpendicular to $v(t)$ (or $T(t)$) and in the plane determined by $v(t)$ and $a(t)$. While that's not hard to do geometrically, it does cause some problems algebraically. Second, there's a third dimension in which our curve may be turning. In order to describe that phenomenon accurately, we'll need a third unit vector perpendicular to both $T(t)$ and $N(t)$. It's called the **binormal**. We'll leave that as a topic for further investigation.

LINES IN THREE DIMENSIONS

An important special case of a vector function is the straight line. We know that, in two dimensions, straight lines can be represented by linear equations of the form $y = mx + k$, where m is the slope and k is the y-intercept. If we try to do something similar in three dimensions, we run into a problem. The slope of a line is the tangent of the angle between the line and the positive x-axis. In two dimensions, this is well-defined. In three dimensions, it is not. There are infinitely many lines through a given point that make, say, a $30°$ angle with the x-axis. (They form a cone-shaped surface around the x-axis.) Hence, we need another approach.

Let $P(x_0, y_0)$ be a fixed point on the line and let $Q(x, y)$ be any other point on the line. Let $v = \langle a, b \rangle$ be a vector parallel to line PQ. The vector from P to Q has coordinates $\langle x - x_0, y - y_0 \rangle$. This vector is parallel to v and must therefore be a scalar multiple of v. Hence, $\langle x - x_0, y - y_0 \rangle = t \langle a, b \rangle$, where t is a scalar. By equating coordinates, we find that the line PQ can be represented parametrically by:

$$x = x_0 + at, \quad y = y_0 + bt$$

or equivalently, PQ is traced by the vector function

$$r(t) := \langle x_0 + at, y_0 + bt \rangle.$$

So, in order to write parametric equations for a line in two dimensions, we need a point on the line and a vector parallel to the line. This same information suffices in three dimensions as well. Hence, we have:

THEOREM 12.5: The line parallel to the vector $v = \langle a, b, c \rangle$ and passing through the point (x_0, y_0, z_0) can be represented by the parametric equations $x = x_0 + at, \; y = y_0 + bt, \; z = z_0 + ct$ or, equivalently, as the vector function $r(t) := \langle x_0 + at, y_0 + bt, z_0 + ct \rangle$.

The vector v is called the **direction vector** for the line and is the three-dimensional counterpart to the notion of slope. Note that $r(t)$ can be written as $r(t) = u + tv$, where $u = \langle x_0, y_0, z_0 \rangle$ and $v = \langle a, b, c \rangle$. This is represented geometrically in Figure 12.4.

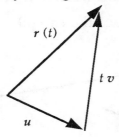

Fig. 12.4

As t increases from 0, the vector tv becomes longer but its direction does not change. If t is negative, the vector points in the opposite direction but is still parallel to v. Therefore, $r(t)$ traces the straight line determined by tv.

EXAMPLE 12.4:

Write parametric equations for the line that passes through the points $P(1, -6, 3)$ and $Q(2, 4, 8)$.

First note that the vector from P to Q has coordinates $\langle 1, 10, 5 \rangle$ and is parallel to the desired line. Using P as the "starting point", we find that PQ has parametric representation $x = 1 + t, y = -6 + 10t, z = 3 + 5t$. ◆

It follows that any two lines with the same direction vector (or with parallel direction vectors) are parallel. For example, the lines $L_1: x = 1 + 5t$, $y = 2 - 3t, z = 2t$ and $L_2: x = 2 + 5t, y = -4 - 3t, z = 6 + 2t$ are parallel since both have $\langle 5, -3, 2 \rangle$ as a direction vector. Two lines are perpendicular if they intersect and if the dot product of their direction vectors is 0. The line $L_3: x = 1 - t, y = 2 + 3t, z = 7t$ is perpendicular to L_1 since both lines pass through $(1, 2, 0)$ and the dot product of their direction vectors is $\langle 5, -3, 2 \rangle \cdot \langle -1, 3, 7 \rangle = -5 - 9 + 14 = 0$.

Although any pair of lines drawn in two dimensions must either be parallel or intersecting, in three dimensions, a third possibility exists. It might be that the lines are neither parallel nor intersecting, in which case they are said to be **skew**. The lines L_1 and L_2 in Figure 12.5 are skew. (Think of the line formed by the floor and the left wall of a room and the line formed by the ceiling and the front wall of the room.)

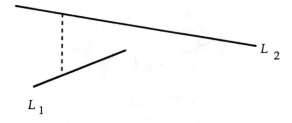

Fig. 12.5

---

6. Let L be represented parametrically by $x = 1 - t, y = 4 + 2t, z = 3 + t$. Write parametric equation for the line parallel to L that passes through $(0, 1, 4)$.

7. Does the line L in TYU #6 pass through the point $(4, -2, 1)$? Explain.

8. Let M be the line represented by $x = 1 + 2t, y = 4 + 3t, z = 3 + ct$, where c is a constant. For what value of c will M be perpendicular to the line L in TYU #6?

EXAMPLE 12.5:

Line L_1 is represented by the vector function $r(t) := \langle 1 + 3t, 2 - t, 4 + t \rangle$ and line L_2 is represented by $q(t) := \langle 2 + t, \ 5 - 2t, \ -1 + 3t \rangle$. Do L_1 and L_2 have any points in common?

What we are really asking is if there are some values of t, say t_1 and t_2, such that $r(t_1) = q(t_2)$. Equating components, this is equivalent to the system of equations:

$$1 + 3t_1 = 2 + t_2$$
$$2 - t_1 = 5 - 2t_2$$
$$4 + t_1 = -1 + 3t_2$$

In most cases, systems of 3 equations in two unknowns do not have a solution. Here, upon solving the first equation for t_2 in terms of t_1 and substituting in the second equation, we have:

$$2 - t_1 = 5 - 2(3t_1 - 1)$$

which implies $t_1 = 1$. Substituting in the first equation gives $t_2 = 2$. Since these values also satisfy the third equation, then $t_1 = 1, t_2 = 2$ is a solution to the system. Indeed, $r(1) = \langle 4, 1, 5 \rangle = q(2)$, so $(4, 1, 5)$ is the point in common to both lines. ◆

EXERCISES FOR SECTION 12.1:

1. Find the length of the line segment joining $(4, 2, -1)$ and $(3, 3, 3)$.

2. Which of the following vectors are perpendicular to $\langle 3, 2, -1 \rangle$?

      (a) $\langle 1, 2, 3 \rangle$ (b) $\langle 1, -1, 1 \rangle$ (c) $\langle 2, -3, 0 \rangle$ (d) $\langle 2, -1, 4 \rangle$

3. For what values of c are the points $O(0, 0, 0)$, $P(-1, 2, 4)$ and $Q(8, 2, c)$ the vertices of a right triangle?

4. Write parametric equations for the line parallel to the vector $\langle 3, 1, -2 \rangle$ that passes through the point $(6, 3, 7)$.

5. Determine the coordinates of the point of intersection of the line in Exercise 4 and the:

(a) xz-plane   (b) yz-plane   (c) the plane $x + y = 5$

6. Write parametric equations for the line parallel to the xz- and yz-planes that passes through the point $(-1, 2, 3)$.

7. Write parametric equations for the line that passes through $(0, 2, 5)$ and $(1, -2, 3)$.

8. Does $(2, -3, -1)$ lie on the line $L: x = 5 - t, y = -9 + 2t, z = 4 - 2t$?

9. Let $r(t) := \langle 4t, e^t, \ln(1 + t) \rangle$.

(a) Determine the velocity vector.

(b) Determine the acceleration vector.

(c) Determine a unit tangent vector at $t = 0$.

(d) Determine the speed of a particle moving along this curve at $t = 0$.

(e) Write an integral that can be used to determine the length of the curve from $t = 0$ to $t = 3$. Do not evaluate.

10. Repeat Exercise 9 with the function $r(t) := \langle t\sin(t), t\cos(t), t^3 \rangle$.

11. Let C be represented parametrically by $x = t, y = 2t + 1, z = t^2$. At what time would a particle travelling along C attain a speed of $\sqrt{105}$?

12. Line L_1 is represented by $x = 1 + t, y = 2 + t, z = 3 + t$ and line L_2 is represented by $x = 2 + 2t, y = 6 + bt, z = 9 - 3t$. For what values of a and b do these lines intersect?

PROBLEMS FOR SECTION 12.1:

1. Let L_1 and L_2 have parametric representations $x = t, y = 3 - 2t, z = 4 + t$ and $x = 1 + 2t, y = -6 + 3t, z = 3 + 4t$, respectively.

   (a) Show that L_1 and L_2 intersect.

   (b) Show that L_1 and L_2 are perpendicular at the point of intersection.

2. Determine a vector u that is perpendicular to both $v = \langle -1, 3, 1 \rangle$ and $w = \langle 4, 2, 0 \rangle$.

3. (a) Show that $v \cdot v = ||v||^2$, for any vector v.

   (b) Use (a) to show that $||v + w||^2 - ||v - w||^2 = 4v \cdot w$.

   (c) Use (b) to show that if v and w are perpendicular, then $||v - w|| = ||v + w||$.

   (d) Argue that the result of (c) is equivalent to the geometric statement that the diagonals of a rectangle are of equal length.

TYU Answers for Section 12.1

1. dist. $= \sqrt{35}$ 2. $x^2 + y^2 + z^2 = 4$; a sphere 3. (a) $\langle 1, 7, 3 \rangle$ (b) $\langle 13, 11, -33 \rangle$

(c) -8 (d) $\sqrt{29}$ 4. $t = 1, -4$ 5. (a) $v(t) := \langle 1, 2t, 0 \rangle$ (b) $s(t) := \sqrt{1 + 4t^2}$

(c) $L = \int_0^1 \sqrt{1 + 4t^2}\, dt = \dfrac{\sqrt{5}}{2} + \dfrac{\ln(2 + \sqrt{5})}{4} \approx 1.479$ 6. $x = -t, y = 1 + 2t, z = 4 + t$

7. No. 8. $c = -4$

12.2 FUNCTIONS OF SEVERAL VARIABLES

Until now, we have dealt only with functions of one variable--that is, $y = f(x)$. There are many situations in which a quantity depends on more than one variable. For example, the volume of a cylinder depends on its height and radius. The amount of time required to stop a car depends on the strength of the brakes, the speed at which the car is moving and the reaction time of the driver, among other things. The temperature at any point in the United States depends on the location of the point. Since we generally specify the location of such a point with a pair of coordinates (perhaps latitude and longitude), then the temperature is a function of two variables.

Note: One of the most difficult questions in mathematical modeling is deciding which variables have a significant effect on the quantity being studied and which can be ignored. For example, the yield of a crop of wheat may depend on the amount of rainfall, the amount of sunlight, the type of wheat, the type of fertilizer used and many other factors. The effect of some of these factors, however, may be negligible. Think about how to design an experiment to determine which factors are important and which are not.

Let's look at an example of how a function of two variables might arise.

EXAMPLE 12.6:

A rectangular box without a top is to be constructed using 1000 square inches of cardboard. Express the volume of the box in terms of its length and width?

Suppose the box is x inches long, y inches wide and z inches high. Then the problem is to maximize $V = xyz$ subject to a constraint on the surface area. Looking at Figure 12.6(a), we see that the area of the bottom is xy, of one pair of sides is $2xz$ and of the other pair of sides is $2yz$. Thus we must have $xy + 2xz + 2yz = 1000$, or $z = \dfrac{1000 - xy}{2(x + y)}$, as our constraint. Therefore, $V(x, y) := \dfrac{xy(1000 - xy)}{2(x + y)}$ is the volume. Note that in order for the volume to be positive, we must have $x > 0, y > 0$ and $xy < 1000$. This restricts the domain of V to a certain portion of the xy-plane, as shown in Figure 12.6(b).

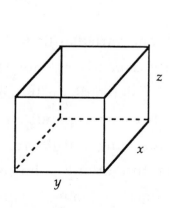

Fig. 12.6(a)

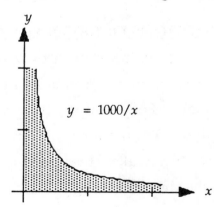

$y = 1000/x$

Fig. 12.6(b)

♦

Here, we've written the volume V of the box as a function of two independent variables. In general, let $z = f(x, y)$. We say that "z is a function of x and y". When we say this, we mean that we may choose any value of x and any value of y for our function as long as the pair (x, y) is in the domain of f. For a function of two variables, the domain is a region in an xy-plane, such as the one in Example 12.6, or perhaps the entire xy-plane, which is denoted R^2.

EXAMPLE 12.7:

Determine the domain of the function $f(x, y) := \dfrac{1}{x - y}$.

The only restriction on the domain is that the denominator can't be 0. Therefore, $D = \{(x, y) \mid y \neq x\}$. This is the entire xy-plane with the line $y = x$ deleted as shown in Figure 12.7.

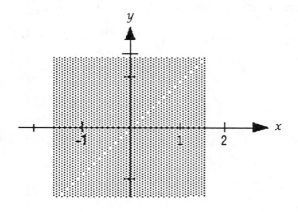

Fig. 12.7

♦

EXAMPLE 12.8:

Determine the domain of $f(x, y) := \dfrac{x}{\sqrt{x^2 + y^2 - 4}}$.

Here, we require the expression under the square root sign to be strictly positive; that is, $x^2 + y^2 > 4$. This corresponds to the portion of the xy-plane outside the circle of radius 2 centered at the origin as shown in Figure 12.8.

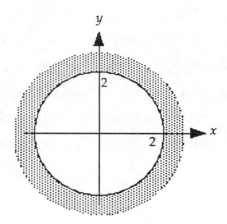

Fig. 12.8

◆

TEST YOUR UNDERSTANDING

1. Describe and sketch the domain of each of the following functions:

(a) $f(x, y) := \dfrac{y}{x^2}$ (b) $g(x, y) := \sqrt{1 - x - y}$

(c) $z = \dfrac{x - 1}{\sqrt{y - 2}}$ (d) $f(x, y) := \ln(x + y)$

Determining the range for a function of two variables is at least as hard as for functions of one variable and we shall not pursue it here.

¤ We now turn to the problem of sketching functions. As we said earlier, the graphs will be in three dimensions and we will have to do the best we can with two-dimensional paper. Since there is a unique z-value for each point in the domain, the graph of a function of two variables generally looks like some kind of surface. See Figure 12.9.

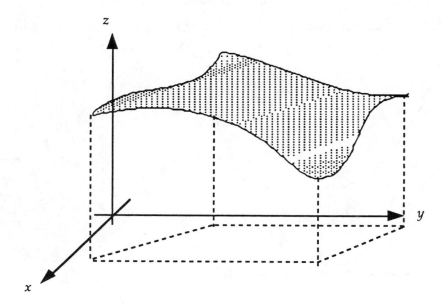

Fig. 12.9

Determining what these surfaces look like if we are given an equation of the function is difficult, certainly more difficult than the problem of sketching graphs of functions of one variable. There are, however, some techniques that can help us.

One useful technique for visualizing surfaces is to examine the curves formed by slicing the surface with a vertical plane. These curves are called **vertical cross-sections**. Although we are free to use any vertical plane, we usually restrict ourselves to planes that, in the case of $z = f(x, y)$, are perpendicular to either the x- or the y-axis.

EXAMPLE 12.9:

Graph the vertical cross-sections of the surface $z = x^2 + y^2$. Then use them to describe the surface.

Letting $y = c$, we see that $z = x^2 + c^2$, a parabola opening upward and having its vertex at $x = 0$ and $z = c^2$. Thus, we have a family of similar parabolas which rise as c increases from $c = 0$ (or as c goes to $-\infty$ from zero). Fixing $x = c$ produces the same family. The graph in Figure 12.10(a) shows some members of the family, all sketched on the same set of axes. The graph in Figure 12.10(b) shows the bowl-like surface, called a **paraboloid**.

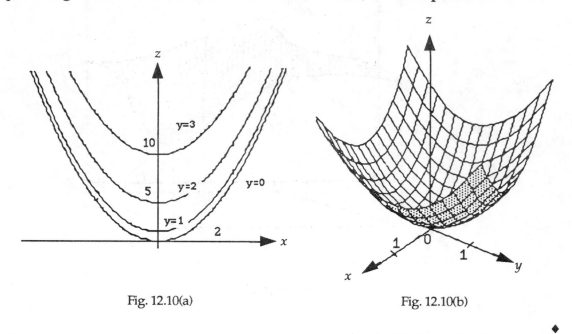

Fig. 12.10(a)   Fig. 12.10(b)

EXAMPLE 12.10:

Graph the vertical cross-sections of the surface $z = \sqrt{x^2 + y^2}$. Then use them to describe the surface.

For $y = 0, z = \sqrt{x^2} = |x|$, whose graph comes to a sharp point. For $y = c$, where $c \neq 0$, we get $z = \sqrt{x^2 + c^2}$ or $z^2 - x^2 = c^2$ with the restriction that $z \geq 0$. This is a branch of a hyperbola. Although parabolas and hyperbolas look alike, they are not the same, so there is a difference between this surface and the one in Example 12.9. The point in the graph of $z = |x|$ suggests that perhaps this surface comes to a point at the bottom, and indeed it does. This surface is a **cone**. See Figures 12.11(a) and 12.11(b).

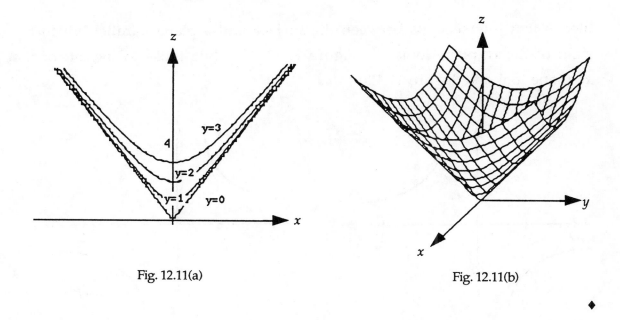

Fig. 12.11(a)   Fig. 12.11(b)

♦

<u>TEST YOUR UNDERSTANDING</u>

2. Picture a cone lying on its side with its center along the x-axis. Describe the vertical cross-sections in two different directions.

While it's not easy to picture surfaces from their cross-sections, it is possible to get better at it. Here's an exercise you might try. Take an object that you have in your room, like a pillow, a doughnut, or a coffee mug and try to picture the cross-section of the object at various spots and in various directions. Unlike the last two examples, most objects have different cross-sections in different directions.

EXAMPLE 12.11:

Analyze the vertical cross-sections for the function $z = f(x, y) := \frac{y}{x}$.

If $x = c$, then $z = \frac{y}{c}$, which is a straight line with slope $1/c$. On the other hand, if $y = c$, then $z = \frac{c}{x}$, which is a hyperbola in the first and third quadrants if $c > 0$ and in the second and fourth quadrants if $c < 0$. This means that intersections between the surface and a plane parallel but to the right of the *xz*-plane look like Figure 12.12(a) while those to the left of the *xz*-plane look like Figure 12.12(b)

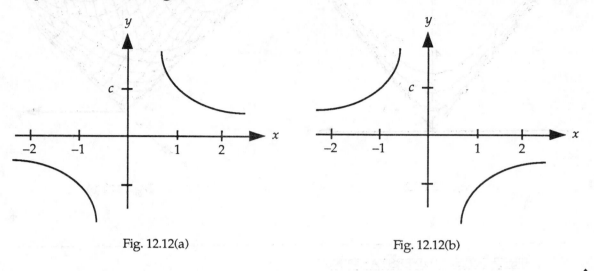

Fig. 12.12(a)   Fig. 12.12(b)

◆

▢ In many applications of functions of two variables, one of the independent variables represents time and the other represents another physical quantity such as distance, mass, temperature, etc. Consider the following problem:

A seesaw 16 feet long pivots on a fulcrum 2 feet off the ground. One end of the seesaw is attached to a spring that has a natural length of 2 feet (so that the spring is neither stretched nor compressed when the seesaw is level). The end of the seesaw attached to the spring is pressed down 0.5 feet and released. See Figure 12.13.

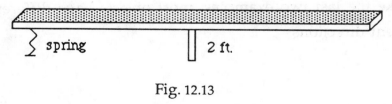

spring   2 ft.

Fig. 12.13

As time goes on, each point on the seesaw oscillates up and down. The amplitude of the oscillation depends on which point we're watching. Points close to the fulcrum don't move very far; those near the end oscillate with greater amplitude. Establish a coordinate plane with the center of the seesaw at the origin and the seesaw at rest lying along the x-axis. Thus, the seesaw goes from -8 to 8 along the x-axis. If z represents the displacement from horizontal of the seesaw at some point, then z is a function of x and of the time since the seesaw was released; that is, $z = f(x, t)$.

In Section 7.2, we showed that the displacement of a spring released from initial position z_0 is given by $z(t) := z_0 \cos(\omega t)$, where ω is a constant that depends on the strength of the spring. Here, the initial displacement at $x = 8$ is 0.5; hence, $f(8, t) := .5\cos(\omega t)$. Moreover, at any other x-value, $\dfrac{f(x, t)}{x} = \dfrac{f(8, t)}{8}$, by similar triangles. (See Figure 12.14.)

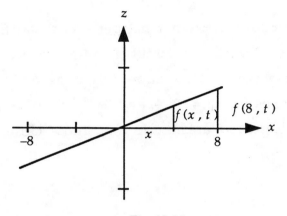

Fig. 12.14

Thus we have

$$f(x, t) := x\,\frac{f(8, t)}{8} = \frac{x\cos(\omega t)}{16}, \quad -8 \le x \le 8,\ t \ge 0.$$

TEST YOUR UNDERSTANDING

3. Sketch the domain of the function above.

Let's look at the vertical cross-sections of this function. If we fix a value of t and slice the surface with a plane parallel to the xz-plane, we get a straight line (the see-saw) passing through the origin (fulcrum) at some angle that depends on t. See Figure 12.15.

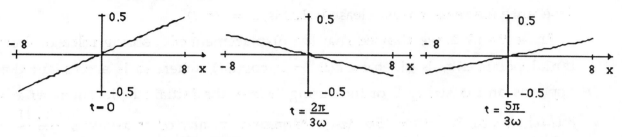

Fig. 12.15

Alternatively, we could ask what happens to a particular point on the seesaw as time passes. That is, we could slice the surface with the plane $x = x_0$ parallel to the tz-plane and examine $f(x_0, t)$ as a function of t. Figure 12.16 shows these curves for $x_0 = 2, 4$, and 8. Notice that points far from the fulcrum oscillate with greater amplitude than those close to the fulcrum, as we said before.

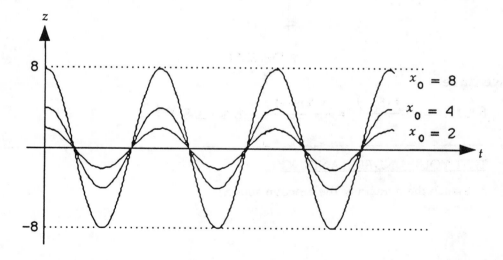

Fig. 12.16

If we put this all together, we can get some idea of what the surface looks like. Figure 12.17 shows a two dimensional representation of this surface. (Admittedly, we've drawn the axes a bit unconventionally to make it easier to see what's going on.)

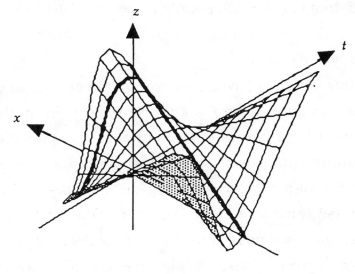

Fig. 12.17

Look at the lines and curves on the surface. Each one is one of the cross-sections that we talked about earlier. In particular, we've darkened one of the lines that represents the position of the seesaw at a particular time t_0. This straight line is like those in Figure 12.15. Then we darkened one of the curves crossing this darkened line corresponding to a particular x-value, x_0. This is one of the cosine curves shown in Figure 12.16. Again we see that the curves for x-values near zero have smaller amplitude than those for x-values near ± 8.

¤ Now let's return to an example we mentioned at the beginning of the section. The temperature at any point in the United States (at a particular time) is a function of its latitude and longitude. How can we best understand this function? We could find the vertical cross-sections. Such a graph would show, for instance, the temperature at every point in the United States with a particular latitude. While this might be interesting, it might be better to look at the temperature in a region around a given point, not just along straight lines through the point. Weather maps try to provide this information by looking at **horizontal cross-sections** of the temperature function and plotting them all on a single map of the country.

We get a horizontal cross section by fixing a value of z, say $z = c$, in the range of f and looking for all points (x, y) at which $f(x, y) = c$. More formally, let

$$S_c = \{(x, y) \mid f(x, y) = c\}.$$

The set of points S_c is called a **contour** or **level curve** (rather than a horizontal cross-section). Since f is a function, no point in the xy-plane can be on two different level curves (lest that point have two different function values). A **contour plot** consists of the superimposition of several level curves on the same xy-plane. By labelling the contours with their respective z-values, we can get some idea of the behavior of the function.

On a weather map, we often find the contour lines for the temperature in increments of ten degrees. These contour lines are called **isotherms**, meaning "places where the temperature (that's the "therm" part) is the same (that's the "iso" part)". The names "contour" and "level curve" come from topographic maps which show how far above sea level a particular point is. That is, for a given point (x, y), $f(x, y)$ is its altitude. Thus a level curve for this function connects points at the same altitude and its shape gives an idea of the shape or contour of the land.

Let's compute a few level curves for the function $f(x, y) := x^2 + y^2$ in Example 12.9. First note that $f(x, y) \geq 0$ for all x and y, so S_c is only defined for $c \geq 0$. For $c = 0$, we have $S_0 = \{(x, y) \mid x^2 + y^2 = 0\}$, a set which consists only of the origin. For $c = 2$, we have $S_2 = \{(x, y) \mid x^2 + y^2 = 2 \}$, which is a circle centered at the origin with a radius of $\sqrt{2}$. It is not hard to see that, in general, S_c is a circle centered at the origin with a radius of $\sqrt{c}$. A contour plot is given in Figure 12.18(a).

For the function $g(x, y) := \sqrt{x^2 + y^2}$ in Example 12.10, the level curves are also circles centered at the origin. This time, however, S_c is a circle of radius c, rather than $\sqrt{c}$. A contour plot is shown in Figure 12.18 (b).

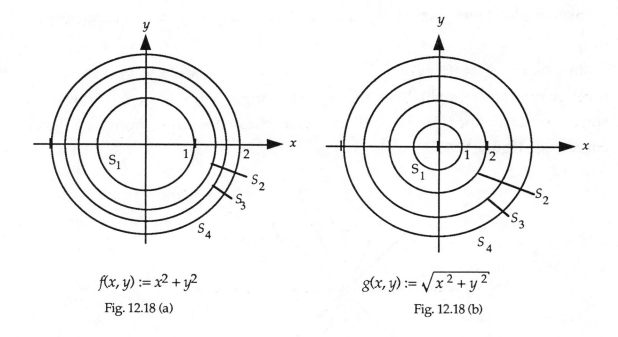

$$f(x, y) := x^2 + y^2$$

Fig. 12.18 (a)

$$g(x, y) := \sqrt{x^2 + y^2}$$

Fig. 12.18 (b)

Let's consider the similarities and differences between the two parts of Figure 12.18. In both plots we used the same evenly spaced values of c. Notice that in the plot on the right the circles are also spaced evenly, showing that that surface rises uniformly. On the other hand, the plot on the right shows circles that are growing closer as c increases. (You can see this clearly for c going from 0 to 1 to 2; the others are a little less obvious but nonetheless true.) That means that the surface is steeper for larger values of c. That point bears repeating: If a surface is rising sharply, the level curves for evenly spaced levels are closer together.

Now look at the level curves for both surfaces for $c = 1$ and $c = 2$. Note that for $c = 1$, both circles have radius one. For $c = 2$, however, the circle for f has a smaller radius than the circle for g. This indicates that for z-values between 1 and 2, the paraboloid is growing more quickly than the cone. Similarly, the graph of f is flatter near the origin than the graph of g.

EXAMPLE 12.12:

Sketch the level curves S_0, S_1, S_2, S_{-1} and S_{-2} for the function $f(x, y)$ $:= \frac{y}{x}$.

In general, $S_c = \{(x, y) \mid \frac{y}{x} = c\} = \{(x, y) \mid y = cx, x \neq 0\}$. Thus, the level curves are straight lines through the origin with slope c. However, since f is not defined for $x = 0$, we must delete the origin from each level curve. See Figure 12.19.

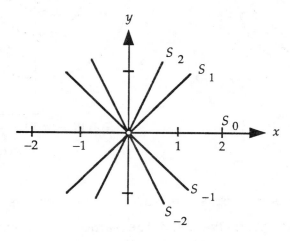

Fig. 12.19

♦

EXAMPLE 12.13:

Sketch the level curves $S_0, S_{1/2}$ and $S_{1/4}$ for the function $g(x, y) := \frac{x}{x^2 + y^2}$.

$S_0 = \{(x, y) \mid \frac{x}{x^2 + y^2} = 0\} = \{(x, y) \mid x = 0\} = y\text{-axis}.$

$S_{1/2} = \{(x, y) \mid \frac{x}{x^2 + y^2} = 1/2\} = \{(x, y) \mid 2x = x^2 + y^2\}$

$\qquad = \{(x, y) \mid (x - 1)^2 + y^2 = 1\}$ upon completing the square. This is a circle of radius 1 centered at (1, 0).

Similarly, $S_{1/4} = \{(x, y) \mid \frac{x}{x^2 + y^2} = 1/4\} = \{(x, y) \mid (x - 2)^2 + y^2 = 4\}$, which is a circle of radius 2 centered at (2, 0).

Again, we must delete the origin from each level curve since $f(0, 0)$ is not defined. See Figure 12.20.

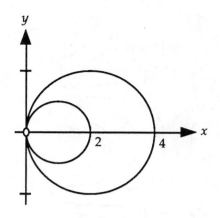

Fig. 12.20

♦

- -

TEST YOUR UNDERSTANDING

4. Determine $S_{-1/2}$ for the function in Example 12.13.

5. Sketch the level curves S_0, S_1 and S_2 for each of the following:

    (a) $f(x, y) := 3x + y$ (b) $f(x, y) := x^2 - y$ (c) $g(x, y) := xy$

- -

Before we leave this topic, let's go back to the seesaw problem and look at the level curves for its solution, the surface $f(x, t) := \dfrac{x \cos(\omega t)}{16}$. See Figure 12.21.

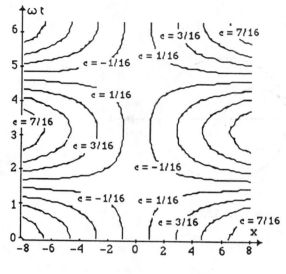

Fig. 12.21

Although this is a pretty picture, it doesn't seem to provide us with any additional information about the problem. In this case, we were better able to understand the function using the vertical cross-sections. In other cases, for example on weather maps, the contours are more useful. Which set of cross-sections, the vertical or the horizontal, is most appropriate in a particular case is difficult to determine in advance. Often, you'll have to try everything and then decide what's helpful.

EXERCISES FOR SECTION 12.2:

1. Let $f(x, y) = x^2 + xy$.

   (a) What is $f(2, 3)$?

   (b) What is $f(x, 2)$?

   (c) Determine all values of x for which $f(x, 2) = 3$.

   (d) Determine $\dfrac{f(x+h, y) - f(x, y)}{h}$.

2. The gravitational attraction between the earth and an object of mass m at a distance r from the center of the earth is given by $f(m, r) := \dfrac{km}{r^2}$, where k is a constant.

   (a) What happens to the force if m is doubled?

   (b) What happens to the force if r is doubled?

3. Sketch the domain of:

    (a) $f(x, y) := \sqrt{x^3 - y}$　　　　　　　(b) $f(x, y) := \ln[x(y + 1)]$

    (c) $f(x, y) := \arcsin(x + y)$

4. Sketch the level curves S_0, S_2 and S_4 for each of the following:

    (a) $z = x + y$　　　(b) $z = \dfrac{y}{1 + x}$　　　(c) $z = x^2 + 4y^2$

    (d) $z = \dfrac{x^2}{x^2 + y^2}$

5. Sketch the vertical cross-sections $x = 0, x = 1, x = 2, y = 1$ for each of the surfaces in Exercise 4.

6. A box has a square base.

    (a) Express the volume V of the box as a function of its height and the length of the base.

    (b) Assuming the box has an open top, express its surface area as a function of its height and the length of the base.

    (c) Suppose the cardboard used to make the box costs 10 cents per square foot and all the edges of the box (except along the top) are reinforced with tape that costs 4 cents per foot. Express total cost of making the box as a function of its height and the length of the base.

7. Sketch the level curves corresponding to $V = 10, 20$ and 30 for the function in Exercise 6(a).

PROBLEMS FOR SECTION 12.2:

1. A repairman is in charge of fixing certain machinery in a factory. Suppose that, on average, q machines per week require fixing and the repairman can fix p machines per week. It can be shown that, under certain conditions, the average amount of time a machine will remain broken before the repairman can get to fix it is given by the function $w = \dfrac{1}{p - q}$, if $p > q$. Show that this function is intuitively plausible by assessing the effect that increasing p or q has on w.

2. Let $f(x, y, z) := \sqrt{x^2 + y^2 + z^2 - 9}$.

    (a) What is the domain of f?

    (b) Describe the "level surfaces" of f.

3. Suppose a manufacturer can use either eye of newt or hair of bat in the manufacture of snake oil. The amount of snake oil produced is $z = f(x, y)$, where x is the amount of eye of newt and y is the amount of hair of bat. What do the vertical cross-sections parallel to the yz-plane show? parallel to the xz-plane? What do the level curves show?

4. In the next chapter, we'll show that under certain conditions, the density of an organism growing at a point x meters from one end of a long tube at time t is given by $r(x, t) := e^{kt} \sin(\pi x / L)$, $0 \le x \le L$, $t \ge 0$, where k is a constant and L is the length of the tube.

   (a) Show that at any time t, the maximum density occurs at $x = L/2$.

   (b) Suppose $k > 0$. What happens to the density for any x as time passes?

   (c) Repeat (b) if $k < 0$.

5. The "wind chill factor" is used by meteorologists to indicate the effective temperature (in terms of its effect on losing body heat) on a cold windy day. The wind chill factor $R = f(T, W)$, where T is the actual temperature and W is the wind speed. For example, when the air temperature is $T = 20$ and the wind speed is $W = 30$, the wind chill factor is $R = -20$, which means that it feels like it is 20 degrees below zero.

   (a) Sketch a typical vertical cross-section parallel to the WR-plane.

   (b) Sketch a typical vertical cross-section parallel to the TR-plane.

   (c) Sketch and interpret the level curves of this function.

   (Note: We don't have a formula for R. The idea is to sketch what you think the cross-sections and level curves might look like.)

TYU Answers for Section 12.2

1. (a) $D = \{(x, y) \mid x \ne 0\}$ (b) $D = \{(x, y) \mid x + y \le 1\}$ (c) $D = \{(x, y) \mid y > 2\}$

    (d) $D = \{(x, y) \mid x + y > 0\}$

2. Cross-sections perpendicular to x-axis are circles, cross-sections perpendicular to y-axis are hyperbolas (the one through the x-axis is a pair of intersecting lines)

3.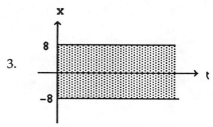

4. $\{(x, y) \mid (x + 1)^2 + y^2 = 1\}$; circle of radius 1, center $(-1, 0)$

5. (a)   Lines   (b)   Parabolas   (c) Hyperbolas (S_0 is the x- and y-axes)

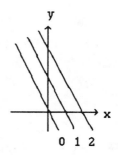
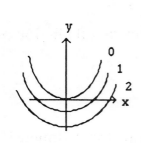
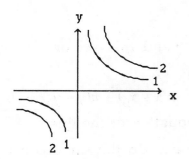

12.3 SOME COMMON SURFACES

Just as there are some curves you needed to know to ease your way in the calculus of a single variable, so too there is a small collection of surfaces with which you ought to be familiar. Not surprisingly, they are analogs of the curves we met in Chapter 1. We'll use these as examples throughout the remainder of the book.

1. PLANES

Recall from Chapter 1 that a straight line is uniquely determined by specifying its slope and a point on the line. Equivalently, we could specify a point on the line and a vector parallel to the line, as we did in Section 12.1. Alternatively, as long as we stay in two dimensions, we could specify a point on the line and a vector *perpendicular* to the line. Specifically, let L be the line passing through $P(x_0, y_0)$ perpendicular to the vector $v = \langle a, b \rangle$. Let $Q(x, y)$ be any other point on L. Then the vector from P to Q has components $\langle x - x_0, y - y_0 \rangle$. See Figure 12.22.

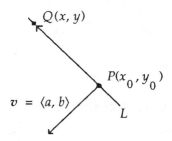

Fig. 12.22

Since v and this vector are perpendicular, their dot product must be zero. Therefore,

$$a(x - x_0) + b(y - y_0) = 0$$

is an equation of the line.

We can do the same construction in three dimensions. Let $v = \langle a, b, c \rangle$ be a vector and let $P(x_0, y_0, z_0)$ be a point. Where are all the points $Q(x, y, z)$ such that the vector from P to Q is perpendicular to v? To help answer this question, mark a point P on your desk and hold a pencil perpendicular to the desk at P. Now pick any other point Q on the desk. The vector from P to Q is perpendicular to the pencil. This will be true for every point on the desk and will be false for every point not on the desk. Since the desk top constitutes a plane, we see that a **plane** is uniquely determined by specifying a point on the plane and a vector v perpendicular to the plane. Moreover, any line in the plane is perpendicular to v. See Figure 12.23.

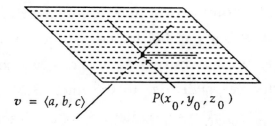

Fig. 12.23

Now let's use an argument similar to the one above to derive an equation of the plane passing through $P(x_0, y_0, z_0)$, perpendicular to $v = \langle a, b, c \rangle$. Choose any other point $Q(x, y, z)$ in the plane. The vector from P to Q has components $\langle x - x_0, y - y_0, z - z_0 \rangle$. Since this vector must be perpendicular to v, then $\langle x - x_0, y - y_0, z - z_0 \rangle \cdot \mathbf{v} = 0$ from which we have:

THEOREM 12.6: An equation of the plane passing through the point $P(x_0, y_0, z_0)$, perpendicular to the vector $v = \langle a, b, c \rangle$ is
$$a(x - x_0) + b(y - y_0) + c(z - z_0) = 0.$$

The vector v is called the **normal vector** for the plane. ("Normal" is a word that is sometimes used in mathematics to mean perpendicular.) We can rewrite this as
$$ax + by + cz = d,$$
where $d = ax_0 + by_0 + cz_0$. Notice that in this form the components of the normal vector are the coefficients of x, y and z.

Of course, this can be solved for z explicitly in terms of x and y, if $c \neq 0$. However, very little is gained by doing so. Nevertheless, this shows that the graph of any function of the form $f(x, y) := mx + ny + p$, where m, n and p are constants, is a plane. So, in two dimensions, linear functions (functions with variables to the first degree only) represent lines; in three dimensions, they represent planes. You can convince yourself of this even further by looking at the level curves and cross-sections. (For a plane, what should they all be?)

Every equation of the form given by Theorem 12.6 represents a plane, as long as a, b and c are not all 0. Let's look at the special case where exactly one of the coefficients is 0. Suppose, for instance, $a = 0$. Then the equation becomes $b(y - y_0) + c(z - z_0) = 0$. If we were working in two dimensions, we'd say this represented a line in the yz-plane. Since we're operating in three dimensions, we can say that the intersection of the given plane with any plane parallel to the yz-plane (that is, of the form $x = c$) is this line. This, in turn, implies that the plane is perpendicular to the yz-plane or, equivalently, parallel to the x-axis. Put differently, the vector $v = \langle 0, b, c \rangle$ is a normal vector for the plane. Since $v \cdot i = 0$ (where $i = \langle 1, 0, 0 \rangle$ is a unit vector in the positive direction of the x-axis), then v and i must be perpendicular. Hence, v is perpendicular to both the x-axis and the plane and, therefore, the plane must be parallel to the x-axis. Similarly, if $b = 0$, then plane is parallel to the y-axis and if $c = 0$, the plane is parallel to the z-axis.

EXAMPLE 12.14:

Write an equation of the plane perpendicular to the line L: $x = 2t, y = 1 - 4t, z = 3 + 6t$ at the point $(8, -15, 27)$.

The vector $v = \langle 2, -4, 6 \rangle$ is parallel to L. (How did we get that?) Since the plane is perpendicular to L, then it must be perpendicular to v. Thus, by Theorem 12.6, an equation of the plane is

$$2(x - 8) - 4(y + 15) + 6(z - 27) = 0 \text{ or, equivalently,}$$
$$2x - 4y + 6z = 238. \qquad \blacklozenge$$

EXAMPLE 12.15:

Find the point of intersection of the line $x = 2t, y = 1 - 4t, z = 3 + 6t$ and the plane whose equation is $7x + 5y - z = 14$.

Any point (x, y, z) on both the line and the plane must satisfy both the equation of the line and the equation of the plane. Substituting the parametric equations of the line into the equation of the plane gives

$$7(2t) + 5(1 - 4t) - (3 + 6t) = 14.$$

Upon solving, we get $t = -1$. Substituting back into the equations of the line gives the point of intersection as $(-2, 5, -3)$. $\qquad \blacklozenge$

Notice that, while there is only one plane perpendicular to a given vector through a given point, there are infinitely many planes through a given point that are *parallel* to a given vector. To visualize this, fold a piece of paper in half. Let v be a vector along the crease and let P be any point on the crease. Then both halves of the paper are parallel to v and pass through P. This will be true no matter what the angle between the two halves of the paper and, hence, there are infinitely many planes through P parallel to v.

Any two planes either are parallel or intersect in a line. See Figure 12.24. If the planes are parallel, then they will have parallel normal vectors. Since parallel vectors are multiples of one another, the coefficients of x, y and z in the two equations will be the same multiples of each other. The constant terms, however need not be related. For example, the planes $3x - y + 2z = 4$ and $-6x + 2y - 4z = 0$ are parallel because their normal vectors $\langle 3, -1, 2 \rangle$ and $\langle -6, 2, -4 \rangle$ are parallel.

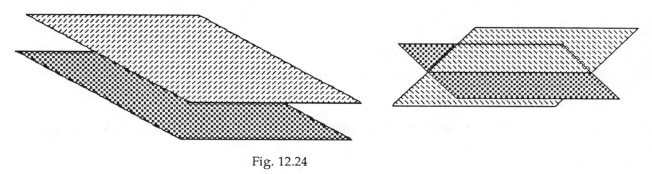

Fig. 12.24

The next example illustrates how to find a set of parametric equations for the line of intersection between two planes.

EXAMPLE 12.16:

Determine parametric equations of the line of intersection of $x + 3y - z = 2$ and $-2x + 5y - 9z = -15$.

This is a system of two equations in three variables. Generally, such systems have infinitely many solutions. In this case, there is a solution corresponding to each point on the line of intersection.

In order to solve such a system, we can assign an arbitrary value to one of the variables and then solve for the other two variables. For instance, we can let $z = t$. Upon substituting and rearranging, we get

$$x + 3y = 2 + t$$

$$-2x + 5y = -15 + 9t$$

Now solve for x and y as with any system of two equations in two variables. For example, multiply the first equation by 2 and add to the second, obtaining $11y = -11 + 11t$ from which $y = -1 + t$. Substituting back and solving for x gives $x = 5 - 2t$.

Thus, one set of parametric equations for the line of intersection is $x = 5 - 2t$, $y = -1 + t$, $z = t$. This is not the only set; there are infinitely many others. Had we started by assigning a value to either x or y, we would have gotten a different set of equations representing the same line. Notice that this line is parallel to $\langle -2, 1, 1 \rangle$, which is perpendicular to both $\langle 1, 3, -1 \rangle$ and $\langle -2, 5, -9 \rangle$, the normal vectors for the two planes. ◆

- -

TEST YOUR UNDERSTANDING

1. Determine a normal vector for the plane $z = 4x - y + 8$.

2. Write an equation for the plane parallel to the one in TYU#1 passing through $(2, 2, -2)$.

3. Write an equation of the plane perpendicular to the xy-plane and passing through $(1, 1, 0)$ and $(3, 5, 0)$.

- -

2. SPHERES AND HEMISPHERES

By definition, a **sphere** is the set of points in three-dimensional space that are a given distance r from a given point (x_0, y_0, z_0). Using the distance formula, any other point (x, y, z) on the sphere must satisfy
$$(x - x_0)^2 + (y - y_0)^2 + (z - z_0)^2 = r^2.$$

This is an equation of the sphere.

We can rewrite this as $(z - z_0)^2 = r^2 - (x - x_0)^2 - (y - y_0)^2$ or, upon solving for z,

$$z = z_0 \pm \sqrt{r^2 - (x - x_0)^2 - (y - y_0)^2}.$$

This is not a function due to the presence of the "$\pm$" sign (meaning that there are two z-values for each x and y. However, if we just want the top half of the sphere, we can use the positive square root; the bottom half is obtained by using the negative square root.

For example, the function $z = f(x, y) := 3 + \sqrt{4 - (x - 5)^2 - (y + 1)^2}$ represents the top half of a sphere whose center is $(5, -1, 3)$ and whose radius is 2.

TEST YOUR UNDERSTANDING

4. (a) Write an equation of the sphere with center $(-2, 3, 5)$ and radius 4.

(b) Write an equation for the bottom half of the sphere in (a).

----

3. CYLINDERS

The word cylinder usually evokes an image of a tin can or pipe or something similar. However, those are a special type of cylinder, a **right circular cylinder**, so named because the cross-sections are circles and the axis through the middle of the cylinder is perpendicular to the base. Mathematically, a **cylinder** is any solid with the property that all its cross-sections perpendicular to some axis are the same size and shape. Those cross-sections may be circles, squares, triangles or any other shape. They don't even have to be closed figures; we can have, for example, a parabolic cylinder. (We are dealing with the surface of the cylinder, not the solid contained in it.)

Suppose the function $z = f(x, y)$ is actually independent of y; that is, y

does not appear in the formula for f. Then all cross-sections with planes of the form $y = c$ will be identical. In other words, every time we slice the surface with a plane parallel to the xz-plane, we get exactly the same shape. Thus, the surface is a cylinder. Similarly, if $f(x, y)$ is independent of x, we also get a cylinder. For example, suppose $f(x, y) := x^2$. Every cross-section with a plane parallel to the xz-plane (i.e. $y = c$) has the form $z = x^2$, which is parabolic. Thus, the surface is a parabolic cylinder, as shown in Figure 12.25.

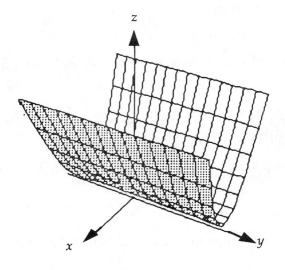

Fig. 12.25

TEST YOUR UNDERSTANDING

   5. Sketch the surface $z = \sin(x)$.

---

4. PARABOLOID

   Any surface for which all vertical cross-sections are parabolas is called a **paraboloid**. Consider the function $z = x^2 + y^2$ that we studied in Example 12.9 and later. We showed that every cross-section with planes of the form $x = c$ or $y = c$ is parabolic. Hence this surface is a paraboloid.

In fact, the cross-sections with any vertical plane (not just those parallel to the xz- and yz-planes) are also parabolic. To show this, note that any such plane has equation $y = mx + b$. Upon substituting, we get $z = x^2 + (mx + b)^2 = (1 + m^2)x^2 + 2bmx + b^2$, which, for any m and b, is a parabola.

Although many of the cross-sections of the cylinder $z = x^2$ are parabolas, not all of them are. Cross-sections parallel to the xz-plane are straight lines. Hence, this surface is not a paraboloid.

We've shown that the level curves for the surface $z = x^2 + y^2$ are circles. This is not necessarily true for all paraboloids. For example, let $z = x^2 + 4y^2$. This also represents a paraboloid; however, the level curve $S_c = \{(x, y) \mid x^2 + 4y^2 = c\}$ is an ellipse. As such, this is sometimes called an elliptical paraboloid, as opposed to the circular paraboloid above. See Figure 12.26.

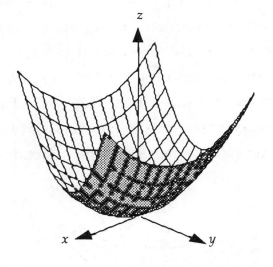

Fig. 12.26

Note that for each of these paraboloids, all of the parabolic cross-sections "point the same way"--that is, they are all concave up or all concave down. It is possible to have a paraboloid in which the cross-section parallel to the xz-plane are concave down and those parallel to the yz-plane are concave up. Suppose $z = y^2 - x^2$. Intersections with planes of the form $x = c$ are $z = y^2 - c^2$, which are concave up parabolas. Intersections with planes of the form $y = c$ are $z = c^2 - x^2$ which are concave down parabolas. Thus, the surface is bent up around the xz-plane and bent down around the yz-plane. See Figure 12.27.

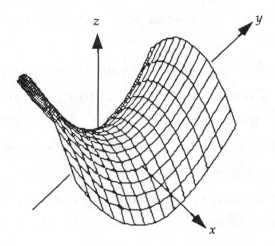

Fig. 12.27

The level curve $S_c = \{(x, y) \mid y^2 - x^2 = c\}$ is a hyperbola symmetric about the y-axis if $c > 0$ and symmetric about the x-axis if $c < 0$. The surface is called a **hyperbolic paraboloid,** although it is informally called a "saddle surface" due to its resemblance to a similarly named piece of equestrian equipment. A contour plot for this surface is given in Figure 12.28. We shall refer to this surface many times in later chapters since it illustrates some of the difficulties that can arise when studying functions of more than one variable.

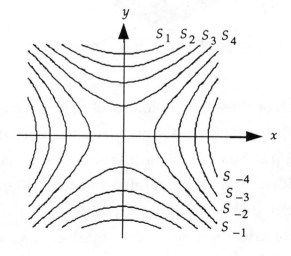

Fig. 12.28

EXERCISES FOR SECTION 12.3:

1. Identify each of the surfaces below. Be as specific as you can.

   (a) $3x + 4y - 2z = 7$ (b) $f(x, y) := e^y$ (c) $g(x, y) := 9x^2 - 4y^2$

2. Write an equation of the plane perpendicular to the line $x = -2 + 6t$, $y = 3t$, $z = 1$ at the point $(10, 6, 1)$.

3. Write an equation of the plane through $(1, 3, 5)$ parallel to $2x - y + z = 9$.

4. Write an equation of the plane through $(0, 1, 4)$ that is perpendicular to the line joining $(1, -2, 3)$ and $(6, 1, 1)$.

5. Write an equation of the plane that is perpendicular to the xy-plane and passes through $(-1, 3, 0)$ and $(4, 1, 0)$.

6. Write an equation of the plane that passes through $(3, 3, -2)$ perpendicular to the z-axis.

7. Write an equation of the sphere whose center is at $(1, 2, -4)$ and which passes through $(3, 5, 0)$.

8. The endpoints of a diameter of a sphere are $(0, 1, 2)$ and $(4, 5, 6)$. Write an equation for the sphere.

9. Sketch the cylinders:

   (a) $z = x^3$ (b) $z = 4 - y^2$ (c) $z = e^{-x}$

10. Write an equation for the plane tangent to the sphere $x^2 + y^2 + z^2 = 9$ at $(1, 2, 2)$. [Hint: The tangent plane is perpendicular to the radius.]

PROBLEMS FOR SECTION 12.3:

1. (a) Find the point of intersection between the line $x = t$, $y = 1 + t$, $z = 2 - 2t$ and the plane $2x + 3y + z = 14$.

   (b) Show that the line $x = 2 + t$, $y = 7t$, $z = 3 - 2t$ and the plane $-3x + y + 2z = 4$ do not intersect.

2. A **tetrahedron** (pyramid with triangular base) is formed by the coordinate planes and the plane $x + 2y + 5z = 10$. Determine the volume of the tetrahedron. (Hint: The volume of a tetrahedron is $V = \frac{1}{3} Bh$, where B is the area of the base and h is the height.)

3. The **dihedral angle** between two planes is the angle between their normal vectors.

   (a) Determine the dihedral angle between $2x + 3y - z = 7$ and
   $-x + y + 4z = 13$.

   (b) Show that the planes $3x - y - z = 9$ and $4x + 2y + 5z = -4$ are perpendicular.

4. Let $\Pi: ax + by + cz + d = 0$ be a plane and let $P(x_0, y_0, z_0)$ be any point not on the plane.

   (a) Determine parametric equations for the line through P perpendicular to Π.

   (b) Determine the point of intersection of Π and the line from (a).

   (c) Show that the distance from P to Π is $\dfrac{|ax_0 + by_0 + cz_0 + d|}{\sqrt{a^2 + b^2 + c^2}}$.

   (d) Determine the distance from $(1, 2, 3)$ to $3x - y - z = 9$.

5. Let $f(x, y, z) := \sqrt{x^2 + y^2 + z^2 - 9}$.

   (a) What is the domain of f?

   (b) Describe the "level surfaces" of f.

6. Show that any function of the form $f(x, y) := ax^2 + by^2 + c$ is a paraboloid. Under what conditions on a, b and c will the paraboloid be circular? elliptical? hyperbolic?

1. $\langle 4, -1, -1 \rangle$ 2. $4x - y - z = 8$ 3. $2x - y = 1$

4. (a) $(x + 2)^2 + (y - 3)^2 + (z - 5)^2 = 16$ (b) $z = 5 - \sqrt{16 - (x + 2)^2 - (y - 3)^2}$

5. For $x \geq 0, y \geq 0$, the surface looks like

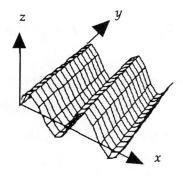

12.4 DESCRIBING FUNCTIONS OF TWO VARIABLES

In Chapter 1, we defined concepts such as direction and concavity for functions of one variable. For example, a function f is increasing on an interval I if for every choice of x_1 and x_2 on I with $x_1 < x_2$, then $f(x_1) < f(x_2)$. In other words, if we move from left to right in the interval, the function values have to get bigger. In this section, we will attempt to do something similar for functions of two variables. The key word is "attempt" since we will quickly find out that the task is not an easy one.

To give you an idea of why we have so much trouble extending these concepts to higher dimensions, consider a typical surface such as the paraboloid $z = x^2 + y^2$. Pick a point on the surface, say $(1, 1, 2)$. Is the surface increasing or decreasing there? The answer to this question is "both"--it depends on which way you look. Remember, for functions of one variable, we always look left to right. Here, we have infinitely many choices of direction. As an analogy, think of standing on a mountain. If you move in some directions, your altitude will increase; move in other directions, it will decrease or even remain the same.

For this particular surface, it is certainly true that if we hold x fixed and increase y, then z increases. Also, if we hold y fixed and increase x, then z increases. Even if we increase both x and y simultaneously, then z increases. But what happens if we increase x and decrease y? It is not clear. So we'll need to be very specific when defining what we mean by the "direction" of a surface.

One way to approach a new problem is to turn it into an old one, since often the tools that solved the old problem will then solve the new one. In this case, the old problem is deciding whether or not a curve in a plane is increasing or decreasing. We know a great deal about solving this problem from Chapters 2 and 3. So let's "reduce" our new problem to this old one.

We say that a function of a single variable is increasing provided the values of $f(x)$ get larger as the values of x get larger. That is, $f(x)$ gets larger as x moves in the direction of the vector $i = \langle 1, 0 \rangle$. We could therefore describe "increasing" more pedantically as "increasing in the direction of i". Admittedly, this is a pretty awkward way of putting it, considering that there are only two possible directions on the real line. On the other hand, with functions of two variables, there are an infinite number of directions to choose, each one represented by a different vector.

Now suppose $z = f(x, y)$. Choose a point $P(x_0, y_0)$ and an arbitrary two-dimensional vector $v = \langle a, b \rangle$. We can ask what happens to the values of $f(x, y)$ when we move through P in the direction of v. The line through P parallel to v has parametric representation $x = x_0 + at$, $y = y_0 + bt$. As t changes, the z-values change according to the function $\phi(t)$ $:= f(x_0 + at, y_0 + bt)$, a function of t alone. Furthermore, $\phi(0) = f(x_0, y_0)$ is the function value at P and as t increases, we move in the direction of v. See Figure 12.29. We are asking how the values of $\phi(t)$ change as t increases in some interval surrounding $t = 0$. If the values of $\phi(t)$ increase as t increases through this interval, as in Figure 12.29, we'll say that "f is increasing at P in the direction of v".

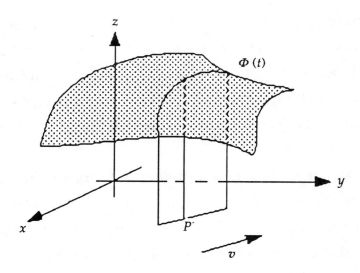

Fig. 12.29

EXAMPLE 12.17:

Let $f(x, y) := x^2 + y^2$ and P be the point $(1, 1)$. Show that f is increasing at P in the direction of $v_1 = \langle 1, 2 \rangle$ and decreasing at P in the direction of $v_2 = \langle -2, 1 \rangle$.

Let $x = 1 + t$, $y = 1 + 2t$ represent the line through P parallel to v_1 and let

$$\phi_1(t) := f(1 + t, 1 + 2t) = (1 + t)^2 + (1 + 2t)^2 = 2 + 6t + 5t^2.$$

Applying the techniques of Chapter 3, we see that $\phi_1(t)$ is increasing for $t > -0.6$. Since $\phi_1(t)$ is increasing for t near 0, then f is increasing at P in the direction of v_1.

Similarly, let $x = 1 - 2t$, $y = 1 + t$ represent the line through P parallel to v_2 and let

$$\phi_2(t) := f(1 - 2t, 1 + t) = 2 - 2t + 5t^2.$$

Since $\phi_2(t)$ is decreasing for $t < 0.2$, we can conclude that f is decreasing at P in the direction of v_2. ◆

TEST YOUR UNDERSTANDING

1. Let $f(x, y) := x^2 - y^2$ and suppose P is the point $(2, 1)$. Show that f is increasing at P in the direction of $v_1 = \langle 1, 1 \rangle$ and decreasing in the direction of $v_2 = \langle 1, 3 \rangle$.

◻ We can look at this geometrically. Note that the point P and the vector v determine a unique plane that contains P, is parallel to v, and is perpendicular to the xy-plane. Imagine slicing the surface $z = f(x, y)$ with this plane. This forms a vertical cross-section, although not necessarily one of the special ones we discussed in Section 12.2, since this cross-section may not be parallel to one of the coordinate planes. See Figure 12.30. On the other hand, the intersection of the surface with the plane produces a curve in the plane which we can analyze exactly as we did in Chapters 2 and 3, if we agree that the positive direction of the horizontal axis is the direction of v.

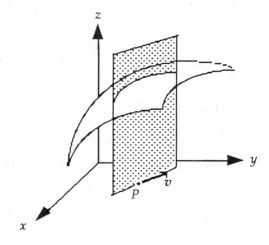

Fig. 12.30

We now see that we have really reduced our difficult problem to one that we solved previously. Unfortunately, we have not solved the new problem in an entirely satisfactory manner. When we asked about the direction of a function of one variable, we could give all of the information by specifying the intervals on which the function was increasing and those on which it was decreasing (understanding that we always go from left to right). We now must specify both a point and a vector (or, alternatively, a plane) to talk about the direction of a function of two variables.

EXAMPLE 12.18:

Let $z = f(x, y) := x^2 - 2y^2$. Show that f is increasing at $P(1, 0)$ in the direction of the $Q(2, 1)$ and decreasing at P in the opposite direction.

The the vector v from P to Q is $\langle 1, 1 \rangle$. Thus, $\phi(t) := (1 + t)^2 - 2t^2 = 1 + 2t - t^2$. $\phi'(t) = 2 - 2t = 2(1 - t)$ which is positive for $t < 1$. Therefore, f is increasing in the direction of v. On the other hand, $-v = \langle -1, -1 \rangle$ and $z = (1 - t)^2 - 2t^2 = 1 - 2t - t^2$. This function of t is decreasing around $t = 0$, so f is decreasing at P in the direction $-v$.   ◆

Extending this technique slightly, we can talk about the concavity of a surface at a point in the direction of a vector v. Once again, we use our techniques from Chapter 3.

EXAMPLE 12.19:

Let $z = f(x, y) := x^2 - 2y^2$. Determine the direction and concavity of this function at the point $P(-2, 1)$ in the direction of $v = \langle 3, -1 \rangle$.

The line through P and parallel to v is represented parametrically by $x = -2 + 3t$, $y = 1 - t$. Thus, $\phi(t) := (-2 + 3t)^2 - 2(1 - t)^2 = 2 - 8t + 7t^2$. Now $\phi'(t) := -8 + 14t$, which is negative for t near zero, and $\phi''(t) := 14$, which is always positive. Thus, f is decreasing and concave up at P in the direction of v.   ◆

TEST YOUR UNDERSTANDING

2. Let $f(x, y) := x^2 y$. Is f increasing or decreasing at $(1, 1)$ in the direction of $v = \langle 1, -1 \rangle$?

3. Is the function in TYU #2 concave up or down at $(1, 1)$ in the direction of $v = \langle 1, -1 \rangle$?

❑ There is another difficulty with our approach to this problem. Slices of a surface through a point may not reveal all of the complexity of the surface at that point. We'll shortly run into some functions that are very well-behaved on every vertical cross-section through a point, but are not well-behaved in any neighborhood of the point. On the other hand, the technique that we've developed is easy to apply and, when used with care, will tell us a great deal about the surface near the point. We'll explore this in Chapter 13. First, let's explore two ideas for which the examination of vertical cross-sections is insufficient.

The first of these is the concept of local extrema. Recall from Chapter 1 that f has a local minimum at $x = x_0$ if $f(x) > f(x_0)$ for all x near x_0. The phrase "near x_0" can be interpreted as "for values of x a little bigger than x_0 and for values of x a little smaller than x_0". For functions of two variables, we certainly want $f(x, y) > f(x_0, y_0)$ for all (x, y) near (x_0, y_0) in order to have a local minimum. The question is what we mean by the phrase "(x, y) near (x_0, y_0)".

It is easy to see that the circular paraboloid $f(x, y) := x^2 + y^2$ has a local minimum at the origin. Indeed, for all points (x, y) which are different from $(0, 0)$, $f(x, y) > f(0, 0) = 0$. On the other hand, consider the hyperbolic paraboloid $g(x, y) := x^2 - y^2$. Look at the origin. If we move in either direction along the x-axis, we go up. If we move in either direction along the y-axis, we go down. So the origin is a local maximum when viewed in the direction $i = \langle 1, 0 \rangle$ and a local minimum when viewed in the direction $j = \langle 0, 1 \rangle$. Indeed, there are many directions in which the origin appears to be a maximum and many in which it appears to be a minimum. A point which is a local maximum in some direction and a local minimum in another direction is called a **saddle** point and will be discussed in greater detail in Chapter 13.

We could define the phrase "local minimum (or maximum) at P in the direction v" as we did for the direction and concavity of a surface, but this is not particularly satisfying. What we really expect of a local minimum is that it be a low point on the surface, a point at which water would collect if it were poured over the surface from above. That is, we expect a local minimum to be a minimum for every direction in which we might look. Thus, we'll take the phrase "near (x_0, y_0)" to mean "in a small circle surrounding (x_0, y_0)" and leave our definition intact. Hence, we'll expect that if (x_0, y_0) is a local minimum, no matter which way you leave (x_0, y_0), the surface goes up.

Now consider the parabolic cylinder $z = x^2$ from Figure 12.25. We might be tempted to say that all the points on the y-axis are local minima. This is not correct since, if we pick one such point and move along the y-axis, we stay at the same z-value, whereas our definition of local minimum says that we'd have to go up.

TEST YOUR UNDERSTANDING

4. Does $f(x, y) := 4 - x^2 - y^4$ have a local extremum at $(0, 0)$? Explain.

5. Does $g(x, y) := x^4 - y^2$ have a local extremum at $(0, 0)$? Explain.

¤ A second example of a concept for which examining vertical cross-sections is not enough is the concept of limit. Recall that $\lim_{x \to a} f(x) = L$ if the values of $f(x)$ can be made arbitrarily close to L by taking x sufficiently close to a. Implicit in this statement is the fact that $f(x)$ must approach L no matter how x approaches a. If $f(x)$ should approach different values as x approaches a from the right and the left, then the limit does not exist.

For functions of two variables, we can make almost the same definition; that is, $\lim_{(x,y) \to (a,b)} f(x, y) = L$ if the values of $f(x, y)$ can be made arbitrarily close to L by considering points (x, y) sufficiently close to (a, b). Again, "close" has to mean "in a small circle surrounding (a, b)". The problem here is that (x, y) can approach (a, b) from infinitely many directions, not just from the left and the right. In order for us to claim that the limit exists, we must ensure that the same limit is attained for every possible approach.

Fortunately, for "nice" functions, we can evaluate the limit by substitution, much as we did for functions of one variable. For example, suppose $f(x, y) := 3x + 4y^3$. Then $\lim\limits_{(x,y) \to (1,-2)} f(x,y) = 3(1) + 4(-2)^3 = -29$.

The problem occurs when $f(a, b)$ is an indeterminate form such as 0/0. The next example illustrates.

EXAMPLE 12.20:

Let $f(x, y) := \dfrac{xy}{x^2 + y^2}$, for $(x, y) \neq (0, 0)$. Show that $\lim\limits_{(x,y) \to (0,0)} f(x,y)$ does not exist.

Let's see what happens as $(x, y) \to (0, 0)$ along several different paths. Suppose $(x, y) \to (0, 0)$ along the x-axis. Then $y = 0$ and $\lim\limits_{(x,y) \to (0,0)} \dfrac{xy}{x^2 + y^2}$ $= \lim\limits_{x \to 0} \dfrac{0}{x^2} = 0$. Similarly, if $x = 0$, then $\lim\limits_{(x,y) \to (0,0)} \dfrac{xy}{x^2 + y^2} = 0$. Now suppose $(x, y) \to (0, 0)$ along the line $y = mx$. Then $\lim\limits_{(x,y) \to (0,0)} \dfrac{xy}{x^2 + y^2} =$ $\lim\limits_{x \to 0} \dfrac{mx^2}{x^2 + (mx)^2} = \dfrac{m}{1 + m^2}$. So, for every different straight line through the origin, we get a different limit. Hence, $\lim\limits_{(x,y) \to (0,0)} \dfrac{xy}{x^2 + y^2}$ does not exist. ◆

Even if every straight line in the example above had yielded the same limit, that is not a guarantee the limit exists, since there might by some curved path that yields a different limit. So, while it is sometimes easy to show that limits do not exist, it is often harder to show that they do. We won't explore this any further here but you should remember that limits for functions of more than one variable are much more complicated than they were for functions of a single variable. Indeed, Murphy might have been thinking of such functions when he said, "Anything that can go wrong will go wrong".

TEST YOUR UNDERSTANDING

6. Evaluate each limit, if it exists:

(a) $\lim\limits_{(x,y) \to (2,1)} e^{x+y}$

(b) $\lim\limits_{(x,y) \to (0,0)} \dfrac{y}{xy + y - 1}$

7. Show that $\lim\limits_{(x,y)\to(0,0)}\dfrac{y}{x-y}$ does not exist by showing that two different paths yield different limits.

EXERCISES FOR SECTION 12.4:

1. Evaluate each of the following limits or show that they do not exist.

   (a) $\lim\limits_{(x,y)\to(3,2)}\dfrac{xy}{x+y}$ (b) $\lim\limits_{(x,y)\to(1,1)}\dfrac{x^2-y^2}{x-y}$ (c) $\lim\limits_{(x,y)\to(0,0)}\dfrac{x^3}{x^2+y^2}$

2. Determine the direction and concavity of each function at the given point P in the direction of the given point Q:

   (a) $f(x,y) := x^2 - y$; $P(0,1)$; $Q(1,0)$

   (b) $f(x,y) := x^3 + 3xy$; $P(1,2)$; $Q(-1,3)$

   (c) $f(x,y) := \sin(xy)$; $P(1,\pi/2)$; $Q(0,\pi)$

PROBLEMS FOR SECTION 12.4:

1. Show that $\dfrac{x^2 y}{x^4+y^2}$ goes to 0 if (x,y) approaches the origin along $y = mx$, but $\lim\limits_{(x,y)\to(0,0)}\dfrac{x^2 y}{x^4+y^2}$ does not exist. [Hint: Let (x,y) approach the origin along any parabola $y = mx^2$.]

2. Determine whether or not $\lim\limits_{(x,y)\to(0,0)}\dfrac{\sin(xy)}{x^2+y^2}$ exists.

3. Show in general that if $z = f(x,y)$ is increasing at $P(x_0,y_0)$ in the direction of v, then it is decreasing at $P(x_0,y_0)$ in the direction of $-v$.

TYU Answers for Section 12.4

1. $x = 2+t, y = 1+t$, $\phi_1(t) = 3+2t$ which is increasing near $t = 0$

   $x = 2+t, y = 1+3t$, $\phi_2(t) = 3-2t-8t^2$ which is decreasing near $t = 0$

2. increasing   3. concave down   4. Local max since $f(x,y) \le f(0,0) = 4$ for all x, y.

5. No local extremum since f is incr. along the x-axis and decr. along the y-axis

6. (a) e^3 (b) does not exist   7. Along $x = 0$, limit is -1; along $y = 0$, limit is 0

12.5 VECTOR FIELDS

We've now seen functions that assign a three-dimensional vector to a number and that assign a number to a point in R^2. What other kinds of functions might there be? One common and important type is a function that assigns a vector to a point.

Imagine water flowing down a river. At each point in the river, the water has a certain velocity--that is, a speed and direction. Due to various obstacles and currents, the velocity may differ from point to point. This suggests that we could define a function that associates a velocity with each point in the river. We'll restrict ourselves just to the surface of the river so that we can describe each point with an ordered pair (x, y). Then, assuming the velocity vectors are also two-dimensional, let $v = F(x, y) = \langle g(x, y), h(x, y) \rangle$ be the velocity of the water at the point (x, y). The function F is a two-dimensional vector function of two variables. Functions of this type, which associate a two-dimensional vector with each point in some domain of the xy-plane, are called **vector fields**. They are, in some sense, a combination of the functions that we studied in this chapter.

Note: It would probably be more realistic to treat the river as a three-dimensional space and the velocity as a three-dimensional vector. Then we would have $v = F(x, y, z) = \langle g(x, y, z), h(x, y, z), k(x, y, z) \rangle$. This is a three-dimensional vector field. Although for simplicity we will stick to two-dimensional fields, most of what we say here can easily be extended to higher dimensions.

For example, consider the vector field $F(x, y) := \langle y, -x \rangle$. Then, $F(0, 0) = \langle 0, 0 \rangle$, $F(1, 1) = \langle 1, -1 \rangle$, $F(3, 2) = \langle 2, -3 \rangle$, etc. Frequently, we represent vector fields graphically by drawing the vector $F(x, y)$ with its tail at (x, y) for various points in the xy-plane. Figure 12.31 shows several vectors in the vector field F.

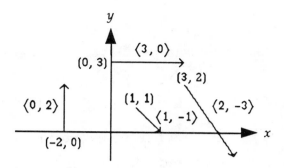

Fig. 12.31

Note that, for this vector field, $\|F(x,y)\| = \sqrt{y^2 + (-x)^2} = \sqrt{y^2 + x^2}$. Thus, all the points whose associated vectors are of length 1 lie on the circle $x^2 + y^2 = 1$, all the points whose associated vectors are of length 2 lie on the circle $x^2 + y^2 = 4$, etc. In general, all the points with associated vectors of length c lie on the circle $x^2 + y^2 = c^2$. Furthermore, for this particular vector field, the vector at each point (x, y) is perpendicular to the vector from the origin to (x, y). To see why, note that $\langle x, y \rangle \cdot F(x, y) = \langle x, y \rangle \cdot \langle y, -x \rangle = xy - xy = 0$. Physically, this field might represent the velocity field for a rotating wheel. A more complete graphical representation of this field is given in Figure 12.32.

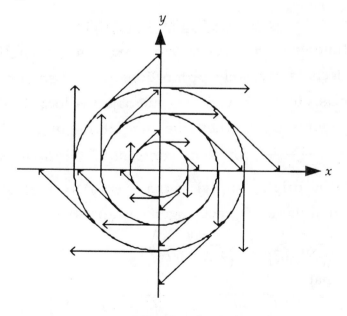

Fig. 12.32

EXAMPLE 12.21:

Sketch some vectors in the vector field $F(x, y) := \langle x + y, x - y \rangle$.

Since $\|F(x,y)\| = \sqrt{(x+y)^2 + (x-y)^2} = \sqrt{2x^2 + 2y^2}$, then all vectors of length 1 lie on the circle $x^2 + y^2 = \frac{1}{2}$. More generally, all vectors of length k lie on the circle $x^2 + y^2 = \frac{k^2}{2}$. Some typical vectors in this vector field are $F(1, 1) = \langle 2, 0 \rangle$, $F(0, 1) = \langle 1, -1 \rangle$ and $F(1, 0) = \langle 1, 1 \rangle$. These, along with a few others are represented in the Figure 12.33.

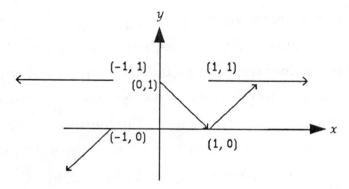

Fig. 12.33

◆

A SPECIAL VECTOR FIELD

It is a well-known fact from physics that the gravitational attraction between two objects is inversely proportional to the square of the distance between the objects. In other words, if one object is located at the origin and the other at the point (x, y), then the magnitude of the force exerted is $\|F(x,y)\| = \frac{k}{r^2} = \frac{k}{x^2 + y^2}$, for some constant k. Furthermore, the force is directed toward the origin, implying that $F(x, y)$ is a negative multiple of $\langle x, y \rangle$. We claim that these two facts together imply that

$$F(x, y) := \left\langle \frac{-kx}{(x^2 + y^2)^{3/2}}, \frac{-ky}{(x^2 + y^2)^{3/2}} \right\rangle .$$

To see why, note that

$$\|F(x,y)\| = \sqrt{\left(\frac{-kx}{(x^2 + y^2)^{3/2}}\right)^2 + \left(\frac{-ky}{(x^2 + y^2)^{3/2}}\right)^2}$$

$$= \sqrt{\frac{k^2(x^2 + y^2)}{(x^2 + y^2)^3}} = \frac{k}{x^2 + y^2} \text{ , as required.}$$

Some vectors in this field are shown in Figure 12.34.

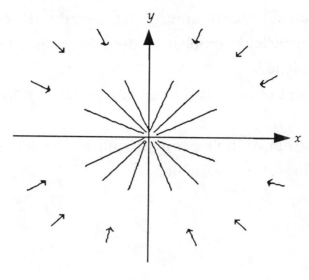

Fig. 12.34

EXERCISES FOR SECTION 12.5:

1. Sketch a few vectors in each of the following vector fields:

   (a) $F(x, y) := \langle x, 1 \rangle$ (b) $F(x, y) := \langle 2x, 3y \rangle$

   (c) $F(x, y) := \langle x - y, xy \rangle$

2. For the vector field in Exercise 1(b), determine the set of points in the xy-plane for which $\|F(x, y)\| = 4$.

3. Show that every vector in the field in Exercise 1(a) is at least 1 unit in length.

PROBLEMS FOR SECTION 12.5:

1. Determine a vector field that obeys the "inverse cube law"; that is, one for which the magnitude of the vectors is inversely proportional to the cube of the distance from the origin.

QUESTIONS TO THINK ABOUT

1. Describe some techniques that can be used to help visualize what a surface in three dimensions looks like.

2. Explain how we describe the direction and concavity of a surface. In particular, point out the differences between the three-dimensional case and the two-dimensional problem of describing direction and concavity of a curve in the plane.

3. Define the concept of local extremum of a surface. What types of extrema are there?

4. How is the concept of limit more difficult for functions of two variables than for functions of one variable?

PROJECT 12.1

THE CROSS PRODUCT

OBJECTIVE: In Problem 1 of Section 12.2, we asked you to find an equation of the plane containing 3 given points P, Q and R. One way to do this is to find a vector w perpendicular to the vector u joining P and Q and the vector v joining Q and R. Then w must be a normal vector for the desired plane. In this project, we investigate the problem of finding a vector perpendicular to two given vectors u and v. Of course, there are infinitely many such vectors, all of which are scalar multiples of each other. One of these vectors has some special properties and we will call it the **cross product** of u and v, written $u \times v$.

PROCEDURE:

Part 1: Defining the cross product

Let $u = \langle u_1, u_2, u_3 \rangle$ and $v = \langle v_1, v_2, v_3 \rangle$. Suppose $w = \langle a, b, c \rangle$ is to be perpendicular to u and v.

a. Argue that a, b and c must satisfy the system of equations
$u_1 a + u_2 b + u_3 c = 0$ and $v_1 a + v_2 b + v_3 c = 0$. Note that this system has infinitely many solutions since there are only two equations with three variables.

b. Show that the equations in 1a can be rewritten as $a = \left(\dfrac{u_2 v_3 - u_3 v_2}{u_1 v_2 - u_2 v_1} \right) c$

and $b = \left(\dfrac{u_3 v_1 - u_1 v_3}{u_1 v_2 - u_2 v_1} \right) c$. Thus, given a value of c, we can compute the corresponding values of a and b.

To get the cross-product, set $c = u_1 v_2 - u_2 v_1$ from which $a = u_2 v_3 - u_3 v_2$ and $b = u_3 v_1 - u_1 v_3$. Hence, we define the cross product:

$$u \times v = \langle u_2 v_3 - u_3 v_2, u_3 v_1 - u_1 v_3, u_1 v_2 - u_2 v_1 \rangle$$

c. Compute $u \times v$, where $u = \langle 3, 1, -2 \rangle$ and $v = \langle 1, 5, 3 \rangle$.

d. Let i, j, and k be unit vectors in the x-, y- and z-directions, respectively. Show that $i \times j = k$, $j \times k = i$ and $k \times i = j$.

e. Use the cross product to help you write an equation of the plane containing the points $(1, 0, 4)$, $(-2, 1, 3)$ and $(7, 2, -4)$.

Part 2: Properties of the cross product
  a. Show that the cross product of any vector with itself gives the zero vector.
  b. Prove that $u \times v = -v \times u$. (That is, the cross product is anti-commutative.)
  c. Prove that $u \cdot (v \times w) = (u \times v) \cdot w$.
  d. In the text, we claimed that $u \cdot v = \| u \| \| v \| \cos(\theta)$, where θ is the angle between u and v. Use this to show that $\| u \| \| v \| \sin(\theta) = \sqrt{\| u \|^2 \| v \|^2 - (u \cdot v)^2}$.
  e. Substitute for $\| u \|$, $\| v \|$ and $u \cdot v$ in terms of $u_1, v_1, u_2,...$, in the expression under the square root, multiply it all out and factor to show that $\| u \| \| v \| \sin(\theta) = \| u \times v \|$.
  f. Use 2e to determine the angle between the vectors in 1c.
  g. Use 2e to show that two non-zero vectors are parallel if and only if their cross product is the zero vector.

Part 3: Other geometric properties of the cross product
  a. Let u and v be vectors drawn so that they have the same tail. Draw a parallelogram with u and v as adjacent sides (much as we do when adding vectors). Show that the area of this parallelogram is $\| u \times v \|$.
  b. Use 3a to find the area of the parallelogram with vertices at $(1, 3, 4)$, $(2, 5, 8)$, $(7, 10, 16)$ and $(8, 12, 20)$.
  c. Let u, v and w be vectors not all in the same plane drawn so that they have the same tail. Consider the parallelepiped (three-dimensional parallelogram) with u, v and w as adjacent sides. It is not hard to show that the volume of this parallelepiped is given by
  $V = u \cdot (v \times w)$. Use this to find the volume of the parallelepiped with vertices at $(0, 0, 0)$, $(0, 0, 4)$, $(1, 0, 3)$, $(1, 0, 7)$, $(0, 6, 0)$, $(0, 6, 4)$, $(1, 6, 3)$ and $(1, 6, 7)$.
  d. Use the formula in 3c to show that non-zero vectors u, v and w are co-planar (lie in the same plane) if and only if $u \cdot (v \times w) = 0$.

PROJECT 12.2

ACCELERATION AND CURVATURE IN 3 DIMENSIONS

OBJECTIVE: In Chapter 9 and, in particular, Project 9.3, we showed how to write the acceleration vector for a curve as the sum of two components--one in the direction of motion (i.e. a scalar multiple of the unit tangent vector T) and one perpendicular to the direction of motion (i.e. a scalar multiple of the unit normal vector N). This, in turn, led to the notion of the curvature of a curve in 2 dimensions. Since we chose N to be counterclockwise to T, the curvature is positive if the curve is bent to the left (counterclockwise); otherwise, the curvature is negative.

In this project, we extend the notion of curvature to three-dimensional curves. The problem is complicated by the fact that in three dimensions, there is no such thing as "counterclockwise"--clocks are inherently two-dimensional objects--and so we'll have to be careful about how we define the unit normal vector N.

PROCEDURE:

Part 1: The unit tangent and unit normal vectors

Let $r(t) := \langle x(t), y(t), z(t) \rangle$ be the equation of a curve in three-dimensional space and let $v(t) := r'(t) := \langle x'(t), y'(t), z'(t) \rangle$ be the corresponding velocity vector. The speed is $v(t) := \| v(t) \|$.

a. Argue that $T(t) := \dfrac{v(t)}{v(t)}$ is a *unit* vector tangent to the curve.

b. Let $T'(t)$ represent the derivative of T with respect to t. Show that T' and T are perpendicular. [Hint: Since T is a unit vector, then $T \cdot T = 1$. Take the derivative of this equation with respect to t, making sure to invoke the product rule.]

It follows that $N(t) := \dfrac{T'(t)}{\| T'(t) \|}$ is a unit vector perpendicular to T. We call $N(t)$ the **principal unit normal vector**.

c. Compute $T(t)$ and $N(t)$ for the curve $r(t) := \langle \sin(t), \cos(t), 3t \rangle$. Show that they are indeed perpendicular.

d. Let $r(t) := \langle -\cos(t), \sin(t) \rangle$ be a two-dimensional curve. Compute $T(t)$ and $N(t)$ for this curve (using the definitions in 1a and b) and sketch them at $t = 0$. Is $N(t)$ $90°$ counterclockwise to $T(t)$.

e. Repeat 1d for $r(t) := \langle \cos(t), \sin(t) \rangle$.

Part 2: Tangential and normal components of acceleration

Let $a(t) := v'(t) = r''(t) := \langle x''(t), y''(t), z''(t) \rangle$ be the acceleration vector. We would like, if possible, to write $a(t) = a_T T(t) + a_N N(t)$, for some scalars a_T (called the **tangential coordinate**) and a_N (called the **normal coordinate**).

a. Differentiate $v(t) = v(t)T(t)$ with respect to t.

b. Substitute $T'(t) = \|T'(t)\| N(t)$ and conclude that
$$a(t) = v'(t)T(t) + v(t)\|T'(t)\| N(t).$$

It follows that the tangential coordinate of the acceleration is $a_T = v'(t)$ and the normal coordinate is $a_N = v(t)\|T'(t)\|$. Unfortunately, calculating the coordinates from these formulas can be messy, except in very simple cases such as those where $v(t)$ is constant, as in 1c. (Otherwise, the calculation of $T'(t)$ is particularly onerous.) Notice that $a(t)$, $T(t)$ and $N(t)$ are coplanar.

c. Starting with $a(t) = a_T T(t) + a_N N(t)$, show that $a_T = a(t) \cdot T(t)$ and $a_N = a(t) \cdot N(t)$.

d. Conclude that $a_T = \dfrac{a(t) \cdot v(t)}{v(t)}$

e. Use the fact that $\|a(t)\|^2 = a(t) \cdot a(t)$
$$= [a_T T(t) + a_N N(t)] \cdot [a_T T(t) + a_N N(t)]$$
to show that $a_N = \sqrt{\|a(t)\|^2 - a_T^2}$.

f. Compute the tangential and normal coordinates for the curve in 1c.

g. Repeat 2f for the curve $r(t) := \langle 2t, t^2, t \rangle$.

Part 3: Curvature

For curves in three-dimensions, we define the **curvature** by $\kappa(t) := \dfrac{\|T'(t)\|}{v(t)}$. [Note: This is not quite the same definition we gave in Project 9.3 for curvature in two-dimensions. There we allowed curvature to be positive when the curve bends counterclockwise and negative when it bends clockwise. As we stated earlier, these terms are meaningless in three dimensions. In this definition, curvature is always positive; however, the greater the curvature, the sharper the bend.]

a. Compute the curvature for the curve in 1c.

b. Use 2b to show that $a_N = \kappa(t)[v(t)]^2$.

c. Show that the curvature is always positive. What does this imply about the normal coordinate a_N?

d. Use the result in 3b to find the curvature for the curve in 2g.

e. Let C be the curve traced by the vector function $r(t)$ and let $\tilde{C}$ be the curve traced by the vector function $\tilde{r}(t) := 2r(t)$. How are the curvatures of C and $\tilde{C}$ related?

CHAPTER 13

PARTIAL DERIVATIVES

13.1 THE TANGENT LINE PROBLEM

In Section 12.4, we examined the problem of describing the direction and concavity of a function of two variables. We saw that the problem was complicated by the fact that a surface may be both increasing and decreasing at a given point, depending upon which way you look. For example, at a given point, $f(x, y)$ may increase if x increases but $f(x, y)$ may decrease if y increases. To clarify this problem, we specified a two-dimensional vector v = $\langle a, b \rangle$ and a point $P(x_0, y_0)$. Then we could say that $f(x, y)$ was either increasing or decreasing at P in the direction of v.

Specifically, let $x = x_0 + at, y = y_0 + bt$ be parametric equations for the line L that passes through P parallel to v. Let Π be the plane perpendicular to the xy-plane along L. Π intersects the surface $z = f(x, y)$ in some curve C. $S(x_0, y_0, f(x_0, y_0))$ is the point on the surface directly above P. See Figure 13.1.

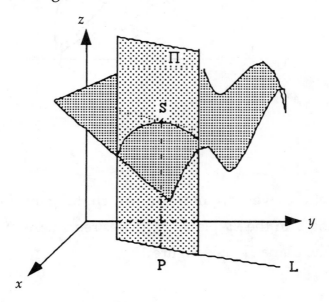

Fig. 13.1

C can be represented parametrically by $x = x_0 + at, y = y_0 + bt, z = \phi(t) = f(x_0 + at, y_0 + bt)$. We were able to determine whether the surface was increasing or decreasing at P by looking at the sign of $\phi'(t)$ for values of t near 0. (Remember that the point P corresponds to $t = 0$.)

To illustrate, consider the function $f(x, y) := x^2 + y^2$ in Example 12.17. Let P be the point $(1, 1)$ and let $v = \langle 1, 2 \rangle$. The line L through P parallel to v has parametric representation $x = 1 + t, y = 1 + 2t$, from which $\phi(t) := (1 + t)^2 + (1 + 2t)^2 = 2 + 6t + 5t^2$. Since $\phi'(t) := 6 + 10t$ is positive near $t = 0$, we conclude that the surface is increasing at P in the direction of v.

◻ The next thing to consider is the line tangent to the surface at S. Again, without additional information, this is not a well-defined problem since there are infinitely many such tangent lines. See Figure 13.2.

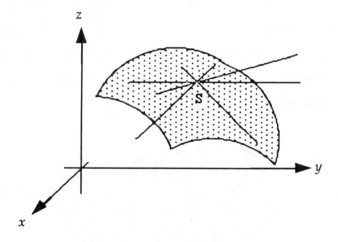

Fig. 13.2

As with direction, we can indicate which tangent line we want by specifying a vector v in the xy-plane. The desired line is the line T tangent to the curve C in the plane Π. See Figure 13.3.

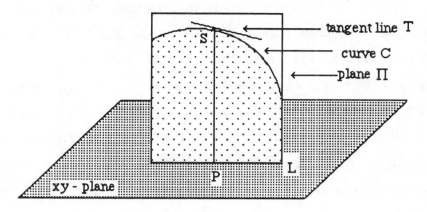

Fig. 13.3

If we restrict ourselves to the plane Π, then T is a line in two dimensions, so it makes sense to talk about its slope. Since T is tangent to C, and C is represented by the function $\phi(t)$, and the point of tangency S corresponds to $t = 0$, our first inclination might be that the slope of T is simply $\phi'(0)$. Hence, in the example above, we'd say that the slope of T is 6.

Unfortunately, this is wrong!! To see why, recall that we specified the vector v in order to tell us which way to look. Thus, only the direction, but not the magnitude of v, is used. In other words, any positive scalar multiple of v should lead to the same conclusions about the direction and concavity of the surface. In particular, let $w = \langle 2, 4 \rangle = 2v$. Then L is represented parametrically by $x = 1 + 2t, y = 1 + 4t$ and $\phi(t) := (1 + 2t)^2 + (1 + 4t)^2 = 2 + 12t + 20t^2$. Since $\phi'(t) := 12 + 40t$, we would claim that the slope of the tangent line is $\phi'(0) = 12$. A line cannot have two different slopes, so something is wrong.

Let's think again about what we mean by "slope". To say that the line $y = mx + b$ has slope m means that every time we move one unit in the x direction, the line goes up m units in the y direction. The key phrase is "one unit". Here, when we used the vector v to parameterize L, as t goes from 0 to 1, we move from $(1, 1)$ to $(2, 3)$ in the xy-plane, a distance of $\sqrt{5}$, which is not one unit. Using w moves us from $(1, 1)$ to $(3, 5)$ as t goes from 0 to 1, a distance of $2\sqrt{5}$.

The remedy for this problem is to pick the right vector with which to parameterize L--that is, pick a positive scalar multiple of v such that when t increases from 0 to 1 (or any other one unit increase), we move exactly one unit along L. In our example, let $u = kv = \langle k, 2k \rangle$, where $k > 0$. Then $x = 1 + kt, y = 1 + 2kt$ are parametric equations of L. When $t = 0$, we're at $(1, 1)$; when $t = 1$, we're at $(1 + k, 1 + 2k)$. The distance between these points is $\sqrt{k^2 + (2k)^2} = k\sqrt{5}$. In order for this distance to be 1, we should take $k = \frac{1}{\sqrt{5}}$ so that $u = \langle \frac{1}{\sqrt{5}}, \frac{2}{\sqrt{5}} \rangle$. Now $\phi(t) := (1 + \frac{1}{\sqrt{5}} t)^2 + (1 + \frac{2}{\sqrt{5}} t)^2 = 2 + \sqrt{5}t + t^2$, from which $\phi'(0) = \sqrt{5}$. This truly is the slope of the tangent line T.

Note that to get u, we divided v by $\sqrt{5}$. But $\sqrt{5}$ is the magnitude of v and, as we learned in Chapter 9, when we divide a vector by its magnitude, we get a unit vector in the same direction. Hence, u is a unit vector in the same direction as v. So, the key to getting the slope of the tangent line is to use a unit vector to parameterize L.

More generally, if we want to find the slope of the line tangent to a surface at a given point P in the direction of the vector v, we first find a unit vector $u = \langle u_1, u_2 \rangle$ in the same direction as v. Let $x = x_0 + u_1 t, y = y_0 + u_2 t$ be a parametric representation of L and let $\phi_u(t) := f(x_0 + u_1 t, y_0 + u_2 t)$ describe the curve C. Then the slope of the tangent line is $\phi'_u(0)$.

Note: Since the equation describing C depends on the vector used to parameterize L, we have introduced the subscript u on $\phi(t)$ to indicate which vector we are using.

EXAMPLE 13.1:

Let $f(x, y) := xy$. Determine the slope of the line tangent to this surface at $P(6, -1)$ in the direction of the vector $v = \langle 3, 4 \rangle$.

Since $\| v \| = 5$, then $u = \frac{1}{5} v = \langle \frac{3}{5}, \frac{4}{5} \rangle$ is a unit vector in the same direction as v. The line L through P in the direction of v is represented by $x = 6 + \frac{3}{5} t, y = -1 + \frac{4}{5} t$, so $\phi_u(t) := (6 + \frac{3}{5} t)(-1 + \frac{4}{5} t) = -6 + \frac{21}{5} t + \frac{12}{25} t^2$. Hence, the desired slope is $\phi'_u(0) = \frac{21}{5}$.   ◆

----

1. Find the slope of the line tangent to the surface in Example 13.1 at (1, 2) in the direction of the unit vector $u = \left\langle \dfrac{5}{13}, \dfrac{12}{13} \right\rangle$.

2. Find the slope of the line tangent to the surface in Example 13.1 at (1, 2) in the direction of the vector $v = \langle -1, 3 \rangle$.

3. Find the slope of the line tangent to $z = x^2 - 4y$ at (0, 2) in the direction of $v = \langle 2, -2 \rangle$.

¤ While the question of determining the slope of a tangent line is interesting in its own right, there is a much broader interpretation to the quantity $\phi'_u(0)$--it measures how fast the function values are increasing or decreasing as we move from point P in some specified direction. The use of unit vectors "standardizes the scale" and allows us to compare the rates of increase or decrease in different directions.

At this point, we'd like to introduce some terminology and notation. The slope of the tangent line clearly depends on the function f, the point P and the unit vector u, so our notation ought to encompass these aspects. Furthermore, $\phi'_u(0)$ is just a special type of derivative--a derivative in a specific direction. Hence, we have:

DEFINITION: Let $f(x, y)$ be a function, $P(x_0, y_0)$ be a point and $u = \langle u_1, u_2 \rangle$ be a unit vector.   Let $\phi_u(t) := f(x_0 + u_1 t, y_0 + u_2 t)$.   Then the **directional derivative of f at P in the direction of u** is $D_u f(x_0, y_0) = \phi'_u(0)$.

Invoking the definition of the derivative from Chapter 3, we have the equivalent statement $D_u f(x_0, y_0) = \lim\limits_{t \to 0} \dfrac{f(x_0 + t u_1, y_0 + t u_2) - f(x_0, y_0)}{t}$.

So we can now restate the result of Example 13.1 as follows: The directional derivative of $f(x, y) := xy$ at $(6, -1)$ in the direction of $u = \left\langle \frac{3}{5}, \frac{4}{5} \right\rangle$ is $D_u f(6, -1) = \frac{21}{5}$.

TEST YOUR UNDERSTANDING

4.   Determine the directional derivative of $f(x, y) := x + y^3$ at $(2, 0)$ in the direction of the unit vector $u = \left\langle \frac{2}{\sqrt{5}}, \frac{1}{\sqrt{5}} \right\rangle$.

◻ Now that we have the directional derivative, we should be able to write an equation of the line tangent to the surface in the given direction. Since this line is in three dimensions, we need to use parametric equations, as we learned in Chapter 12. First, we need to find a direction vector for the line.

Let's go back to functions of one variable for a minute. If $y = f(x)$, then the slope of the line tangent to f at $x = x_0$ is $f'(x_0)$. This means that the vector $\langle 1, f'(x_0) \rangle$ is parallel to the tangent line.

If we confine ourselves to the plane Π in Figure 13.3, then the slope of the line tangent to C at S is $D_u f(x_0, y_0)$. Hence, the vector $\langle 1, D_u f(x_0, y_0) \rangle$ is parallel to the tangent line. In other words, if we move 1 unit along L, the tangent line goes up by $D_u f(x_0, y_0)$. However, that 1 unit move along L is equivalent to a movement of u_1 in the x-direction and u_2 in the y-direction. Therefore, we claim:

THEOREM 13.1: The vector $v = \langle u_1, u_2, D_u f(x_0, y_0) \rangle$ is parallel to the line tangent to the surface $z = f(x, y)$ at the point (x_0, y_0) in the direction of the unit vector u. Consequently, the tangent line can be represented parametrically by:

$$x = x_0 + u_1 t, \quad y = y_0 + u_2 t, \quad z = f(x_0, y_0) + D_u f(x_0, y_0)t$$

EXAMPLE 13.2:

Write parametric equations for the line tangent to $f(x, y) := xy$ at $(6, -1)$ in the direction of $u = \left\langle \frac{3}{5}, \frac{4}{5} \right\rangle$.

We've shown in Example 13.1 that $D_u f(6, -1) = \frac{21}{5}$. Since $f(6, -1) = -6$, then the equations are $x = 6 + \frac{3}{5} t$, $y = -1 + \frac{4}{5} t$, $z = -6 + \frac{21}{5} t$. ◆

We end this section with some practical interpretations of the directional derivative.

EXAMPLE 13.3:

The temperature at the point (x, y) is given by the function $f(x, y) := xy^2 + x + 20$. What is the instantaneous rate of change in the temperature felt by a bug that leaves $P(3, 2)$ and moves in a straight line towards $Q(5, 1)$?

We're looking for the directional derivative of f at $(3, 2)$ in the direction of a unit vector u, where u is parallel to the vector PQ. The vector PQ has coordinates $\langle 3, -1 \rangle$ and magnitude $\sqrt{10}$. Hence, $u = \left\langle \frac{3}{\sqrt{10}}, \frac{-1}{\sqrt{10}} \right\rangle$ is the desired unit vector. Then $x = 3 + \frac{3}{\sqrt{10}} t$, $y = 2 - \frac{1}{\sqrt{10}} t$ and

$$\phi_u(t) := \left(3 + \frac{3}{\sqrt{10}} t\right)\left(2 - \frac{1}{\sqrt{10}} t\right)^2 + 3 + \frac{3}{\sqrt{10}} t + 20$$

$$= 35 + \frac{3}{\sqrt{10}} t - \frac{9}{10} t^2 + \frac{3}{10\sqrt{10}} t^3.$$

Thus, $D_u f(3, 2) = \phi_u'(0) = \frac{3}{\sqrt{10}}$ is the rate of change in temperature. ◆

In this example, the temperature is a function of x and y, two variables that describe the location of a point in the xy-plane. Hence, the directional derivative has the interpretation as the rate of change in temperature as we move from one point in the plane towards another point. Sometimes, however, the independent variables for the function being considered do not have quite the same geometric flavor. In particular, there are many applications in which one independent variable measures location and the other measures time. In cases like this, the directional derivative is somewhat harder to interpret physically, except in special instances.

For example, in Chapter 12, we studied the problem of a see-saw attached to a spring. We showed that the height of the see-saw at a point x units from its fulcrum at time t is given by the function $f(x, t) := \dfrac{x \cos(\omega t)}{16}$, where ω is a constant. After a bit of algebra, it can be shown that if we keep x fixed and change t--that is, move in the direction of the unit vector $j = \langle 0, 1\rangle$--we get $D_j f(x, t) := \dfrac{-x \, \omega \sin(\omega t)}{16}$. This tells us how fast a person sitting at coordinate x on the seesaw is moving up and down. For example, $D_j f(0, t)$ = 0 for all t since the fulcrum (x = 0) never moves. On the other hand, $D_j f(x, t)$ increases in absolute value as x increases for any time t. This means that person far from the fulcrum is moving faster than one close to the fulcrum.

It also can be shown that the directional derivative in the direction of the unit vector $i = \langle 1, 0\rangle$ is $D_i f(x, t) = \dfrac{\cos(\omega t)}{16}$. This tells us how fast the height of a person sitting on the seesaw changes as the person slides along the seesaw at any given time t. Since the seesaw is a straight line (with constant slope), this rate of change ought to be independent of x for any t, and indeed it is.

It is these special cases of directional derivatives--those in which the direction is either i or j--that are the subject of the next section.

EXERCISES FOR SECTION 13.1:

1. Let $f(x, y) := x^2 - 2xy$ and let $P(3, -1)$ be a point in the xy-plane.

   (a) Determine the directional derivative of f at P in the direction of $u = \left\langle \frac{2}{3}, \frac{\sqrt{5}}{3} \right\rangle$.

   (b) Determine the directional derivative of f at P in the direction of $v = \langle 2, 3 \rangle$.

   (c) Write parametric equations for the line tangent to the graph of f at P in the direction of $v = \langle 2, 3 \rangle$.

2. The directional derivative of a function f at the point (x, y) in the direction of $u = \left\langle \frac{1}{\sqrt{2}}, \frac{1}{\sqrt{2}} \right\rangle$ is $D_u f(x, y) = (y - 2)\frac{1}{\sqrt{2}} + (x + 6y)\frac{1}{\sqrt{2}}$.

   (a) Write parametric equations for the line tangent to f at $(3, 4)$ in the direction of u.

   (b) Determine all points (x, y) at which the line tangent to the graph of f in the direction of u is horizontal.

3. A plane perpendicular to xy-plane through $P(1, -2)$ in the direction of some unit vector u intersects a surface $z = f(x, y)$ in some curve C. If C is defined by the function $\phi_u(t) := 8 - 7t + 14t^2$, what is:

   (a) $f(1, -2)$ (b) $D_u f(1, -2)$

4. The directional derivative of a function f at the point $P(2, -3)$ in the direction of some unit vector u is $D_u f(2, -3) = -12u_1 + 4u_2$. Write parametric equations for the line tangent to the graph of f at P that is parallel to the xz-plane.

5. Determine parametric equations for the curve formed by the intersection of $f(x, y) := x^2 y^2$ and the plane $x + y = 4$.

6. Write parametric equations for the line tangent to the curve in Exercise 5 at $(2, 2, 16)$.

PROBLEMS FOR SECTION 13.1:

1. Suppose f is a function such that $D_u f(3, 1) = u_1 - 3u_2$.

   (a) Determine a unit vector u such that line tangent to the graph of f at $(3, 1)$ is horizontal.

(b) Show that there is no unit vector such that $D_u f(3, 1) = 4$.

2. Let f be the function in Problem 1 and suppose $f(3, 1) = 5$.

(a) Let L_1 be the line tangent to the graph of f at $(3, 1)$ in the direction of $\left\langle \frac{3}{5}, \frac{4}{5} \right\rangle$ and L_2 be the line tangent to the graph of f in the direction of $\left\langle \frac{4}{5}, \frac{-3}{5} \right\rangle$. Write parametric equations for L_1 and L_2.

(b) Show that L_1 and L_2 both lie on the plane $x - 3y - z = -5$.

(c) Show that the line tangent to f at $(3, 1)$ in any direction also lies on the plane in (b).

TYU Answers for Section 13.1

1. $\dfrac{22}{13}$ 2. $\dfrac{1}{\sqrt{10}}$ 3. $\dfrac{4}{\sqrt{2}} = 2\sqrt{2}$ 4. $\dfrac{2}{\sqrt{5}}$

13.2 PARTIAL DERIVATIVES AND GRADIENTS

So far, we've computed directional derivatives by first determining $\phi_u(t)$, an equation for the curve C formed by the intersection of the surface $z = f(x, y)$ and a plane perpendicular to the xy-plane in the direction of the unit vector u. Then $D_u f(x_0, y_0) = \phi_u'(0)$. Admittedly, if f is complicated, this can be algebraically messy; hence, we seek a more efficient method for finding directional derivatives.

The key is to look at the special cases we mentioned in the last section. Suppose $u = i$. Then

$$D_u f(x_0, y_0) = \lim_{t \to 0} \frac{f(x_0 + t, y_0) - f(x_0, y_0)}{t}.$$

Look at this carefully: y remains fixed at y_0 so f is really just a function of x. Let $g(x) := f(x, y_0)$. Then, by the definition of the derivative,

$$g'(x_0) := \lim_{t \to 0} \frac{g(x_0 + t) - g(x_0)}{t} = \lim_{t \to 0} \frac{f(x_0 + t, y_0) - f(x_0, y_0)}{t}.$$

Hence, the directional derivative in this case is nothing more than the derivative of f with respect to x, treating y as a constant.

Similarly, if $u = j$, then

$$D_u f(x_0, y_0) = \lim_{t \to 0} \frac{f(x_0, y_0 + t) - f(x_0, y_0)}{t} = \lim_{t \to 0} \frac{h(y_0 + t) - h(y_0)}{t},$$

where $h(y) := f(x_0, y)$. Here, the directional derivative is the derivative of f with respect to y, treating x as a constant.

These special cases are very important and we give them special names. Let $z = f(x, y)$ be a function of two variables. Then:

DEFINITION: The **partial derivative of f with respect to x** is:
$$f_x(x, y) = \lim_{\Delta x \to 0} \frac{f(x + \Delta x, y) - f(x, y)}{\Delta x}.$$

The **partial derivative of f with respect to y** is:
$$f_y(x, y) = \lim_{\Delta y \to 0} \frac{f(x, y + \Delta y) - f(x, y)}{\Delta y}.$$

In other words, $f_x(x, y) = D_i f(x, y)$ and $f_y(x, y) = D_j f(x, y)$. Note the similarity to the definition of the derivative for functions of one variable in Chapter 3. The only difference is that here we have two variables, one of which is changing, the other remaining fixed. Remember that, for the partial derivative with respect to x, y remains fixed and x changes. For the partial derivative with respect to y, x remains fixed and y changes.

There are several different notations for partial derivatives. In addition to $f_x(x, y)$, you may also see $\frac{\partial z}{\partial x}$, $f_1(x, y)$ or $D_x f(x, y)$ to represent the partial derivative with respect to x. The subscript "1" in the second notation indicates that the derivative is with respect to the first variable listed. Note that the "∂" in the first notation is different from the "d" used for ordinary derivatives. Similarly, the partial derivative with respect to y is denoted $f_y(x, y)$, $\frac{\partial z}{\partial y}$, $f_2(x, y)$ or $D_y f(x, y)$. As always, we shall use the notations interchangeably.

Calculating partial derivatives is easy; certainly, we won't ever need to use the definition. Just remember which variable remains fixed, treat it as a constant, and differentiate with respect to the other variable, as we have always done.

EXAMPLE 13.4:

Let $f(x, y) := x^2 + xy$. Determine $f_x(x, y)$ and $f_y(x, y)$.

Treating y as a constant and differentiating with respect to x, we find

$$f_x(x, y) = 2x + y.$$

Treating x as a constant and differentiating with respect to y, we find

$$f_y(x, y) = x. \qquad \blacklozenge$$

EXAMPLE 13.5:

Let $f(x, y) := x^3 e^{2y}$. Determine $f_x(x, y)$ and $f_y(x, y)$.

For $f_x(x, y)$, treat y (and hence e^{2y}) as a constant. Therefore,

$$f_x(x, y) := 3x^2 e^{2y}.$$

For $f_y(x, y)$, treat x (and hence x^3) as a constant. Therefore,

$$f_y(x, y) := x^3 (e^{2y})(2) = 2x^3 e^{2y}. \qquad \blacklozenge$$

EXAMPLE 13.6:

Let $f(x, y) := xy \ln(y)$. Find $f_y(x, y)$.

Treating x as a constant and using the product rule, we have

$$f_y(x, y) := x[y(1/y) + \ln(y)] = x[1 + \ln(y)]. \qquad \blacklozenge$$

EXAMPLE 13.7:

Let $z = \dfrac{x}{x^2 + y^2}$. Determine $\dfrac{\partial z}{\partial x}$.

Treating y as a constant and invoking the quotient rule, we have

$$\frac{\partial z}{\partial x} = \frac{(x^2 + y^2)(1) - (2x)x}{(x^2 + y^2)^2} = \frac{y^2 - x^2}{(x^2 + y^2)^2}. \qquad \blacklozenge$$

EXAMPLE 13.8:

Let $z = \sin(x^2 y)$. Determine $\dfrac{\partial z}{\partial y}$.

Treating x as constant, we differentiate with respect to y using the chain rule. So,

$$\frac{\partial z}{\partial y} = [\cos(x^2 y)](x^2) = x^2 \cos(x^2 y). \qquad \blacklozenge$$

TEST YOUR UNDERSTANDING

1. Determine $\dfrac{\partial z}{\partial x}$ for the function in Example 13.8.

2. Determine $\dfrac{\partial z}{\partial x}$ and $\dfrac{\partial z}{\partial y}$ for each of the following:

   (a) $z = \dfrac{x}{y^2}$ (b) $z = e^{xy}$ (c) $z = \ln(x^2 + 3y)$ (d) $z = x\cos(xy^2)$

¤ Now let's see how the directional derivative in an arbitrary direction u is related to the partial derivatives. Look at the function in Example 13.4. Let (x_0, y_0) be an arbitrary point in the xy-plane and let $u = \langle u_1, u_2 \rangle$ be a unit vector. Then

$$\phi_u(t) := (x_0 + tu_1)^2 + (x_0 + tu_1)(y_0 + tu_2)$$
$$= x_0^2 + x_0 y_0 + 2x_0 t u_1 + t^2 u_1^2 + x_0 t u_2 + y_0 t u_1 + t^2 u_1 u_2$$

Thus, $\phi_u{}'(t) := 2x_0 u_1 + 2t u_1^2 + x_0 u_2 + y_0 u_1 + 2t u_1 u_2$ from which

$$D_u f(x_0, y_0) = \phi_u{}'(0) = 2x_0 u_1 + x_0 u_2 + y_0 u_1$$

or, upon generalizing to an arbitrary point, we have:

$$D_u f(x, y) := 2x u_1 + x u_2 + y u_1$$
$$= (2x + y)u_1 + x u_2.$$

Written in this form, it should remind you of the dot product of two vectors. Indeed, after a bit of thought, we realize that:

$$D_u f(x, y) = \langle 2x + y, x \rangle \cdot \langle u_1, u_2 \rangle .$$

The second vector on the right side is just u. The first vector, $\langle 2x + y, x \rangle$ has components which are the partial derivatives of f, first with respect to x and then with respect to y. Hence, we might be tempted to claim that

(1) $D_{\boldsymbol{u}}f(x,y) = \langle f_x(x,y), f_y(x,y)\rangle \cdot \boldsymbol{u}$.

Let's try another example. Suppose $f(x,y) := x^3 e^{2y}$ as in Example 13.5. Then $\phi_{\boldsymbol{u}}(t) := f(x+tu_1, y+tu_2) = (x+tu_1)^3 e^{2(y+tu_2)}$. After a bit of work, we can show that $\phi_{\boldsymbol{u}}'(t) := e^{2(y+tu_2)}[2u_2(x+tu_1)^3 + 3u_1(x+tu_1)^2]$ so

$$D_{\boldsymbol{u}}f(x,y) = \phi_{\boldsymbol{u}}'(0) = e^{2y}[2u_2 x^3 + 3u_1 x^2] = \langle 3x^2 e^{2y}, 2x^3 e^{2y}\rangle \cdot \boldsymbol{u}.$$

Again, the vector containing the partial derivatives appears in the answer.

To show that Eq.(1) is true in general, recall that $D_{\boldsymbol{u}}f(x_0, y_0)$ measures the instantaneous rate of change in values of f as we move from (x_0, y_0) in the direction of $\boldsymbol{u}$. This motion can be broken down into two components, one in the x-direction and one in the y-direction. See Figure 13.4.

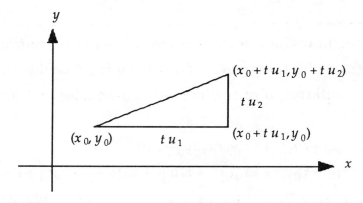

Fig. 13.4

Clearly, $f(x_0 + tu_1, y_0 + tu_2) - f(x_0, y_0) =$
    $[f(x_0 + tu_1, y_0 + tu_2) - f(x_0 + tu_1, y_0)] + [f(x_0 + tu_1, y_0) - f(x_0, y_0)].$

$f(x_0 + tu_1, y_0) - f(x_0, y_0)$ represents the change in function values as we move in the x-direction, keeping y fixed. Recall that for functions of one variable, we can approximate changes in function values using the derivative; that is, if g is differentiable,

    $g(x + \Delta x) - g(x) \approx g'(x)\Delta x,$

for small Δx. So, if t is small and f_x exists, we can write

$$f(x_0 + t u_1, y_0) - f(x_0, y_0) \approx f_x(x_0, y_0)tu_1.$$

Similarly, $f(x_0 + t u_1, y_0 + t u_2) - f(x_0 + t u_1, y_0)$ represents the change in function values as we move in the y-direction, keeping x fixed. By the same argument,

$$f(x_0 + tu_1, y_0 + tu_2) - f(x_0 + tu_1, y_0) \approx f_y(x_0 + tu_1, y_0)tu_2$$

if f_y exists. Therefore,

(2) $f(x_0 + t u_1, y_0 + t u_2) - f(x_0, y_0) \approx f_x(x_0, y_0)tu_1 + f_y(x_0 + tu_1, y_0)tu_2.$

Upon dividing by t and taking the limit as $t \to 0$, we get:

$$D_u f(x_0, y_0) = \lim_{t \to 0} \frac{f(x_0 + t u_1, y_0 + t u_2) - f(x_0, y_0)}{t}$$

$$= \lim_{t \to 0} \left[f_x(x_0, y_0)u_1 + f_y(x_0 + t u_1, y_0)u_2 \right]$$

$$= f_x(x_0, y_0)u_1 + f_y(x_0, y_0)u_2 = \langle f_x(x_0, y_0), f_y(x_0, y_0) \rangle \cdot u$$

as we surmised.

There are some technicalities which we must take into account. For reasons beyond the scope of this book, the proof above requires not only that f_x and f_y exist at (x_0, y_0) but that they be continuous in some region around (x_0, y_0). Although mathematicians would use the phrase "continuously differentiable" to describe such functions, we shall simply describe them as **nice**. Now we can state:

THEOREM 13.2: If f is nice in a region around (x_0, y_0), then the directional derivative of f in the direction of the unit vector **u** is given by

$$D_u f(x_0, y_0) = \langle f_x(x_0, y_0), f_y(x_0, y_0) \rangle \cdot u.$$

So, to find the directional derivative of f at (x_0, y_0) in the direction of **u**, just find the partial derivatives of f, evaluate them at (x_0, y_0), put them in a vector and take the dot product of that vector with the unit vector **u**.

EXAMPLE 13.9:

Let $f(x, y) := x^3 + 3x^2y^4 + 7$. Determine the directional derivative of f at (2, 1) in the direction of the unit vector $u = \left\langle \frac{1}{\sqrt{5}}, \frac{2}{\sqrt{5}} \right\rangle$. (Note that polynomials such as this are nice.)

The partial derivatives are $f_x(x, y) := 3x^2 + 6xy^4$ and $f_y(x, y) := 12x^2y^3$. Thus, $\langle f_x(2,1), f_y(2,1) \rangle = \langle 24, 48 \rangle$ from which

$$D_u f(2, 1) = \langle 24, 48 \rangle \cdot \langle u_1, u_2 \rangle = 24u_1 + 48u_2 = \frac{120}{\sqrt{5}} = 24\sqrt{5} . \qquad \blacklozenge$$

◻ The vector containing the partial derivatives that appears in Theorem 13.2 is very special and we give it a name.

DEFINITION: Let $f(x, y)$ be a function of two variables. The **gradient** of f is the vector $\nabla f(x, y) = \langle f_x(x, y), f_y(x, y) \rangle$; that is, the vector whose components are the partial derivatives of f with respect to x and with respect to y.

The ∇ is an upside-down capital delta and is pronounced either "del" or "grad". Hence, Theorem 13.2 can be restated as:

THEOREM 13.2': If f is nice in a region around (x_0, y_0), then the directional derivative of f in the direction of the unit vector u is given by

$$D_u f(x_0, y_0) = \nabla f(x_0, y_0) \cdot u .$$

Do not overlook the hypothesis of this theorem requiring that f be nice near (x_0, y_0). In Example 12.21, we considered the function

$$f(x, y) := \begin{cases} \dfrac{xy}{x^2 + y^2} & \text{if } x^2 + y^2 \neq 0 \\ 0 & \text{if } x^2 + y^2 = 0 \end{cases} .$$

It can be shown (see the problems at the end of this section) that for this function, $f_x(0, 0) = 0$ and $f_y(0, 0) = 0$ but if $u \neq i$ or j, the directional derivative $D_u f(0, 0)$ does not exist. Hence, $D_u f(0, 0)$ is certainly not equal to $\nabla f(0, 0) \cdot u$ for this function. Fortunately, most of the functions we'll deal with throughout this chapter are nice, so we won't have to worry about this very much.

TEST YOUR UNDERSTANDING

3. For the function in Example 13.9, evaluate

   (a) $D_u f(2, 1)$ where $u = \left\langle \frac{3}{5}, \frac{-4}{5} \right\rangle$ (b) $D_u f(1, -1)$ where $u = \left\langle \frac{3}{5}, \frac{-4}{5} \right\rangle$.

4. Let $f(x, y) := xy^2$. Determine:

   (a) $\nabla f(x, y)$.

   (b) $D_u f(-3, 3)$ where $u = \left\langle \frac{8}{17}, \frac{15}{17} \right\rangle$

EXERCISES FOR SECTION 13.2:

1. For each function below, determine f_x and f_y.

   (a) $f(x, y) := (x + 4y)^3$ (b) $f(x, y) := \dfrac{x^2}{y^2 + 1}$

   (c) $f(x, y) := \sqrt{x^2 + y^2}$ (d) $f(x, y) := \sin(x^3 y)$

   (e) $f(x, y) := (1 + xy)^5$ (f) $f(x, y) := x^2 e^{-x^2 y^2}$

   (g) $f(x, y) := \arctan(y/x)$ (h) $f(x, y) := \sqrt{\dfrac{x}{y + 1}}$

   (i) $f(x, y) := \ln(x - y^3)$ (j) $f(x, y) := x \cos(y^2)$

2. For each function in Exercise 1, evaluate the gradient of f at $(2, 1)$.

3. Compute the directional derivative for the function in Exercise 1(d) at $(1, 0)$ in the direction of $u = \left\langle \frac{5}{13}, \frac{-12}{13} \right\rangle$.

4. If $f_x(2, 3) = -1, f_y(2, 3) = 4$ and $f(2, 3) = 6$, determine:

  (a) $\nabla f(2, 3)$.

  (b) $D_u f(2, 3)$ where $u = \left\langle \dfrac{-5}{13}, \dfrac{12}{13} \right\rangle$.

5. If $f_x(-2, 0) = 3$ and $f_y(-2, 0) = 6$, determine the directional derivative of f at $(-2, 0)$:

  (a) in the direction of the unit vector $u = \left\langle \dfrac{3}{\sqrt{13}}, \dfrac{2}{\sqrt{13}} \right\rangle$.

  (b) in the direction from $(-2, 0)$ toward the point $(1, 1)$.

6. Let $f(x, y) := 4x^3 y^2$.

  (a) Determine the partial derivatives $f_x(x, y)$ and $f_y(x, y)$.

  (b) Evaluate the gradient of f at $(1, -1)$.

  (c) Compute the directional derivative of f at $(1, -1)$ in the direction of $(5, 2)$.

  (d) Write parametric equations of the line tangent to the graph of f at $(1, -1)$ in the direction of $(5, 2)$.

7. Let L be the line tangent to the graph $f(x, y) := 9 - x^2$ at $(1, 1)$ in the direction of the point $(2, 2)$. At what point does L intersect the xy-plane?

8. Let M be the line tangent to the surface in Exercise 7 at $(1, 1)$ in the direction of the point $(4, 5)$. At what point does M intersect the plane $x + y = 19$?

9. The wind chill factor R is a function of air temperature T and wind speed W. (See Example 1.3 in Section 1.1 and Problem 5 in Section 12.2.) R measures how cold it actually feels to the skin. What is the interpretation of the partial derivatives R_T and R_W? Would you expect them to be positive or negative?

10. The average time w an arbitrary customer would expect to wait in a queue (waiting line, perhaps at the grocery store or bank) depends on the arrival rate c of the customers and the rate s at which the servers serve. (Both c and s are measured in units such as customers per hour.) Is the partial derivative of w with respect to s positive or negative? What about the partial derivative of w with respect to c?

PROBLEMS FOR SECTION 13.2:

1. Prove that $\nabla[f(x, y)g(x, y)] = f(x, y)\nabla g(x, y) + g(x, y)\nabla f(x, y)$.

2. Suppose $x = g(u, v)$ and $y = h(u, v)$. The **Jacobian** of x and y with respect to u and v is defined to be $J = \dfrac{\partial x}{\partial u}\dfrac{\partial y}{\partial v} - \dfrac{\partial x}{\partial v}\dfrac{\partial y}{\partial u}$. Compute the Jacobian if $x = u^2 + v^2$ and $y = uv$.

3. Let $f(x, y) = \begin{cases} \dfrac{xy}{x^2 + y^2} & \text{if } x^2 + y^2 \neq 0 \\ 0 & \text{if } x^2 + y^2 = 0 \end{cases}$.

    (a) Use the definition of the partial derivatives of f with respect to x and with respect to y to show that $f_x(0, 0) = 0$ and $f_y(0, 0) = 0$.

    (b) Use the definition of the directional derivative to show that if $u = \langle u_1, u_2 \rangle$, then $D_u f(0, 0) = \lim\limits_{t \to 0} \dfrac{u_1 u_2}{t}$.

    (c) Conclude from (b) that if neither u_1 nor u_2 is 0, then $D_u f(0, 0)$ does not exist and so can't be equal to $f_x(0, 0)u_1 + f_y(0, 0)u_2 = 0$.

4. Consider the function in Problem 3.

    (a) Show that, for $(x, y) \neq (0, 0)$, $f_x(x, y) = \dfrac{y(y^2 - x^2)}{(x^2 + y^2)^2}$.

    (b) We know from Problem 3(a) that $f_x(0, 0) = 0$. Show that $\lim\limits_{y \to 0} f_x(0, y) = \lim\limits_{y \to 0} \dfrac{1}{y}$ does not exist and hence, f_x is not continuous in any region around $(0, 0)$.

13.3 USES AND PROPERTIES OF THE GRADIENT

The gradient is a very important quantity and plays much the same role for functions of two variables that derivatives play for functions of one variable. Let's look at some instances.

1. Approximating functions and the tangent plane

We know from Chapter 3 that an equation for the line tangent to the graph of $y = f(x)$ at $x = x_0$ is $y = f(x_0) + f'(x_0)(x - x_0)$. We can use this tangent line to approximate $f(x)$ for x-values near x_0. Equivalently, if $\Delta x = x - x_0$, then

$$f(x_0 + \Delta x) - f(x_0) \approx f'(x_0)\Delta x.$$

Here, we'd like to approximate $f(x_0 + \Delta x, y_0 + \Delta y)$ in terms of $f(x_0, y_0)$. One approach is to look at the tangent line through $P(x_0, y_0)$ in the direction of the point $Q(x_0 + \Delta x, y_0 + \Delta y)$. The slope of this line is the directional derivative of f in the direction of u, where u is a unit vector in the same direction as PQ. Hence, the z-component of the tangent line is given by

$$z = f(x_0, y_0) + t\, D_u f(x_0, y_0) = f(x_0, y_0) + t[\nabla f(x_0, y_0) \cdot u]$$

if f is nice.

Let t_0 be the value of t corresponding to Q. Since we've coordinatized PQ in terms of the unit vector u with P as the origin ($t = 0$), then the length of PQ is just t_0. Then,

$$f(x_0 + \Delta x, y_0 + \Delta y) \approx f(x_0, y_0) + t_0[\nabla f(x_0, y_0) \cdot u].$$

The coordinates of the vector from P to Q are $\langle \Delta x, \Delta y \rangle$ so $t_0 = \sqrt{(\Delta x)^2 + (\Delta y)^2}$ and $u = \frac{1}{t_0}\langle \Delta x, \Delta y \rangle$. See Figure 13.5.

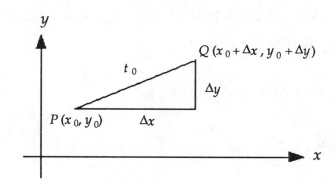

Fig. 13.5

Thus,

(3) $f(x_0 + \Delta x, y_0 + \Delta y) \approx f(x_0, y_0) + t_0 \dfrac{1}{t_0} \nabla f(x_0, y_0) \cdot \langle \Delta x, \Delta y \rangle$

$= f(x_0, y_0) + \nabla f(x_0, y_0) \cdot \langle \Delta x, \Delta y \rangle.$

Note the similarity to the one-dimensional result. The difference is that the derivative is replaced by the gradient, the Δx factor is replaced by the vector $\langle \Delta x, \Delta y \rangle$ and ordinary multiplication is replaced by the dot product. This is a very common theme.

EXAMPLE 13.10:

Let $f(x, y) := x^3 + 3x^2 y^4 + 7$ as in Example 13.9.   Use Eq.(3) to approximate the value of $f(2.1, 1.05)$.

Set $x_0 = 2, y_0 = 1, \Delta x = .1$ and $\Delta y = .05$. Since $f(2, 1) = 27$ and we've already determined $\nabla f(2, 1) = \langle 24, 48 \rangle$, then $f(2.1, 1.05) \approx 27 + \langle 24, 48 \rangle \cdot \langle .1, .05 \rangle = 31.8.$ ◆

TEST YOUR UNDERSTANDING

1. For a certain function, $f(3, 2) = 4$ and $\nabla f(3, 2) = \langle -1, 5 \rangle$. Estimate the value of $f(2.5, 2.2)$.

¤   Eq.(3) has a geometric interpretation. If we expand the dot product in terms of its components, we get:

(4) $z = f(x_0, y_0) + f_x(x_0, y_0)\Delta x + f_y(x_0, y_0)\Delta y$

$$= f(x_0, y_0) + f_x(x_0, y_0)(x - x_0) + f_y(x_0, y_0)(y - y_0)$$

or, equivalently, $f_x(x_0, y_0)x + f_y(x_0, y_0)y - z = d$,   for some constant d. Written in this form, it reminds us of the equation of a plane that we encountered in Chapter 12. Indeed, the set of all points satisfying Eq.(4) does constitute a plane, called the **tangent plane** for the surface. Figure 13.6 shows a surface and the tangent plane drawn at a point.

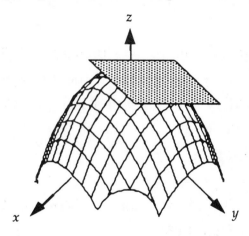

Fig. 13.6

In view of Theorem 12.3, we have:

THEOREM 13.3: If f is nice near (x_0, y_0), then an equation of the plane tangent to $z = f(x, y)$ at (x_0, y_0, z_0) is
$$f_x(x_0, y_0)(x - x_0) + f_y(x_0, y_0)(y - y_0) - (z - z_0) = 0.$$

An immediate consequence of this theorem is that the three-dimensional vector $v = \langle f_x(x_0, y_0), f_y(x_0, y_0), -1 \rangle$ is perpendicular (normal) to the tangent plane and, consequently, to the surface at the point $(x_0, y_0, f(x_0, y_0))$. Furthermore, we know that the vector $w = \langle u_1, u_2, D_u f(x_0, y_0) \rangle$ is a direction vector for the line tangent to the graph of f in the direction of u. Now $v \cdot w = f_x(x_0, y_0)u_1 + f_y(x_0, y_0)u_2 - D_u f(x_0, y_0) = D_u f(x_0, y_0) - D_u f(x_0, y_0) = 0$ for every u. Thus, the direction vector for every tangent line is perpendicular to the normal vector for the tangent plane. This means that every tangent line is parallel to the tangent plane. However, since all the tangent lines pass through the point of tangency, then we can conclude that <u>all the tangent lines to a given surface through a given point lie in the same plane</u>!

EXAMPLE 13.11:

Write an equation of the plane tangent to the surface $f(x, y) := x^3 + 3x^2y^4 + 7$ at the point (2, 1, 27). (See Examples 13.9 and 13.10.)

In view of Theorem 13.3, an equation of the tangent plane is

$$24(x - 2) + 48(y - 1) - (z - 27) = 0, \quad \text{or} \quad 24x + 48y - z = 69. \qquad \blacklozenge$$

- -

<u>TEST YOUR UNDERSTANDING</u>

2. Write an equation of the plane tangent to the surface in Example 13.11 at the point (1, –1, 11).

3. Write an equation of the plane tangent to the surface $f(x, y) := xy^2$ at (1, 2, 4).

- -

2. The chain rule

Remember that the directional derivative gives us the rate of change in function values as we move along *straight lines* through a given point. We'd now like to investigate what happens if we move along a curved path. Specifically, let $r(t) := \langle x(t), y(t) \rangle$ define a curve K in the xy-plane. Construct a cylinder perpendicular to the xy-plane along K. (Remember that cylinders need not look like tin cans; any surface with identical cross-sections perpendicular to some axis is a cylinder.) See Figure 13.7. The cylinder intersects the surface in some curve C. We want to know the rate of change in function values along C.

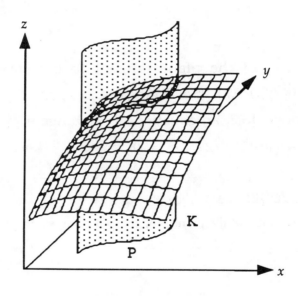

Fig. 13.7

C is defined by the function $\phi_K(t) = f(x(t), y(t))$. We want $\phi_K{}'(t)$. As we move along K during the time interval $[t, t + \Delta t]$, the x-coordinate changes by

$$\Delta x = x(t + \Delta t) - x(t),$$

the y-coordinate changes by

$$\Delta y = y(t + \Delta t) - y(t)$$

and the function values along C change by

$$\Delta z = \phi_K(t + \Delta t) - \phi_K(t)$$

$$= f(x(t + \Delta t), y(t + \Delta t)) - f(x(t), y(t))$$
$$= f(x(t) + \Delta x, y(t) + \Delta y) - f(x(t), y(t)).$$

Using an argument similar to one we used earlier,

$$\Delta z = f(x(t) + \Delta x, y(t) + \Delta y) - f(x(t), y(t))$$
$$= [f(x(t) + \Delta x, y(t) + \Delta y) - f(x(t) + \Delta x, y(t))]$$
$$+ [f(x(t) + \Delta x, y(t)) - f(x(t), y(t))]$$

$$\approx f_y(x(t) + \Delta x, y(t))\Delta y + f_x(x(t), y(t))\Delta x$$

assuming f is nice. Thus, $\dfrac{\Delta z}{\Delta t} \approx f_y(x(t) + \Delta x, y(t))\dfrac{\Delta y}{\Delta t} + f_x(x(t), y(t))\dfrac{\Delta x}{\Delta t}$.
Upon taking the limit as $\Delta t \to 0$ and noting that $\Delta x \to 0$ and $\Delta y \to 0$ simultaneously, we have:

THEOREM 13.4 (THE CHAIN RULE): Let $z(t) := f(x(t), y(t))$, where $x(t)$ and $y(t)$ are differentiable functions such that $x(t_0) = x_0$ and $y(t_0) = y_0$. If f is nice near (x_0, y_0), then

$$z'(t_0) = f_x(x_0, y_0) x'(t_0) + f_y(x_0, y_0) y'(t_0)$$
$$= \nabla f(x_0, y_0) \cdot \langle x'(t_0), y'(t_0) \rangle.$$

This theorem is often abbreviated as $\dfrac{dz}{dt} = \dfrac{\partial z}{\partial x}\dfrac{dx}{dt} + \dfrac{\partial z}{\partial y}\dfrac{dy}{dt}$.

Note the resemblance to the chain rule for functions of one variable. In particular, if $z = f(x(t))$, then $\dfrac{dz}{dt} = \dfrac{dz}{dx}\dfrac{dx}{dt}$. Here, much like for the tagnent plane, the $\dfrac{dz}{dx}$ factor is replaced by the gradient $\left\langle \dfrac{\partial z}{\partial x}, \dfrac{\partial z}{\partial y} \right\rangle$, the $\dfrac{dx}{dt}$ is replaced by $\left\langle \dfrac{dx}{dt}, \dfrac{dy}{dt} \right\rangle$ and ordinary multiplication is replaced by the dot product of two vectors.

Note further that if x and y are linear functions--$x = x_0 + u_1 t$, $y = y_0 + u_2 t$--then $\dfrac{dz}{dt}$ is just the directional derivative and Theorem 13.4 simplifies to Theorem 13.2.

EXAMPLE 13.12:

Suppose $z = x^2y^3$, where $x = \sin(t)$ and $y = e^{2t}$. Determine $\frac{dz}{dt}$ in terms of t.

Since $\frac{\partial z}{\partial x} = 2xy^3$, $\frac{dx}{dt} = \cos(t)$, $\frac{\partial z}{\partial y} = 3x^2y^2$ and $\frac{dy}{dt} = 2e^{2t}$, then

$$\frac{dz}{dt} = (2xy^3)\cos(t) + (3x^2y^2)(2e^{2t})$$
$$= 2\sin(t)\cos(t)e^{6t} + 6\sin^2(t)e^{6t}. \qquad \blacklozenge$$

Admittedly, Theorem 13.4 is not really necessary if x and y are expressed explicitly in terms of t. For instance, we could have gotten the answer to Example 13.12 by first substituting for x and y and then differentiating with respect to t. The real need for the chain rule is when the functions x and y are not known explicitly.

EXAMPLE 13.13:

The radius of a cylinder is increasing at a rate of 2 cm./min. At a certain instant, the height is decreasing at a rate of 3 cm./min. How fast is the volume of the cylinder changing when the radius is 8 and the height is 10 cm.? Is the volume increasing or decreasing?

The volume of a cylinder is given by the formula $V = \pi r^2 h$. Here, r and h are both changing (functions of time). Let's use the chain rule to find $\frac{dV}{dt}$.

$$\frac{dV}{dt} = \frac{\partial V}{\partial r}\frac{dr}{dt} + \frac{\partial V}{\partial h}\frac{dh}{dt} = 2\pi rh\frac{dr}{dt} + \pi r^2\frac{dh}{dt}.$$

We are given $\frac{dr}{dt} = 2$, $\frac{dh}{dt} = -3$, $r = 8$ and $h = 10$. Thus, $\frac{dV}{dt} = 320\pi - 192\pi = 128\pi$ cm.^{3}/min. Since the answer is positive, the volume is increasing. $\qquad \blacklozenge$

TEST YOUR UNDERSTANDING

4. Find dz/dt at $t = 1$ if $z = \sin(xy)$, where $x = \sqrt{5-t}$ and $y = t^3$.

5. Find dz/dt if $z = \sqrt{x^2+y^2}$, where $x = \ln(t)$ and $y = 1 + t^2$.

----

3. Maximum increase and decrease

We've already seen that the directional derivative $D_u f(x_0, y_0) = \nabla f(x_0, y_0) \cdot u$ gives the slope of the line tangent to the surface at the point (x_0, y_0) in the direction of u. So, if $D_u f(x_0, y_0) > 0$, then f is increasing in that direction. If $D_u f(x_0, y_0) < 0$, f is decreasing in that direction and if $D_u f(x_0, y_0) = 0$, then f is constant in that direction. It is most important to realize that at any given point, f may be increasing, decreasing or constant, depending on the choice of the vector u.

What this means is that at any given point on the surface, there may be many directions in which f is increasing. An interesting question is: In which of these directions is f increasing most rapidly? In other words, for which unit vector u does $D_u f(x_0, y_0)$ attain its maximum value?

To answer this question, we need to recall a fact about vectors that we studied in Chapter 9. Given two vectors, v and u, the angle ϕ between them is given by:

$$\cos(\phi) = \frac{v \cdot u}{\|v\|\|u\|} \quad \text{or} \quad v \cdot u = \|v\|\|u\|\cos(\phi)$$

See Figure 13.8.

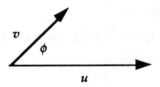

Fig. 13.8

Since $\cos(0) = 1$, the largest value of the cosine, then the largest value of $v \cdot u$ is $\|v\|\|u\|$ and it occurs when u and v are pointed in the same direction. Similarly, since $\cos(\pi) = -1$, then the smallest value of $v \cdot u$ is $-\|v\|\|u\|$ and it occurs when u and v are pointed in opposite directions.

Now, let $v = \nabla f(x_0, y_0)$ and let u be a unit vector (so that $\|u\| = 1$).

Then,

$$D_{\boldsymbol{u}}f(x_0, y_0) = \nabla f(x_0, y_0) \cdot \boldsymbol{u} = \|\nabla f(x_0, y_0)\| \cos(\phi)$$ and we have the following:

THEOREM 13.5: Suppose f is nice near (x_0, y_0). Then the largest possible value of $D_{\boldsymbol{u}}f(x_0, y_0)$ is $\|\nabla f(x_0, y_0)\|$ and occurs when $\boldsymbol{u}$ is in the same direction as $\nabla f(x_0, y_0)$. The smallest possible value of $D_{\boldsymbol{u}}f(x_0, y_0)$ is $-\|\nabla f(x_0, y_0)\|$ and occurs when $\boldsymbol{u}$ is in the opposite direction of $\nabla f(x_0, y_0)$.

What this theorem says is that if you want to increase function values as quickly as possible, go in the direction of the gradient. If you want them to decrease as quickly as possible, go in the direction opposite to the gradient.

EXAMPLE 13.14:

Let $f(x, y) := x^2 y$. What is the largest value of $D_{\boldsymbol{u}}f(3, 1)$ and what is the corresponding vector $\boldsymbol{u}$?

$\nabla f(x, y) = \langle 2xy, x^2 \rangle$ so $\nabla f(3, 1) = \langle 6, 9 \rangle$. Therefore, the largest value of $D_{\boldsymbol{u}}f(3, 1) = \|\langle 6, 9 \rangle\| = \sqrt{117}$.

The unit vector $\boldsymbol{u}$ parallel to the gradient is $\left\langle \dfrac{6}{\sqrt{117}}, \dfrac{9}{\sqrt{117}} \right\rangle$. ◆

TEST YOUR UNDERSTANDING

6. If $D_{\boldsymbol{u}}f(a, b) = \frac{1}{2}\|\nabla f(a, b)\|$, what is the angle between $\boldsymbol{u}$ and $\nabla f(a, b)$?

7. For the function in Example 13.14, what is the smallest value of $D_{\boldsymbol{u}}f(-1, 1)$ and what is the corresponding unit vector?

----

4. Gradients and level curves

Using the language of Section 12.5, we see that the gradient is a vector field, meaning that for each point in the xy-plane, we can draw a vector whose direction and magnitude are given by $\nabla f(x, y)$. For example, suppose $f(x, y) := x^2 y$. Then $\nabla f(x, y) = \langle 2xy, x^2 \rangle$. Figure 13.9 illustrates a few vectors in the vector field.

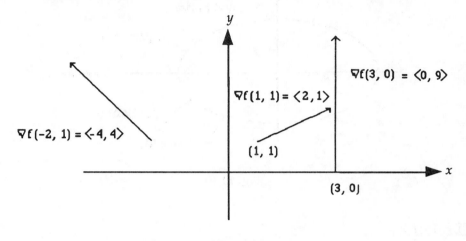

Fig. 13.9

The vector field defined by the gradient has a special geometric property. Suppose we intersect the surface $z = f(x, y)$ with the horizontal plane $z = c$. The curve of intersection is just the level curve S_c for the function f. If we move along the level curve, the z-values do not change. That means the directional derivative in a direction u tangent to the level curve must be 0 at any point along the curve. In other words, $D_u f(x, y) = \nabla f(x, y) \cdot u = 0$ for all (x, y) on the level curve. We know from Chapter 9 that if the dot product of two vectors is 0, then the vectors are perpendicular. Thus, we have:

THEOREM 13.6: Let $P(x_0, y_0)$ be a point in the domain of a function f and let $S = \{(x, y) \mid f(x, y) = f(x_0, y_0)\}$ be the corresponding level curve. If f is nice near (x_0, y_0) and if $\nabla f(x_0, y_0) \neq \langle 0, 0 \rangle$, then the gradient $\nabla f(x_0, y_0)$ is perpendicular to S.

This theorem is illustrated in Figure 13.10. (Remember, level curves are drawn in two dimensions and the gradient is a two-dimensional vector.) At each point, the gradient is perpendicular to the (tangent to the) level curve.

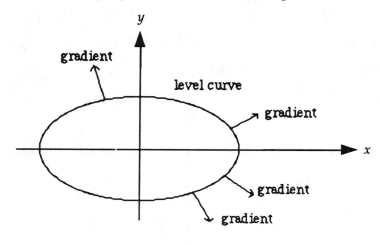

Fig. 13.10

EXAMPLE 13.15:

Let $f(x, y) := x^2 y$ and let $S_9 = \{(x, y) \mid f(x, y) = 9\}$ be the level curve passing through $(3, 1)$. Write parametric equations for the line tangent to this level curve at $(3, 1)$.

First note that the level curve and, hence, the desired tangent line are two-dimensional objects confined to the xy-plane. Since $\nabla f(3, 1) = \langle 6, 9 \rangle = 3\langle 2, 3 \rangle$, then $\langle 2, 3 \rangle$ is perpendicular to the level curve. Furthermore, since $\langle 2, 3 \rangle \cdot \langle 3, -2 \rangle = 0$, then $\langle 3, -2 \rangle$ is perpendicular to $\langle 2, 3 \rangle$ and, consequently, must be parallel to the tangent line. Hence, parametric equations for the tangent line are $x = 3 + 3t, y = 1 - 2t$. ◆

EXERCISES FOR SECTION 13.3:

1. An equation of the plane tangent to the surface $z = f(x, y)$ at the point $(1, -3)$ is $4x + 3y - z = 9$.

   (a) What is $f(1, -3)$?

   (b) What is $\nabla f(1, -3)$?

(c) What is the directional derivative of f at $(1, -3)$ in the direction of the origin?

(d) Estimate $f(1.05, -2.95)$.

2. Write an equation of the plane tangent to $z = xy$ at $(2, 2, 4)$.

3. (a) Write an equation of the plane tangent to surface $z = 4 - x^2 + 3x + y$ at the point where the surface intersects the z-axis.

(b) At what point does the plane in (a) intersect the x-axis?

4. Suppose $f_x(x, y) := y^3 - 1$ and $f_y(x, y) := 3xy^2$.

(a) At which point will the tangent plane be parallel to the xy-plane? (Hint: If a plane is parallel to the xy-plane, what must its normal vector look like?)

(b) At which point will the tangent plane be parallel to the plane $-2x + 9y - z = 14$?

5. Let $z = \ln(xy)$ where $x = t^3$, and $y = 1 + t^2$. Determine $\frac{dz}{dt}$ at $t = 1$.

6. Express $\frac{dz}{dt}$ in terms of t if $z = xy^2$, $x = \cos(t)$ and $y = \sin(t)$.

7. Let $z = 4xy + y^2$ where $x = t^2$, and $y = 4 - t$. Determine $\frac{dz}{dt}$ at the point where $x = 4$ and $y = 6$.

8. Write a unit vector in the direction of maximum increase for $f(x, y) := (x + 4y)^3$ at $(2, 1)$.

9. Write a unit vector in the direction of maximum decrease for $f(x, y) := x^2y^2$ at $(1, 3)$.

10. Suppose $f(2, -3) = 5$ and $\nabla f(2, -3) = \langle -1, 4 \rangle$. Give parametric equations of the line tangent to the level curve $\{(x, y) \mid f(x, y) = 5\}$ at $(2, -3)$.

11. How fast is the area of a rectangle changing if the length is 12 ft. and increasing at a rate of 2 ft./min. and the width is 8 ft. and decreasing at a rate of 3 ft./min.?

12. The base of a box is a square whose side is $x = 3$; its height is $y = 5$. If x increases at 2 units/min, how fast must y decrease in order to keep the volume constant?

13. Consider the paraboloid $f(x, y) := x^2 + 4y^2$. Write an equation of the line in the xy-plane perpendicular to the level curve S_5 at $(1, 1)$.

PROBLEMS FOR SECTION 13.3:

1. Let L be the line perpendicular to the surface $z = x^2 + y^2$ at $(1, 1, 2)$.

    (a) Write parametric equations for L.

    (b) At what other point does L intersect the surface?

2. Suppose that, at some point (a, b), $\nabla f(a, b) = \langle 1, 4 \rangle$. Show that there is no unit vector u such that $D_u f(a, b) = 5$.

3. Find the volume of the tetrahedron formed by the coordinate planes and the plane tangent to $z = 9 - x^2 - y^2$ at $(1, 1, 7)$.

4. Suppose $z = f(x, y)$, where $x = g(s, t)$ and $y = h(s, t)$. Then z is also function of s and t.

    (a) Derive expressions for the partial derivatives of z with respect to s and with respect to t.

    (b) Use your answer to (a) to find $\dfrac{\partial z}{\partial s}$ if $z = x/y$, $x = st$, $y = s^2 t^2 + 1$.

5. Let Π_1 be the plane tangent to $z = 4 - x^2 - y^2$ at $(1, 1, 2)$ and let Π_2 be the plane tangent to the same surface at $(0, 0, 4)$. Determine parametric equations for the line of intersection of Π_1 and Π_2.

6. Two of the level curves of a function f are shown below. Draw the gradient at Q. Will it be shorter or longer than the gradient at P?

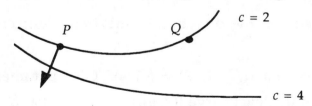

7. The temperature at the point (x, y) on a flat surface is given by the function $T(x, y) := 100 - x^2 - 3y^2$. A bug starts at the point $(2, 1)$ and always moves in the direction of maximum temperature increase. Let $r(t) = \langle x(t), y(t) \rangle$ be a parametric representation of the path followed by the bug.

    (a) Argue that $r'(t) = \nabla T$.

    (b) Show that the condition in (a) is equivalent to the system of differential equations $x'(t) = -2x$, $y'(t) = -6y$.

(c) Solve the equations in (b), making sure to use the initial conditions.

(d) Eliminate t from your solution to (c) and obtain an xy-equation for the path travelled by the bug.

TYU Answers for Section 13.3

1. 5.5 2. $9(x-1) - 12(y+1) - (z-11) = 0$ 3. $4(x-1) + 4(y-2) - (z-4) = 0$

4. $\dfrac{23}{4} \cos(2) \approx -2.393$ 5. $\dfrac{dz}{dt} = \dfrac{x}{\sqrt{x^2 + y^2}} \left(\dfrac{1}{t} \right) + \dfrac{y}{\sqrt{x^2 + y^2}} (2t)$

6. $\pi/3$ 7. $-\sqrt{5}; \; u = \dfrac{1}{\sqrt{5}} \langle 2, -1 \rangle$

13.4 CRITICAL POINTS AND LOCAL EXTREMA

In this section, we look at the problem of determining the local extrema of a function of two variables. Recall that a critical point of a function f is any number c in the domain of f for which $f'(c) = 0$ or $f'(c)$ does not exist. The critical points were candidates for the local maxima and minima of the function. If the function changed from increasing to decreasing at the critical point, then there was a local maximum. A change from decreasing to increasing indicated a local minimum. If there was no change of direction, the critical point was neither a maximum nor a minimum.

For functions of two variables, things are a little more complicated. It seems intuitive that at a local extremum, one possibility is that the directional derivative should be zero in every direction--that is, $D_u f(a, b) = 0$ for every u. A moment's thought should convince you that, if f is nice near (a, b), then the only way this can happen is if $\nabla f(a, b) = \langle 0, 0 \rangle$. This is equivalent to $f_x(a, b) = 0$ and $f_y(a, b) = 0$. Thus, any point (a, b) for which both partial derivatives are 0 is a candidate for a local maximum or minimum.

Another possibility for a local extremum is a point at which the directional derivative does not exist in some direction. Of course such functions are not nice and we'll ignore them in what follows. This leads to the following:

DEFINITION: The point (a, b) is said to be a **critical point** for the function $z = f(x, y)$ if $f_x(a, b) = 0$ and $f_y(a, b) = 0$.

EXAMPLE 13.16:

Determine the critical points for the function $f(x, y) := 8 - x^2 - 10x - y^2 + 6y$.

The partial derivatives are $f_x(x, y) := -2x - 10$ and $f_y(x, y) := -2y + 6$. Since both of these are defined for all x and y, we set them equal to 0 to find the critical points. We get $x = -5$ and $y = 3$. Hence, $(-5, 3)$ is the only critical point. ♦

EXAMPLE 13.17:

Determine the critical points for the function $f(x, y) := 2x^3 + xy - y^2$.

The partial derivatives are $f_x(x, y) = 6x^2 + y$ and $f_y(x, y) = x - 2y$. As in the previous example, we set both of these equal to 0.

If $x - 2y = 0$, then $x = 2y$. Substituting in f_x, we get $6(2y)^2 + y = 0$, or, $24y^2 + y = 0$. This has solutions $y = 0$ and $y = -1/24$. The corresponding x-values are $x = 0, x = -1/12$. Thus, $(0, 0)$ and $(-1/12, -1/24)$ are the only critical points. ♦

<u>TEST YOUR UNDERSTANDING</u>

1. Determine the critical points of $f(x, y) := xy - x^2 - 2y$.

◻ Our next task is to classify the critical points. For functions of one variable, there are three possibilities: local maximum, local minimum or neither. For functions of two variables, there are more. In Chapter 12, we looked at the paraboloid $f(x, y) := x^2 - y^2$. Since $f_x(x, y) := 2x$ and $f_y(x, y) := -2y$, then $(0, 0)$ is the only critical point. At any point $(x, 0)$ along the x-axis, we have $f(x, 0) = x^2$ which is strictly greater than $f(0, 0)$. Hence, $(0, 0)$ is a local minimum along the x-axis. At any point along the y-axis, we have $f(0, y)$ = $-y^2$ which is strictly less than $f(0, 0)$. Hence, $(0, 0)$ is a local maximum along the y-axis. Any point which is a local maximum in one direction and a local minimum in another direction is called a **saddle point** and so we have four possibilities for critical points: local maximum, local minimum, saddle point or none of the above.

Sometimes it is possible to decide the nature of a critical point just by looking at the function. For instance, by completing the square, the function in Example 13.16 can be rewritten as:

$$f(x, y) := 42 - (x + 5)^2 - (y - 3)^2.$$

Since the squared terms are never negative, then $f(x, y)$ must always be less than or equal to 42, with equality when $x = -5$ and $y = 3$. Therefore, the critical point $(-5, 3)$ is a local (indeed, global) maximum.

Arguments of this type can be used only in very special cases. What we would like is a more systematic approach to classifying critical points of a function of two variables.

For functions of one variable, we said that if $x = c$ is a critical point such that $f'(c) = 0$, then f has a local maximum at $x = c$ if f is concave up at $x = c$ and a local minimum at $x = c$ if f is concave down at $x = c$. Since concavity is determined by the second derivative, this suggests that it might be useful to look at second derivatives for functions of two variables.

Think again about the curve C of intersection between the surface $z = f(x, y)$ and the plane Π perpendicular to the xy-plane through $P(x_0, y_0)$ in the direction of the unit vector $u = \langle u_1, u_2 \rangle$ as we did in Section 13.1. (See Figure 13.3.) C is defined by $\phi_u(t) := f(x_0 + tu_1, y_0 + tu_2)$. The directional derivative $D_u f(x_0, y_0) = \phi_u'(0)$ tells us the slope of the line tangent to C in the direction of u. The concavity of C is determined by the second derivative of $\phi_u(t)$. This leads to the following:

DEFINITION: The **directional second derivative** of f at $P(x_0, y_0)$ in the direction of the unit vector u is $D_u^2 f(x_0, y_0) = \phi_u''(0)$, where $\phi_u(t) := f(x_0 + tu_1, y_0 + tu_2)$.

EXAMPLE 13.18:

Let $f(x, y) := xy$ as in Example 13.1. Determine the directional second derivative of this surface at $P(6, -1)$ in the direction of the vector $u = \left\langle \frac{3}{5}, \frac{4}{5} \right\rangle$.

The line L through P in the direction of u is represented by $x = 6 + \frac{3}{5} t$, $y = -1 + \frac{4}{5} t$, so $\phi_u(t) := (6 + \frac{3}{5} t)(-1 + \frac{4}{5} t) = -6 + \frac{21}{5} t + \frac{12}{25} t^2$. Hence, the directional second derivative is $D_u^2 f(6, -1) = \phi_u''(0) = \frac{24}{25}$. ♦

TEST YOUR UNDERSTANDING

2. Determine the directional second derivative of $f(x, y) := x^2 + y^2$ at $(1, 2)$ in the direction of $u = \frac{1}{\sqrt{2}} \langle 1, -1 \rangle$.

Ideally, we would like to be able to compute the directional second derivative without having to first find $\phi_u(t)$, much like Theorem 13.2 allows us to compute the directional derivative in terms of the partial derivatives.

In order to do so, we need to look at a somewhat more complicated example. Let $f(x, y) := x^3 + 2xy^2$ and consider an arbitrary point (x, y) and an arbitrary unit vector u. Then,

$$\phi_u(t) := f(x + tu_1, y + tu_2) = (x + tu_1)^3 + 2(x + tu_1)(y + tu_2)^2$$
$$= (x + tu_1)(x^2 + t^2 u_1^2 + 2y^2 + 2t^2 u_2^2 + 2xtu_1 + 4ytu_2)$$

After some algebra, we find

$$\phi_u'(t) := 3t^2 u_1^3 + 6t^2 u_1 u_2^2 + 6xtu_1^2 + 4xtu_2^2 + 3x^2 u_1 + $$
$$8ytu_1 u_2 + 4xyu_2 + 2y^2 u_1$$

from which $D_u f(x, y) = \phi_u'(0) = 3x^2 u_1 + 4xyu_2 + 2y^2 u_1$.

Then, $\phi_u''(t) := 6tu_1{}^3 + 12tu_1u_2{}^2 + 6xu_1{}^2 + 4xu_2{}^2 + 8yu_1u_2$

so $D_u^2 f(x,y) = \phi_u''(0) = 6xu_1{}^2 + 4xu_2{}^2 + 8yu_1u_2$.

Note that there are three terms: one containing $u_1{}^2$, one containing $u_2{}^2$ and one containing u_1u_2. The question is: What are the coefficients?

In general, let $\phi_u(t) := f(x + tu_1, y + tu_2)$. Then by the chain rule,

(5) $\phi_u'(t) := f_x(x + tu_1, y + tu_2)u_1 + f_y(x + tu_1, y + tu_2)u_2$.

Each term on the right is a function of t, so to get the second derivative of $\phi_u(t)$, we need to use the chain rule on each term. This means we'll have to take the derivatives of f_x and f_y with respect to x and with respect to y. In other words, we are taking the partial derivative of the partial derivatives obtaining, quite naturally, **second partial derivatives**. Since each first partial derivative can be differentiated with respect to either variable, there are, in principle, four possible second partial derivatives.

1. $f_{xx}(x,y)$--differentiate with respect to x twice.
2. $f_{xy}(x,y)$--differentiate with respect to x, then with respect to y.
3. $f_{yx}(x,y)$--differentiate with respect to y, then with respect to x.
4. $f_{yy}(x,y)$--differentiate with respect to y twice.

The second and third cases are sometimes called **mixed partial derivatives**.

Suppose $f(x,y) = x^2y^3 + 4xy^2$. The first partial derivatives are:

$f_x(x,y) = 2xy^3 + 4y^2$ and $f_y(x,y) = 3x^2y^2 + 8xy$.

Upon differentiating $f_x(x,y)$ with respect to x, we get $f_{xx}(x,y) := 2y^3$. Upon differentiating $f_x(x,y)$ with respect to y, we get $f_{xy}(x,y) := 6xy^2 + 8y$. Upon differentiating $f_y(x,y)$ with respect to x, we get $f_{yx}(x,y) := 6xy^2 + 8y$. Upon differentiating $f_y(x,y)$ with respect to y, we get $f_{yy}(x,y) := 6x^2y + 8x$.

Note that $f_{xy}(x,y) = f_{yx}(x,y)$. This is not a coincidence; in fact, we could prove that for mixed partial derivatives, the order in which we differentiate doesn't matter, provided the function, its first partial derivatives and the mixed partial derivatives are continuous. This is a little stronger condition than requiring the function to be "nice" since the mixed partial derivatives also have to be continuous. We shall describe functions satisfying all these conditions as **very nice**.

There are other notations for second partial derivatives. For example, if $z = f(x, y)$, then $f_{xx}(x, y)$ can be denoted by $f_{11}(x, y)$, $D_{xx}f(x, y)$ or $\dfrac{\partial^2 z}{\partial x^2}$.

The mixed partial $f_{xy}(x, y)$ is denoted $f_{12}(x, y)$, $D_{xy}(x, y)$ or $\dfrac{\partial^2 z}{\partial y \, \partial x}$. The last notation is correct, although at first glance you might think the denominator is backwards. When using the ∂-notation, the variables in the denominator are written from right to left.

TEST YOUR UNDERSTANDING

3. Determine all second partial derivatives for the function $z = \dfrac{x}{y^2}$.

4. Determine all second partial derivatives for the function $f(x, y) := \ln(x + 4y)$.

¤ Now let's go back to the problem of finding the derivative of Eq.(5). Since u_1 and u_2 are constants, then

$$\phi_u''(t) := f_{xx}(x + tu_1, y + tu_2)u_1{}^2 + f_{xy}(x + tu_1, y + tu_2)u_1 u_2 +$$
$$f_{yx}(x + tu_1, y + tu_2)u_1 u_2 + f_{yy}(x + tu_1, y + tu_2)u_2{}^2$$

$$= f_{xx}(x + tu_1, y + tu_2)u_1{}^2 + 2f_{xy}(x + tu_1, y + tu_2)u_1u_2 + f_{yy}(x + tu_1, y + tu_2)u_2{}^2$$

if f is very nice. Upon substituting $t = 0$, we have:

THEOREM 13.7: Suppose f is very nice near (x_0, y_0). Then the directional second derivative of f in the direction of the unit vector u is

$$D_u^2 f(x_0, y_0) = f_{xx}(x_0, y_0)u_1{}^2 + 2f_{xy}(x_0, y_0)u_1u_2 + f_{yy}(x_0, y_0)u_2{}^2.$$

To illustrate, let $f(x, y) := x^3 + 2xy^2$. Then $f_x(x, y) := 3x^2 + 2y^2$, $f_y(x, y) := 4xy$, $f_{xx}(x, y) := 6x$, $f_{xy}(x, y) := 4y$ and $f_{yy}(x, y) := 4x$. Hence,

$$D_u^2 f(x, y) := 6xu_1{}^2 + 8yu_1u_2 + 4xu_2{}^2$$

as we got before.

TEST YOUR UNDERSTANDING

5. Determine the directional second derivative at (1, 2) in the direction of the unit vector u for the function in TYU #3.

□   We now return to the problem that motivated this discussion--that of classifying the critical points of a function of two variables. We claim that if (a, b) is a critical point such that the directional second derivative at (a, b) is strictly positive for every unit vector u, then (a, b) is a local minimum on the surface. This is a stronger condition than requiring that (a, b) be a local minimum on every straight line path through (a, b), since it is possible to have a local minimum on a curve when the second derivative is 0. In fact, it is possible to have a surface on which (a, b) is a local minimum on every line through (a, b) but for which there are curved paths through (a, b) on which it is a local maximum. See the problems at the end of this section for an example. Similar arguments can be made for local maxima and saddle points. Hence, we have:

THEOREM 13.8:

Suppose f has a critical point at (a, b) and f is very nice near (a, b). Then f has:

(a) a local minimum at (a, b) if $D_u^2 f(a, b) > 0$ for all u.

(b) a local maximum at (a, b) if $D_u^2 f(a, b) < 0$ for all u.

(c) a saddle point at (a, b) if $D_u^2 f(a, b) > 0$ for some u and $D_u^2 f(a, b) < 0$ for some u.

In all other cases, there is no conclusion.

Notice that parts (a) and (b) of this test fail if there is even one u such that $D_u^2 f(a, b) = 0$. In part (c), we'd expect $D_u^2 f(a, b) = 0$ for at least one u.

EXAMPLE 13.19:

Show that $(-5, 3)$ is a local maximum for the function $f(x, y) := 8 - x^2 - 10x - y^2 + 6y$ of Example 13.16.

Since $f_x(x, y) := -2x - 10$ and $f_y(x, y) = -2y + 6$, then $f_{xx}(x, y) = -2$, $f_{xy}(x, y) = 0$ and $f_{yy}(x, y) = -2$. Thus,

$$D_u^2 f(-5, 3) = -2u_1^2 - 2u_2^2 = -2(u_1^2 + u_2^2).$$

Since u is a unit vector, then $u_1^2 + u_2^2 = 1$. Thus, $D_u^2 f(-5, 3) = -2$ for all u, implying that $(-5, 3)$ is a local maximum. ◆

EXAMPLE 13.20:

Show that $(0, 0)$ is a saddle point of the function $f(x, y) := x^2 - y^2$.

Since $f_x(x, y) := 2x$ and $f_y(x, y) := -2y$, then $f_{xx}(x, y) := 2$, $f_{xy}(x, y) = 0$ and $f_{yy}(x, y) := -2$. Thus,

$$D_u^2 f(0, 0) = 2u_1^2 - 2u_2^2 = 2(u_1^2 - u_2^2).$$

This quantity is positive for some u (e.g. $u = \langle 1, 0 \rangle$) and negative for others (e.g. $u = \langle 0, 1 \rangle$). Thus, $(0, 0)$ is a saddle point. ♦

EXAMPLE 13.21:

Classify the critical points for the function $f(x, y) := e^{-(x^2 + y^2)}$.

The first partial derivatives are $f_x(x, y) := -2xe^{-(x^2 + y^2)}$ and $f_y(x, y) := -2ye^{-(x^2 + y^2)}$. Since $e^{-(x^2 + y^2)} \neq 0$ for any (x, y), then $f_x(x, y) = 0$ only if $x = 0$. Similarly, $f_y(x, y) = 0$ only if $y = 0$. Hence, the only critical point is the origin $(0, 0)$.

The second partial derivatives are $f_{xx}(x, y) := (4x^2 - 2)e^{-(x^2 + y^2)}$, $f_{xy}(x, y) := 4xye^{-(x^2 + y^2)}$ and $f_{yy}(x, y) = (4y^2 - 2)e^{-(x^2 + y^2)}$. Evaluating at the critical point gives $f_{xx}(0, 0) = f_{yy}(0, 0) = -2$ and $f_{xy}(0, 0) = 0$. Thus, the directional second derivative is $D_u^2 f(0,0) = -2u_1^2 - 2u_2^2$ which, by the same argument we used in Example 13.19, is always equal to -2. Therefore, the critical point is a local maximum. ♦

EXAMPLE 13.22:

Determine and classify the critical points of $f(x, y) := x^4 + y^2$.

The first partial derivatives are $f_x(x, y) := 4x^3$ and $f_y(x, y) := 2y$. Clearly, the only critical point is $(0, 0)$.

The second partial derivatives are $f_{xx}(x, y) := 12x^2$, $f_{xy}(x, y) := 0$ and $f_{yy}(x, y) := 2$. Evaluating at the critical point gives $f_{xx}(0, 0) = f_{xy}(0, 0) = 0$ and $f_{yy}(0, 0) = 2$. Thus, the directional second derivative is $D_u^2 f(0,0) = 2u_2^2$ which is 0 for $u = \langle 1, 0 \rangle$ and thus is neither strictly positive, nor strictly negative. Neither is it sometimes negative and sometimes positive. Therefore, Theorem 13.7 leads to no conclusion.

In this case, however, it is clear that $f(x, y) > 0$ for all $(x, y) \neq (0, 0)$. Since $f(0, 0) = 0$, then there is a local minimum at $(0, 0)$. ♦

---

6. Suppose $f_x(a, b) = f_y(a, b) = 0, f_{xx}(a, b) = f_{xy}(a, b) = f_{yy}(a, b) = 1$. What conclusion can you draw about the point (a, b)?

7. Determine and classify all the critical points for the function $f(x, y) :=$ $x^2 + 4xy - y^2$.

◻ While Theorem 13.8 has a nice geometrical interpretation, it is not very easy to implement in practice. Determining by inspection whether an expression of the form

$$D^2_u f(a, b) = f_{xx}(a, b)u_1^2 + 2f_{xy}(a, b)u_1 u_2 + f_{yy}(a, b)u_2^2$$

is strictly positive or strictly negative is a non-trivial task, except in simple cases as we illustrated in the examples above. What we need is an algebraic way of determining the nature of $D^2_u f(a, b)$.

After factoring out u_2^2, $D^2_u f(a, b)$ can be rewritten as:

$$D^2_u f(a, b) = u_2^2 \left[f_{xx}(a, b)\left(\frac{u_1}{u_2}\right)^2 + 2f_{xy}(a, b)\left(\frac{u_1}{u_2}\right) + f_{yy}(a, b) \right].$$

The expression in square brackets is of the form $h(w) := pw^2 + 2qw + r$, where $w = \frac{u_1}{u_2}$, $p = f_{xx}(a, b)$, $q = f_{xy}(a, b)$ and $r = f_{yy}(a, b)$. This is a quadratic function whose graph is, obviously, a parabola. There are three possibilities for the graph, as indicated in Figure 13.11, if $p > 0$ and, turning all of the graphs upside down, there are three more if $p < 0$.

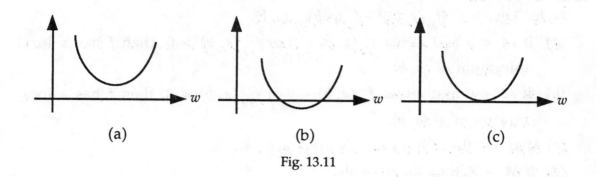

Fig. 13.11

In (a), h has no real roots and $h(w)$ has the same sign for all w. In (b), h has two distinct real roots and $h(w) < 0$ for some w and $h(w) > 0$ for some w. In (c), h has two equal real roots and $h(w) \geq 0$ for all w.

You may recall from your algebra class that the nature of the roots of a quadratic equation depends on the sign of the discriminant (the expression under the square root sign in the quadratic formula). Here, the discriminant is $(2q)^2 - 4pr = 4(q^2 - pr)$. Hence, the nature of the roots can be determined from the quantity $M = q^2 - pr = \left(f_{xy}(a,b)\right)^2 - f_{xx}(a,b) f_{yy}(a,b)$. There are three cases to consider:

1. $M < 0$: In this case, the roots of $h(w) = 0$ are imaginary, meaning that we either have Figure 13.11(a) or its reflection across the w-axis. If $p > 0$, then the function is concave up, so we have Figure 13.11(a); that is, $D_u^2 f(a,b)$ is always positive. If $p < 0$, we have its reflection and $D_u^2 f(a,b)$ is always negative.

2. $M > 0$: In this case, the roots of $h(w) = 0$ are distinct and real. This corresponds to Figure 13.11(b). Thus, $D_u^2 f(a,b)$ is sometimes negative and sometimes positive.

3. $M = 0$: In this case, $h(w) = 0$ has two identical roots. This corresponds to Figure 13.11(c).

Thus, we have the following:

THEOREM 13.9: Suppose f has a critical point at (a, b) and is very nice near (a, b). Let $M = [f_{xy}(a, b)]^2 - f_{xx}(a, b)f_{yy}(a, b)$.

(a) If $M < 0$ and either $f_{xx}(a, b) > 0$ or $f_{yy}(a, b) > 0$, then f has a local minimum at (a, b).

(b) If $M < 0$ and either $f_{xx}(a, b) < 0$ or $f_{yy}(a, b) < 0$, then f has a local maximum at (a, b).

(c) If $M > 0$, then f has a saddle point at (a, b).

(d) If $M = 0$, then the test fails.

EXAMPLE 13.23:

Determine and classify all the critical points of the function $f(x, y) := 12x + 3y - x^3 - y^3$.

The first partial derivatives are $f_x(x, y) := 12 - 3x^2$ and $f_y(x, y) := 3 - 3y^2$. Setting these equal to 0 gives $x^2 = 4$ and $y^2 = 1$. Thus, there are four critical points: $(2, 1)$, $(2, -1)$, $(-2, 1)$ and $(-2, -1)$.

The second partial derivatives are $f_{xx}(x, y) = -6x$, $f_{xy}(x, y) = 0$ and $f_{yy}(x, y) = -6y$. Therefore, $M = 0 - (-6x)(-6y) = -36xy$.

$M(2, 1) = -72 < 0$ and $f_{xx}(2, 1) = -12 < 0$, so $(2, 1)$ is a local maximum.

$M(2, -1) = 72 > 0$, so $(2, -1)$ is a saddle point.

$M(-2, 1) = 72 > 0$, so $(-2, 1)$ is a saddle point.

$M(-2, -1) = -72 < 0$ and $f_{xx}(-2, -1) = 12 > 0$, so $(-2, -1)$ is a local minimum. ◆

- -

TEST YOUR UNDERSTANDING

8. Classify the critical points of $f(x, y) := xy - x^2 - 2y$ from TYU #1.

- -

AN APPLICATION TO METEOROLOGY

When you listen to the weather report on the radio or television, you often hear the weatherman report the atmospheric pressure. Typically, this is reported as a number around 30 inches. (The measurement in inches refers to how high the air pushes a column of mercury in a glass tube called a barometer.)

Let $P(x, y) :=$ atmospheric pressure at the point on the earth's surface whose coordinates (perhaps recorded as latitude and longitude) are (x, y). Level curves for this function are called **isobars**; all points on a given isobar have equal atmospheric pressure. Some isobars are shown in Figure 13.12.

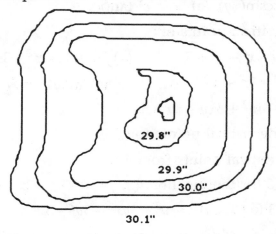

Fig. 13.12

One of the reasons there are winds on the earth's surface is due to changes in air pressure. Air tends to travel from areas of high pressure to areas of low pressure. Furthermore, if we ignore other factors such as the earth's rotation, the wind's velocity is proportional to the gradient of the atmospheric pressure; that is, $w(x, y) = -k\nabla P(x, y)$, for some constant $k > 0$. (Note that $w(x, y)$ is a vector field--it has magnitude and direction.) The reason for the minus sign is that we know the gradient always points in the direction of maximum increase; since the wind blows from high pressure areas to low pressure areas, it must go in a direction opposite to the gradient.

A high pressure center is nothing more than a local maximum of P. Since $\nabla P(x, y) = \langle 0, 0 \rangle$ at a local maximum, then $\|w(x, y)\| = -k\|\nabla P(x, y)\|$

$= -k\|\langle 0, 0\rangle\| = 0$ at a high pressure center. Thus, there is virtually no wind at the center of a high or, by the same argument, low pressure area. For example, the eye of a hurricane, which is characterized by extremely low pressure, is usually very calm. The strong winds are at the edge of the storm where the magnitude of the pressure gradient is much greater.

EXERCISES FOR SECTION 13.4:

1. Determine all the second partial derivatives for:

(a) $f(x, y) := \cos(xy^2)$ (b) $z = \dfrac{1}{x + y}$ (c) $g(x, y) := \dfrac{y}{x^2 + 1}$

(d) $f(x, y) := \arcsin(xy)$ (e) $z = e^x \tan(y)$

2. Determine the critical points of:

(a) $f(x, y) := 4xy - x^4 - y^4 + 7$ (b) $f(x, y) := x^3 - 3x + y^2 + 2y$

(c) $g(x, y) := x^3 + 3x + y^2 + 2y$ (d) $f(x, y) := 4y - y^2$

3. Let $f(x, y) := x^2 - 4y^2 + 6xy - 8y + 5$.

(a) Determine the critical points for f.

(b) Classify the critical points from (a).

4. Repeat Exercise 3 for the function $f(x, y) := 4y^3 - 2xy + 2x$.

5. Repeat Exercise 3 for $f(x, y) := y^3 - 3yx^2 - 3y^2 - 3x^2$.

6. Suppose (a, b) is a saddle point of a very nice function f. If $f_{xy}(a, b) = 6$ and $f_{xx}(a, b) = 2$, what are the possible values of $f_{yy}(a, b)$?

PROBLEMS FOR SECTION 13.4:

1. (a) How many third partial derivatives of a function of two variables would there be? Assuming appropriate continuity, how many of them would be distinct?

(b) Find all the third partial derivatives for the function $f(x, y) := e^{xy}$.

2. Suppose $w = f(x, y, z)$.

(a) How many distinct second-order partial derivatives are there (assuming any necessary continuity)?

(b) Determine all the second-order partial derivatives for $w = x^2yz + 4xyz^3$.

3. Prove that if $f_x(a, b) = f_y(a, b) = 0$ and $f_{xx}(a, b) = 0$ and $f_{xy}(a, b) \neq 0$, then f has a saddle point at (a, b).

4. Let $f(x, y) := (y - x^2)(y - 3x^2)$.

   (a) Show that $(0, 0)$ is the only critical point of f.

   (b) Show that Theorem 13.8 leads to no conclusion.

   (c) Let C_m be the curve formed by the intersection of the graph of f and the plane $y = mx$. Let $g(x) := f(x, mx)$ be the equation of C_m. Show that $x = 0$ is a local minimum on C_m for every $m \neq 0$.

   (d) Let C_0 and C_∞ be the curves formed by the intersection of f and the planes $y = 0$ (the xz-plane) and $x = 0$ (the yz-plane). Show that $x = 0$ is a local minimum on these curves as well.

   (e) Show that the origin is *not* a local minimum on the surface by showing that there are points arbitrarily near the origin for which $f(x, y) < f(0, 0)$ and other points for which $f(x, y) > f(0, 0)$.

TYU Answers for Section 13.4

1. $(2, 4)$ is the only critical point   2. 2   3. $z_{xx} = 0, z_{xy} = z_{yx} = \dfrac{-2}{y^3}, z_{yy} = \dfrac{6x}{y^4}$

4. $f_{xx}(x, y) := \dfrac{-1}{(x + 4y)^2}, f_{xy}(x, y) = f_{yx}(x, y) := \dfrac{-4}{(x + 4y)^2}, f_{yy}(x, y) := \dfrac{-16}{(x + 4y)^2}$

5. $\dfrac{-1}{2} u_1 u_2 + \dfrac{3}{8} u_2^2$ 6. There is no conclusion.

7. $(0, 0)$ is a saddle point.   8. $(2, 4)$ is a saddle point

13.5 CONSERVATIVE VECTOR FIELDS

In Chapter 6, we showed that every continuous function has an antiderivative, even if we can't write it in closed form. In particular, Theorem 6.5 says that if f is continuous and $F(x) := \int_a^x f(t)\, dt$, then $F'(x) := f(x)$, for all x, implying F is an antiderivative of f.

We now consider the following analogous problem for functions of two variables. Given a vector field $g(x, y)$, does there exist a function $f(x, y)$ such that $\nabla f = g$? Suppose $g(x, y) = \langle p(x, y), q(x, y) \rangle$. Then, we're asking if there is a function f such that $f_x(x, y) = p(x, y)$ and $f_y(x, y)$

$= q(x, y)$.

After a bit of thought, you should realize that the answer to this question is usually, "no". It is highly unlikely that arbitrary expressions for $f_x(x, y)$ and $f_y(x, y)$ would come from the same function f. For example, suppose $p(x, y) := 4x^3y^3$ and $q(x, y) := \sin(xy)$. Clearly, there is no function for which $f_x(x, y) = 4x^3y^3$ and $f_y(x, y) = \sin(xy)$. On the other hand, if $p(x, y) := 4x^3y^3$ and $q(x, y) := 3x^4y^2$, then $f(x, y) := x^4y^3$ has these functions as its partial derivatives.

The question then becomes: For what pairs of functions, p and q, does there exist a function f such that $f_x(x, y) = p(x, y)$ and $f_y(x, y) = q(x, y)$, for all (x, y)?

It turns out that this question is not hard to answer, at least for the case when p and q are sufficiently nice. Differentiating $f_x = p$ with respect to y and $f_y = q$ with respect to x gives:

$$f_{xy} = p_y \quad \text{and} \quad f_{yx} = q_x.$$

Assuming appropriate continuity of partial derivatives, then $f_{xy} = f_{y\,x}$. Thus, we have:

THEOREM 13.10: Let $g(x, y) = \langle p(x, y), q(x, y) \rangle$ be a vector field. If p and q are nice and $p_y(x, y) = q_x(x, y)$ for all x and y, then there exists a function f such that $\nabla f(x, y) = g(x, y)$.

Vector fields with this property--that is, those which can be the gradient of some function--are said to be **conservative**. The function f, whose gradient is g, is called a **potential function** for g. (This is the terminology you'll see most often, although it might be better to call f an "antigradient" of g.)

EXAMPLE 13.24:

Determine whether $g(x, y) := \langle y^2 + 2xy - 7, 2xy + x^2 \rangle$ is conservative.

With $p(x, y) := y^2 + 2xy - 7$ and $q(x, y) := 2xy + x^2$, we have $p_y(x, y) := 2y + 2x$ and $q_x(x, y) := 2y + 2x$. Since $p_y = q_x$, then g is conservative.

♦

---

1. Determine whether each of the following are conservative vector fields.

(a) $g(x, y) := \langle 3x^2y^2 + 5y^4, 2x^3y \rangle$ (b) $g(x, y) := \left\langle \dfrac{y}{(x+y)^2}, \dfrac{-x}{(x+y)^2} \right\rangle$

¤ Once we've determined that g is conservative, then we'd like to find its potential function, if possible. As we said before, f must satisfy both of the conditions $f_x(x, y) = p(x, y)$ and $f_y(x, y) = q(x, y)$. If the partial derivative of $f(x, y)$ with respect to x is $p(x, y)$, then it seems logical to say that $f(x, y)$ is the **partial antiderivative** of $p(x, y)$ with respect to x and write $f(x, y) = \displaystyle\int p(x, y)\, dx$. Similarly, since the partial derivative of $f(x, y)$ with respect to y is $q(x, y)$, then $f(x, y) = \displaystyle\int q(x, y)\, dy$.

In Chapter 3, we considered the problem of determining a function given its derivative. We found that there are infinitely many functions with the same derivative, any two of which differ by a constant. The graphs of all these antiderivatives are "parallel" in the sense that the vertical distance between any two graphs is the same for all values of x.

Let's see what happens for functions of two variables. Suppose $p(x, y) :=$ $6x^2y$ is the partial derivative of f with respect to x. Treating y as a constant, we see that one possibility for f is $f(x, y) := 2x^3y$. We might be tempted to say that all possible f's are of the form $f(x, y) := 2x^3y + C$, where C is a constant. However, this is not the whole story. When we differentiate with respect to x, any term that contains only y vanishes. Thus, C does not have to be a constant; it can be any function of y alone. Therefore, if $f_x(x, y) := 6x^2y$, then $f(x, y) := 2x^3y + g(y)$, where g is some function. We'll write this as:

$$\int 6x^2 y \, dx = 2x^3 y + g(y).$$

Similarly, if we want to find a partial antiderivative with respect to y, treat x as a constant, find an antiderivative as usual (if possible) and add a function of x. For example,

$$\int 6x^2 y \, dy = 3x^2 y^2 + h(x).$$

Now, suppose $g(x, y) := \langle y^2 + 2xy - 7, 2xy + x^2 \rangle$ as in Example 13.24. We've already shown that g is conservative. Hence, it follows that

$$f(x, y) := \int (2xy + x^2) \, dy = xy^2 + x^2 y + h(x) \quad \text{for some function } h \text{ and}$$

$$f(x, y) := \int (y^2 + 2xy - 7) \, dx = xy^2 + x^2 y - 7x + k(y) \quad \text{for some } k.$$

In order for these to be the same for all x and y, we could take $h(x) := -7x$ and $k(y) = 0$, in which case

$$f(x, y) := xy^2 + x^2 y - 7x.$$

This is not the only possibility; indeed, $f(x, y) := xy^2 + x^2 y - 7x + c$, for any constant c, is also a potential function for g.

- -

TEST YOUR UNDERSTANDING

2. Determine each of the following partial antiderivatives:

(a) $\int \frac{x}{y} \, dy$ (b) $\int \frac{x}{y} \, dx$ (c) $\int e^{xy^2} \, dx$ (d) $\int \frac{x}{x^2 + y^2 + 4} \, dx$

3. Determine a potential function for each of the following:

(a) $\langle 12x^3 y - 2x, 3x^4 + 4 \rangle$ (b) $\langle 2x e^{x^2} \sin(y), e^{x^2} \cos(y) \rangle$

◻ Conservative vector fields are very common in physics. For example, there are many force fields, such as magnetic fields and gravitational fields, that obey the so-called "inverse square law". That is, in the case of gravity, the attraction between two objects is inversely proportional to the square of the distance between them.

Suppose one object is at the origin and another is at the point $P(x, y)$. The distance between the objects is $r = \sqrt{x^2 + y^2}$. Assume the force is directed towards the origin; i.e., in the direction of the vector $v = \langle -x, -y \rangle$. The force field $F(x, y)$ must be parallel to v in such a way that $\|F(x, y)\| = \frac{1}{r^2}$.

As we saw in Chapter 12, $F(x, y) := \left\langle \frac{-x}{r^3}, \frac{-y}{r^3} \right\rangle$, where $r = \sqrt{x^2 + y^2}$, has these properties since, for any (x, y), $F(x, y)$ is parallel to v and

$$\|F(x, y)\| = \sqrt{\left(\frac{(-x)}{r^3}\right)^2 + \left(\frac{(-y)}{r^3}\right)^2} = \frac{1}{r^3}\sqrt{x^2 + y^2} = \frac{r}{r^3} = \frac{1}{r^2} .$$

Moreover, F is conservative. To see why, let

$$u(x, y) := \frac{1}{\sqrt{x^2 + y^2}} = \frac{1}{r} .$$

Then $u_x(x, y) := \dfrac{-x}{\left(x^2 + y^2\right)^{3/2}} = \dfrac{-x}{r^3}$ and $u_y(x, y) := \dfrac{-y}{\left(x^2 + y^2\right)^{3/2}} = \dfrac{-y}{r^3}$.

Thus, $\nabla u = F$, justifying our claim.

What we have shown is that any force field which obeys the inverse square law is conservative. This is an extremely important fact, the ramifications of which will become evident in Chapter 14 when we discuss line integrals.

EXERCISES FOR SECTION 13.5:

1. Evaluate each partial antiderivative:

(a) $\displaystyle\int \left(3x^2 y^4 + 6xy^3 - 9\right) dx$ (b) $\displaystyle\int \left(3x^2 y^4 + 6xy^3 - 9\right) dy$ (c) $\displaystyle\int y\,\sin(xy)\, dx$

(d) $\displaystyle\int x\,e^{y^2 - x^2}\, dx$ (e) $\displaystyle\int \frac{1}{x^2 + y^2}\, dy$ (f) $\displaystyle\int \frac{x}{x^2 + y^2}\, dx$

2. Determine whether each vector field is conservative. If so, find a potential function.

(a) $g(x, y) := \langle 2x, 2y \rangle$ (b) $g(x, y) := \langle 4xy - y^2, 4xy - x^2 \rangle$

(c) $g(x, y) := \langle y \cos(xy), x \cos(xy) \rangle$.

PROBLEMS FOR SECTION 13.5:

1. Suppose F is a force field that obeys an "inverse cube law". Determine whether F is conservative. If so, find a potential function for it.

TYU Answers for Section 13.5

1. (a) No   (b) Yes   2. (a) $x \ln|y| + g(x)$ (b) $\frac{x^2}{2y} + h(y)$ (c) $\frac{1}{y^2} e^{xy^2} + h(y)$

(d) $\frac{1}{2} \ln(x^2 + y^2 + 4) + h(y)$ 3. (a) $3x^4 y + 4y - x^2 + c$ (b) $e^{x^2} \sin(y) + c$

13.6 OPTIMIZATION AND LAGRANGE MULTIPLIERS

In Chapter 5, we considered the problem of maximizing the area of a rectangular garden that could be enclosed with 100 feet of fence. If x and y represent the dimensions of the garden, then the problem is to maximize $A(x, y) := xy$ subject to the constraint that $2x + 2y = 100$.

We solved this problem by using the constraint to express x in terms of y and rewriting the objective function in terms of x only. Then we differentiated and found the critical points. In this case, the only critical point is $x = 25$, which turns out to be the global maximum.

In this case, the constraint is very simple and it is easy to solve for y in terms of x. There are many cases where this is not true and we will face substantial algebraic difficulty if we attempt this procedure. What we need instead is a method for solving optimization problems in which the objective function and the constraint are functions of two variables. Specifically, our problem is:

Maximize (or minimize) $A = f(x, y)$

subject to $g(x, y) = c$.

We will assume that f, g and their first partial derivatives are continuous.

There is a set $C = S_c(g)$ of points in the xy-plane satisfying the constraint $g(x,y) = c$. This is the level curve for the function g. The solution to the optimization problem, if there is one, must be a point on C.

Now consider the level curves for f; in particular, let $S_k(f) = \{(x,y) \mid f(x,y) = k\}$. For any given k, the set $S_k(f)$ may or may not intersect the set C. In the case of a maximization problem, the goal is to find the largest k for which C and $S_k(f)$ have at least one point in common. This point will be the solution to the maximization problem.

To illustrate, consider the garden problem again. The set of points satisfying the constraint $2x + 2y = 100$ is a straight line in the xy-plane. The level curves $S_k(f) = \{(x,y) \mid xy = k\}$ are hyperbolas. For small values of k, the hyperbola intersects the line in two points. As k increases those two points get closer together until, for some k^*, there is just one point of intersection. For values of $k > k^*$, there is no intersection. See Figure 13.13.

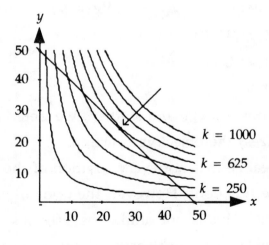

Fig. 13.13

We see that the largest k for which $S_k(f)$ intersects C is $k^* = 625$ which corresponds to the solution $x = 25$, $y = 25$. At this point, the hyperbola is tangent to the line.

For reasons that will be clear in a minute, let's compute the gradients of f and g at the point of tangency. For $f(x, y) := xy$, we have $\nabla f(x, y) = \langle y, x \rangle$ from which $\nabla f(25, 25) = \langle 25, 25 \rangle$. Also, for $g(x, y) := 2x + 2y$, we have $\nabla g(x, y) = \langle 2, 2 \rangle$ for all x and y. Note that the gradients are parallel; that is, there is a constant λ (the Greek letter "lambda") such that $\nabla f(x, y) = \lambda \nabla g(x, y)$. This is not an accident; it is a direct consequence of Theorem 13.6. That theorem says that the gradient of a function is perpendicular to the level curves. If the level curves of f and g are tangent at a point, then any lines perpendicular to those curves at the point of tangency must be parallel.

◻ We are now prepared to describe a method for finding the maximum or minimum value of $f(x, y)$ subject to the constraint $g(x, y) = c$. This method was developed by Joseph Lagrange, a French mathematician of the 18th century. It is called the **method of Lagrange Multipliers**.

The main idea is to write a system of equations that the optimal solution must satisfy. Obviously, the optimal solution must satisfy the constraint

$$g(x, y) = c.$$

Furthermore, in view of our observation about gradients, the optimal solution must also satisfy $\nabla f(x, y) = \lambda \nabla g(x, y)$. Looking at individual components, this is the same as:

$$f_x(x, y) = \lambda g_x(x, y)$$
$$f_y(x, y) = \lambda g_y(x, y).$$

We solve these equations for x, y and λ; then, we determine which solution maximizes (or minimizes) the objective function.

It is important to realize that not every solution of the Lagrange equations optimizes the objective function. However, the optimal solution must satisfy the Lagrange equations. This is not unlike the situation for functions of one variable: Every local extremum must be a critical point but not every critical point is a local extremum.

For the garden problem, $f(x, y) := xy$ and $g(x, y) := 2x + 2y$. Thus, $f_x(x, y) := y, f_y(x, y) := x$ and $g_x(x, y) = g_y(x, y) = 2$. Hence, the Lagrange equations are:

$$2x + 2y = 100$$
$$y = 2\lambda$$
$$x = 2\lambda.$$

The second and third equations imply either $\lambda = 0$ or $x = y$. If $\lambda = 0$, then $x = y = 0$, which would not satisfy the first equation. Thus, $x = y$. Upon substituting in the first equation, we get $2x + 2x = 100$, or $x = 25$ (implying $y = 25$), as we found before.

EXAMPLE 13.25:

Find the minimum value of $f(x, y) := x^2 - y^2$ subject to the constraint $2y - x = 12$.

The graph in Figure 13.14 shows the level curves of f and the constraint. Note that there are two sets of level curves, one for $k > 0$ and one for $k < 0$. The curves for $k > 0$ all intersect the constraint, no matter how big k is. Hence, there is no maximum value of f. Conversely, there appears to be a level curve for $k < 0$ that is tangent to the constraint (somewhere between the second and third curves in the picture). If we make k smaller (more negative) than this, there is no intersection. Hence, f has a minimum value subject to the constraint.

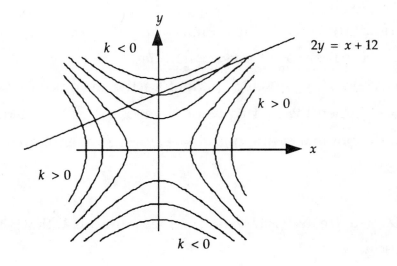

Fig. 13.14

Since $f_x(x, y) := 2x, f_y(x, y) := -2y, g_x(x, y) := -1$ and $g_y(x, y) := 2$, the Lagrange equations are:

$$2y - x = 12, \qquad 2x = -\lambda, \qquad -2y = 2\lambda$$

The third equation implies $y = -\lambda$ and, hence from the second equation, $y = 2x$. Substituting in the first equation gives $4x - x = 12$ or $x = 4$. Thus, the optimal solution is $x = 4, y = 8$. The minimum value of f subject to the constraint is -48.

Note: We can check that this is the minimum, not maximum value by evaluating f at some other point satisfying the constraint. For example, $x = 2, y = 7$ satisfies the constraint. However, $f(2, 7) = -45 > -48$. ♦

EXAMPLE 13.26:

Find two positive numbers, x and y, such that $x + 2y = 1$ and the product $z = x^2y^3$ is a large as possible.

With $f(x, y) := x^2y^3$ and $g(x, y) := x + 2y$, we have $f_x(x, y) := 2xy^3, f_y(x, y) := 3x^2y^2, g_x(x, y) := 1$ and $g_y(x, y) := 2$. Thus, the Lagrange equations are:

$$x + 2y = 1$$
$$2xy^3 = \lambda$$
$$3x^2y^2 = 2\lambda$$

The second and third equations imply $3x^2y^2 = 4xy^3$ or, equivalently, $xy^2(3x - 4y) = 0$. There are three possibilities: $x = 0, y = 0$, or $y = \frac{3x}{4}$. The first two yield $z = 0$ which cannot be the maximum. On the other hand, if $y = \frac{3x}{4}$, then the first equation gives $x + 2(\frac{3x}{4}) = 1$ from which $x = \frac{2}{5}$. Hence, the optimal solution is $x = \frac{2}{5}, y = \frac{3}{10}$ with corresponding $z = \frac{108}{25000} = .00432$. ♦

Notice that we are not interested in the value of λ that produces the optimal solution.

Let's look at another problem that we solved in Chapter 5 (Example 5.3).

EXAMPLE 13.27:

What are the dimensions of the stiffest rectangular beam that can be cut from a circular log of radius 16", where the stiffness is defined to be the product of the width times the cube of the height of the beam?

Let x = width and y = height of the beam. Then the objective is to maximize $S = xy^3$. Since the beam is to be cut from a log of radius 16, then x and y must satisfy the constraint $x^2 + y^2 = 16^2 = 256$.

With $f(x, y) := xy^3$ and $g(x, y) := x^2 + y^2$, we have $f_x(x, y) := y^3$, $f_y(x, y) := 3xy^2$, $g_x(x, y) := 2x$ and $g_y(x, y) := 2x$. Thus, the Lagrange equations are:

$$x^2 + y^2 = 256$$
$$y^3 = 2\lambda x$$
$$3xy^2 = 2\lambda y$$

The third equation implies either $y = 0$ (which is not a reasonable answer since the corresponding stiffness would be 0) or $3xy = 2\lambda$. Hence, the second equation becomes $y^3 = x(3xy) = 3x^2y$, from which $y^2 = 3x^2$. Substituting in the first equation, we get $x^2 + 3x^2 = 256$, implying $x = 8$. The corresponding y-value is $y = 8\sqrt{3}$. Therefore, the stiffest beam is 8" wide and $8\sqrt{3}$" high. ♦

- -

TEST YOUR UNDERSTANDING

1. Suppose we want to minimize $f(x, y) := x^2 + y^2$ subject to $x^2 - y = 4$.

    (a) Write the Lagrange equations for this problem.

    (b) Determine the solution(s) of these equations.

(c) Notice that $x^2 = 4 + y$, so $f(x, y) := y^2 + y + 4$. Does this function have a maximum value?

EXAMPLE 13.28:

A cowboy and his horse are riding near a river. The cowboy wants to ride his horse to the river, let it drink some water, then ride to his ranch. At what point on the river should he ride to minimize the total length of the trip? See Figure 13.15.

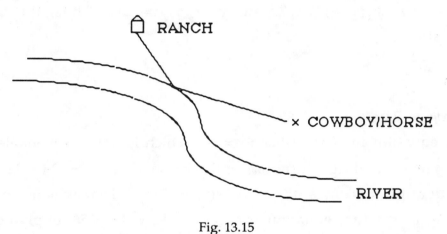

Fig. 13.15

Introduce a coordinate system and let $A(p, q)$ be the location of the cowboy, $B(r, s)$ be the location of the ranch and $P(x, y)$ be the point on the river to which he rides. The total distance he rides is given by $f(x, y) :=$
$\sqrt{(x - p)^2 + (y - q)^2} + \sqrt{(x - r)^2 + (y - s)^2}$.

By definition, the set of points for which the sum of the distances to two fixed points is constant is an ellipse. Hence, the level curves of f are concentric ellipses with A and B as foci, as in Figure 13.16.

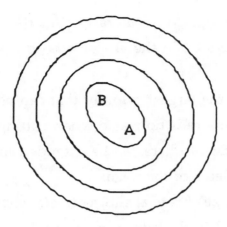

Fig. 13.16

Hence, by the arguments we used in this section, the minimum distance occurs when the level curve is tangent to the constraint. Here, the constraint is the river. So, the cowboy should draw an ellipse with his location and his ranch as foci that is tangent to the river. Then he should ride to the point of tangency. ◆

EXERCISES FOR SECTION 13.6:

1. Find the maximum value of xy subject to $x + y = 20$.

2. Find the point on the circle $x^2 + y^2 = 1$ for which $x + 2y$ is a maximum.

3. Find the smallest value of $2x + y$ such that $xy = 32$, where x and y are positive.

4. Find the largest and smallest values of x^3y, subject to $\sqrt{x} + \sqrt{y} = 1$, where $x, y \geq 0$.

PROBLEMS FOR SECTION 13.6:

1. An economist predicts that the number of items produced by a manufacturer is given by $f(x, y) := 50x^{3/4}y^{1/4}$, where x is the number of units of labor and y is the number of units of capital. If labor costs \$150 per unit and capital costs \$250 per unit, find the maximum number of items that can be produced for \$50000. (Note: The objective function is a special case of the so-called Cobb-Douglas production function.)

2. Use the method of Lagrange Multipliers to find the area of the largest rectangle that can be inscribed in the ellipse whose equation is $x^2 + 4y^2 = 16$.

3. Determine the volume of the largest cylinder that can be made from 100 sq. in. of material. (Assume there is no waste when cutting the pieces.)

4. The method of Lagrange Multipliers can be extended to functions of three variables--that is, to problems of the form:

Maximize (or minimize) $f(x, y, z)$ subject to $g(x, y, z) = c$.

The only change required is the addition of another equation $f_z(x, y, z) = \lambda g_z(x, y, z)$.

(a) Find the minimum value of $x^2 + 2y^2 + z^2$ subject to $x + y + z = 4$.

(b) A rectangular box lies in the first octant with three sides on the coordinate planes and one vertex on the plane $2x + y + 4z = 12$. Find the maximum volume of the box.

<u>TYU Answers to Section 13.6</u>

1. (a) $x^2 - y = 4$, $2x = 2\lambda x$, $2y = -\lambda$ (b) $x = \pm\sqrt{\dfrac{7}{2}}$, $y = \dfrac{-1}{2}$ (c) No

13.7 SOME APPLICATIONS

Many of the interesting applications of calculus that we encountered in earlier chapters arose in the form of differential equations. In this section, we'll look at yet another application of differential equations. This time, however, the equations will involve partial, rather than ordinary, derivatives. As we might expect, partial differential equations are much harder to solve than ordinary differential equations. While there are some techniques we could learn for solving such equations, they are best left for a more advanced course on the subject. Instead, we will concentrate on the analysis that leads to the derivation of the equation. Then we'll claim that a certain function satisfies the equation, a claim that can be verified by substitution.

Imagine a long, glass tube in which some organism--hereinafter known as "stuff"--is growing. Assume that the stuff is uniformly distributed on any cross-section perpendicular to the axis of the tube, but that the density of stuff varies from slice to slice. Figure 13.17 shows slices of low, medium and high densities.

Fig. 13.17

As the stuff suffers from severe claustrophobia, it has a tendency to move from areas of high density to areas of low density. To complicate matters, all the food is inside the tube so any stuff that escapes from the end of the tube dies. Finally, since there isn't much else to do in the tube, the stuff reproduces.

Our goal is to determine what happens to the distribution of stuff inside the tube as time passes. Out of necessity, some stuff is going to escape out the end of the tube and die, to be replaced by new stuff. If the new stuff is produced at a fast enough rate, then it will more than compensate for the losses and, assuming there is an unlimited food supply, the population of stuff will grow without bound (at least until there is no room left in the tube). Conversely, if the birth rate cannot compensate for the losses, then the population will eventually die out. Finally, in the unlikely event that the birth rate exactly compensates for the losses, the population may level off at some constant amount over time.

It seems reasonable that the proportion of stuff that escapes from the end of the tube depends on how long the tube is. For short tubes, a greater fraction of stuff is near the end, so a relatively high proportion of stuff could escape. On the other hand, if the tube is very long, then a smaller percentage of stuff is near the end so relatively little might escape.

This is reminiscent of the song that goes, "There were ten in the bed and the little one said, 'Roll over'. So they all rolled over and one fell out." That's 10 percent of the bed population. If the bed were bigger, with 100 in the bed and they all rolled over and one fell out, then that's only 1 percent of the bed population.

Now let's try to quantify these qualitative ideas. In view of our assumptions about uniformity within cross-sections, we can introduce a one-dimensional coordinate system with $x = 0$ corresponding to one end of the tube and $x = L$ corresponding to the other end. See Figure 13.18.

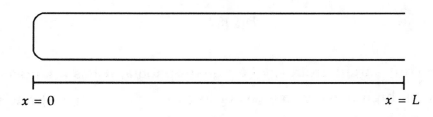

$x = 0$ $\qquad\qquad\qquad\qquad\qquad\qquad\qquad\qquad$ $x = L$

Fig. 13.18

The variable in which we are interested is the density of stuff at any point in the tube at any given time. Hence, the density, measured in units such as grams/meter, is a function of two variables and we'll denote it $\rho(x, t)$.

After much calculus whose details we omit, we have that $\rho(x, t)$ must satisfy the second-order partial differential equation

(6) $\qquad \dfrac{\partial \rho}{\partial t} = k\dfrac{\partial^2 \rho}{\partial x^2} + r\rho,$

where k measures the rate at which diffusion occurs and r is the natural growth rate of the stuff.

As we said earlier, we will not attempt to learn any methods for solving partial differential equations. However, consider the function:

(7) $\qquad \rho(x, t) := e^{\alpha t}[c_1 \cos(\beta x) + c_2 \sin(\beta x)].$

Then, $\dfrac{\partial \rho}{\partial t} = \alpha e^{\alpha t}[c_1 \cos(\beta x) + c_2 \sin(\beta x)] = \alpha \rho$ and

$$\dfrac{\partial^2 \rho}{\partial x^2} = -\beta^2 e^{\alpha t}[c_1 \cos(\beta x) + c_2 \sin(\beta x)] = -\beta^2 \rho.$$

Upon substituting, we get $\alpha \rho = -k\beta^2 \rho + r\rho$, or

(8) $\alpha = r - k\beta^2$.

Thus, the function in Eq.(7) satisfies Eq.(6), if $\alpha = r - k\beta^2$.

The next step is to use information in the problem to solve for the constants c_1, c_2 and β. (Once we have β, α is automatically determined by Eq.(8).) Typically, partial differential equations require two types of information. **Boundary conditions** give information about the variable or its derivatives at specific x-values as a function of t. **Initial conditions** give the distribution of the variable at time $t = 0$ as a function of x.

In our problem, let's assume that the tube is closed at $x = 0$. This means that stuff can't flow through that end. Since the flow is proportional to the derivative of the density with respect to x, then we must have $\dfrac{\partial \rho}{\partial x} = 0$ when $x = 0$. This is one boundary condition. From Eq.(7),

$$\dfrac{\partial \rho}{\partial x} = -\beta e^{\alpha t}[c_1 \sin(\beta x) - c_2 \cos(\beta x)] = c_2 e^{\alpha t}\beta \text{ when } x = 0.$$

This means either $\beta = 0$ or $c_2 = 0$. If $\beta = 0$, then $\rho(x, t) := c_1 e^{\alpha t}$ which is independent of x. Depending upon whether α is positive or negative, the stuff either grows without bound or dies off uniformly throughout the tube as time passes. While this may be possible (assuming the stuff is uniformly distributed to begin with), it isn't terribly interesting. Hence, we'll assume $c_2 = 0$.

The other end of the tube is open but anytime stuff flows out it dies. Hence the density of stuff at that end must be 0--that is, $\rho(L, t) = 0$ for all t. This is another boundary condition. Since $\rho(L, t) = c_1 e^{\alpha t}\cos(\beta L)$, then $\cos(\beta L) = 0$ or $c_1 = 0$. If $c_1 = 0$ (in addition to $c_2 = 0$), then $\rho(x, t) = 0$ for all x, t; again, this is not very interesting. Thus $\cos(\beta L) = 0$ which happens if $\beta L = \frac{\pi}{2}, \frac{3\pi}{2}, \frac{5\pi}{2}, \ldots$ or, equivalently, if $\beta = \frac{\pi}{2L}, \frac{3\pi}{2L}, \frac{5\pi}{2L} \cdots$

So far, we've shown that the family of functions

(11) $\rho_n(x,t) := c_n\, e^{\alpha_n t}\, \cos(\beta_n x)$

where $\beta_n = \frac{2n-1}{2}\frac{\pi}{L}$, $\alpha_n = r - k\beta_n^2$ and c_n is an arbitrary constant, satisfies the partial differential equation and the two boundary conditions. Moreover, it can be shown that the sum of any two (or more) functions in this family also satisfies the equation and the boundary conditions. We still have not imposed any initial conditions; we'll deal with that a little later.

For now, let's look at the behavior of one of these functions, say $\rho_1(x,t)$. Since $\beta_1 = \frac{\pi}{2L}$, then $\alpha_1 = r - k\left(\frac{\pi}{2L}\right)^2$. Depending on the values of r and k, α_1 may be positive or negative. Remember, r measures the per capita birth rate while k measures the rate at which the stuff diffuses from high to low density areas.

Suppose α_1 is positive, which occurs if $r > k\left(\frac{\pi}{2L}\right)^2$. Then the exponential factor has a positive exponent, which increases as t increases. Therefore, the population grows without bound at each x-value. Conversely, if $r < k\left(\frac{\pi}{2L}\right)^2$, then α_1 will be negative and the population will die out. These two behaviors are depicted in Figure 13.19.

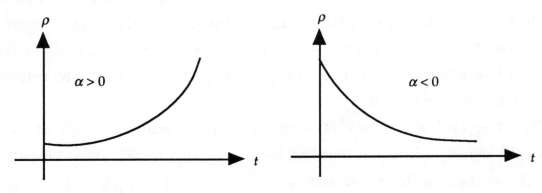

Fig. 13.19

If, by chance, $\alpha_1 = 0$, then the birth rate exactly compensates for the losses and the density will remain constant over time.

Note that $r > k\left(\dfrac{\pi}{2L}\right)^2$ if and only if $L > \dfrac{\pi}{2}\sqrt{\dfrac{k}{r}}$. So, if the length of the tube exceeds this value, the population grows without bound. If $L < \dfrac{\pi}{2}\sqrt{\dfrac{k}{r}}$, the population dies out. If $L = \dfrac{\pi}{2}\sqrt{\dfrac{k}{r}}$, the population remains constant.

Now let's go back to the initial conditions. From Eq.(11), $\rho_n(x,0) = c_n\cos(\beta_n x)$. This function, by itself, is an unreasonable initial distribution since, among other reasons, $\rho_n(x,0)$ would be negative for some x-values. Recall, however, that the sum of functions of the type in Eq.(11) is also a solution. It turns out that, for any suitably well-behaved initial distribution $f(x)$ defined on $[0, L]$, it is possible to choose the coefficients c_n such that

$$f(x) := \sum_{n=1}^{\infty} c_n\cos(\beta_n x) \text{ for all } x \text{ on } [0, L].$$

While this may seem strange, it is really not much different from Taylor series, where we claimed that any nice function could be represented as a power series of the form $\displaystyle\sum_{n=0}^{\infty} c_n x^n$. Series of the form $\displaystyle\sum_{n=1}^{\infty} c_n\cos(\beta_n x)$ are called **Fourier series**, named for the 19th century French mathematician Joseph Fourier. For more details about Fourier series, you'll need to take a course in partial differential equations.

PROBLEMS FOR SECTION 13.7:

1. Consider the special case of Eq.(6) in which there are no births--that is, when $r = 0$.

   (a) What does this imply about α?

   (b) Assuming the same boundary conditions, what do the solutions look like?

   Note: The equation $\dfrac{\partial\rho}{\partial t} = k\dfrac{\partial^2\rho}{\partial x^2}$ that results when $r = 0$ is called the **heat equation** and can be used to describe the way heat diffuses in a rod insulated along its length.

2. Suppose the stuff is not confined to a tube but rather is allowed to grow in a rectangular dish. Now we might expect migration in two directions, "north-south" and "east-west". This requires the need for two coordinates (x, y) to specify the location of the stuff. Let $\rho(x, y, t)$ = density of stuff at location (x, y) at time t. Modify Eq.(6) to account for this.

3. Consider the second-order partial differential equation $\dfrac{\partial^2 z}{\partial t^2} = c^2 \dfrac{\partial^2 z}{\partial x^2}$, where c is a constant. (This particular equation occurs quite frequently in physics and is called the **wave equation**.)

   (a) Show that $z = \sin(x - ct)$ satisfies this equation.

   (b) Let $c = \pi/4$. Sketch, on separate axes, the graphs of z vs. x for $t = 0$, 1 and 2. Can you see why the equation is called the wave equation?

4. Another important example of a partial differential equation is **Laplace's equation** $\dfrac{\partial^2 z}{\partial x^2} + \dfrac{\partial^2 z}{\partial x^2} = 0$. Show that $z = \arctan(y/x)$ satisfies Laplace's equation.

QUESTIONS TO THINK ABOUT

1. Define the directional derivative and give its geometrical interpretation. Why is it necessary to use a unit vector in the definition?

2. Discuss several uses for the gradient. How is the role of the gradient for functions of two variables similar to the role of the derivative for functions of one variable?

3. Describe how you would determine the local extrema for a function of two variables.

4. Explain the theory underlying the Method of Lagrange Multipliers.

5. What does it mean for a vector field to be conservative? How can you tell if it is?

PROJECT 13.1

FOURIER SERIES

OBJECTIVE: In Section 13.7, we saw that functions of the form $\rho_n(x, t) :=$ $e^{\alpha t} \cos(\beta_n x)$ satisfied a certain partial differential equation subject to some boundary conditions. Unfortunately, any particular one of these functions forces us to accept unrealisitic initial conditions $\rho_n(x, 0) = \cos(\beta_n x)$. We then claimed that by taking combinations of these functions, we could make the initial conditions more realistic. That is, if the initial conditions are described by some function $f(x)$, then we can write $f(x) = \displaystyle\sum_{n=1}^{\infty} c_n \cos(\beta_n x)$, for some constants c_n. In this project, we will show more generally how certain functions can be expressed as the sum of terms of the form $a_n \sin(nx)$ and $b_n \cos(nx)$. Such series are called **Fourier series,** named after the French engineer who first exploited them.

PROCEDURE:
Part 1: Some necessary integrals

Recall that a function f is odd if $f(-x) = -f(x)$ for all x and f is even if $f(-x) = f(x)$ for all x. The graph of an odd function is symmetric about the origin while that of an even function is symmetric about the y-axis. The product of two odd functions is even, the product of an even function and an odd function is odd, and the product of two even functions is even. The sum of two odd functions is odd, the sum of two even functions is even and the sum of an even and an odd function is neither even nor odd.

a. Show that $f(x) := \cos(kx)$ is even and $g(x) := \sin(kx)$ is odd, for all k.

b. Show that $\displaystyle\int_{-a}^{a} f(x)\, dx = 0$ if f is odd.

c. Show that $\displaystyle\int_{-a}^{a} f(x)\sin(nx)\, dx = 0$ if f is even and $\displaystyle\int_{-a}^{a} f(x)\cos(nx)\, dx = 0$ if f is odd.

d. Evaluate $\displaystyle\int_{-\pi}^{\pi} \sin(mx)\cos(nx)\, dx$.

e. Use the fact that $\sin(mx)\sin(nx) = \dfrac{\cos[(m-n)x] - \cos[(m+n)x]}{2}$ to

evaluate $\displaystyle\int_{-\pi}^{\pi} \sin(mx)\sin(nx)\,dx$, if $m \neq n$.

f. Use the fact that $\cos(mx)\cos(nx) = \dfrac{\cos[(m-n)x] + \cos[(m+n)x]}{2}$ to

evaluate $\displaystyle\int_{-\pi}^{\pi} \cos(mx)\cos(nx)\,dx$, if $m \neq n$.

g. Use integration by parts or a table of integrals to show that

$$\int_{-\pi}^{\pi} \cos^2(nx)\,dx = \int_{-\pi}^{\pi} \sin^2(nx)\,dx = \pi, \text{ for all positive integers } n.$$

Part 2: The Fourier coefficients

Let f be a function defined on the interval $[-\pi, \pi]$. Our goal is to express f as a Fourier series of the form

(1) $f(x) := a_0 + a_1\cos(x) + a_2\cos(2x) + \ldots + b_1\sin(x) + b_2\sin(2x) + \ldots$

$$= a_0 + \sum_{n=1}^{\infty} [a_n \cos(nx) + b_n \sin(nx)].$$

a. Integrate both sides of (1) from $-\pi$ to π to show that $a_0 = \dfrac{1}{2\pi}\displaystyle\int_{-\pi}^{\pi} f(x)\,dx$.

b. Multiply (1) by $\cos(x)$ and integrate from $-\pi$ to π. Use 1d, 1f and 1g to

show that $a_1 = \dfrac{1}{\pi}\displaystyle\int_{-\pi}^{\pi} f(x)\cos(x)\,dx$.

c. More generally, multiply (1) by $\cos(nx)$ and integrate from $-\pi$ to π to

show that $a_n = \dfrac{1}{\pi}\displaystyle\int_{-\pi}^{\pi} f(x)\cos(nx)\,dx$.

d. Show that $b_n = \dfrac{1}{\pi}\displaystyle\int_{-\pi}^{\pi} f(x)\sin(nx)\,dx$.

e. Use 2d to show that if f is odd, then its Fourier series contains no cosine terms while if f is even, its Fourier series contains no sine terms.

Part 3: Periodic functions

A function f is said to be **periodic with period p** if $f(x + p) = f(x)$ for all x, and p is the smallest number with this property.

a. What is the period of $f(x) := \sin(x)$? of $f(x) := \tan(x)$?

b. Show that $f(x) := \sin(kx)$ has period $p = 2\pi/k$.

c. Graph $y = \sin(x) + 2\sin(3x)$. What is its period?

Any function defined on a closed interval can be turned into a period function by repeating the graph along consecutive intervals of the x-axis. We call this new function the **periodic extension** of f, denoted $\bar{f}(x)$. We'll restrict ourselves to functions defined on intervals of the form $[-c, c]$.

d. Draw the periodic extension of $f(x) := \begin{cases} 1, & 0 \le x \le \pi \\ -1, & -\pi \le x \le 0 \end{cases}$. The resulting picture is called a "square wave". What is its period?

e. Show that the Fourier series for the function in 3d is

$$\frac{4}{\pi}\left[\sin(x) + \frac{\sin(3x)}{3} + \frac{\sin(5x)}{5} + \cdots\right].$$

f. Graph the first four "partial sums" of the series in 3e.

g. Show that $f(\pi)$ does not equal the value of the series at π. What about other values of x?

h. Draw the periodic extension of $g(x) = x, -\pi \le x \le \pi$. This is called a saw-tooth wave.

i. Determine the Fourier series for the function in 3h.

Part 4: Some generalizations and a surprising result

Suppose f is defined on $[-c, c]$ and is extended periodically with period $2c$. (The functions in 3d and 3h are examples of this with $c = \pi$). Now the Fourier series takes the form $a_0 + \sum_{n=1}^{\infty}\left[a_n \cos\left(\frac{n\pi x}{c}\right) + b_n \sin\left(\frac{n\pi x}{c}\right)\right]$. It can be shown that the coefficients are given by $a_0 = \frac{1}{2c}\int_{-c}^{c} f(x)\,dx$, $a_n = \frac{1}{c}\int_{-c}^{c} f(x)\cos\left(\frac{n\pi x}{c}\right)dx$ and $b_n = \frac{1}{c}\int_{-c}^{c} f(x)\sin\left(\frac{n\pi x}{c}\right)dx$.

a. Let $f(x) := |x|, -1 \le x \le 1$. Show that the Fourier series for f is

$$\frac{1}{2} - \frac{4}{\pi^2}\sum_{k=0}^{\infty}\frac{1}{(2k+1)^2}\cos(2k+1)\pi x.$$

Note that f is even so the Fourier series will have no sine terms.

b. Substitute $x = 0$ in 4a and show that $\frac{\pi^2}{8} = 1 + \frac{1}{9} + \frac{1}{25} + \frac{1}{49} + \cdots$.

c. Use 4b to show that $\frac{\pi^2}{6} = 1 + \frac{1}{4} + \frac{1}{9} + \frac{1}{16} + \frac{1}{25} + \frac{1}{36} + \frac{1}{49} + \cdots$.

   Hint:

$$1 + \frac{1}{4} + \frac{1}{9} + \frac{1}{16} + \frac{1}{25} + \frac{1}{36} + \frac{1}{49} + \cdots = 1 + \frac{1}{9} + \frac{1}{25} + \frac{1}{49} + \cdots \frac{1}{4} + \frac{1}{16} + \frac{1}{36} + \cdots =$$

$$1 + \frac{1}{9} + \frac{1}{25} + \frac{1}{49} + \cdots \frac{1}{4}\left(1 + \frac{1}{4} + \frac{1}{9} + \frac{1}{16} + \cdots\right)$$

PROJECT 13.2

THE METHOD OF LEAST SQUARES

OBJECTIVE: Let $\{(x_1, y_1), (x_2, y_2), \ldots, (x_n, y_n)\}$ be a set of points in the xy-plane. If $n = 2$, then there is a unique straight line passing through the two points. If $n > 2$, then it is highly unlikely that all the points lie on the same straight line. The question then becomes: Can we find a line that passes "as closely as possible" through all the points? Statisticians are frequently faced with just such a problem and have developed a method, called the "method of least squares regression", for answering it. We'll investigate this method and some extensions of it in this project.

PROCEDURE:

Part 1: An illustrative example

Consider the set of four points $\{(1, 2), (3, 6), (5, 8), (7, 8)\}$.

a. Plot these points and superimpose the line $y = 2 + x$. How many points are above the line, how many are below the line and how many are on the line?

b. Determine the vertical distance (i.e. difference in y-values) from each point to the line. Compute the sum of the squares of those distances.

c. Repeat 1a and 1b for the line $y = 2.5 + .5x$. Which line do you think fits the data better? Explain.

d. Now consider the line $y = a + bx$. Let r_i = vertical distance from the ith point to the line. Express r_1, r_2, r_3 and r_4 in terms of a and b.

e. Let $Q = \sum_{i=1}^{4} r_i^2$. Express Q in terms of a and b.

f. By setting $\dfrac{\partial Q}{\partial a}$ and $\dfrac{\partial Q}{\partial b}$ equal to 0, show that Q is in fact minimized by taking $b = 1$ and $a = 2$, as in 1a. This line is called the **least squares regression** line for the data.

Part 2: The general case

Let $\{(x_1, y_1), (x_2, y_2), \ldots, (x_n, y_n)\}$ be a set of n points and let $y = a + bx$ be an equation of a straight line.

a. Express r_i in terms of a and b, where r_i is defined in 1d.

b. Let $Q = \sum_{i=1}^{n} r_i^2$ as in 1e. Show that

$$\frac{\partial Q}{\partial a} = -2 \sum_{i=1}^{n} (y_i - a - bx_i) = -2\left(\sum_{i=1}^{n} y_i - b \sum_{i=1}^{n} x_i - na \right) \text{ and}$$

$$\frac{\partial Q}{\partial b} = -2 \sum_{i=1}^{n} x_i (y_i - a - bx_i) = -2\left(\sum_{i=1}^{n} x_i y_i - b \sum_{i=1}^{n} x_i^2 - a \sum_{i=1}^{n} x_i \right).$$

c. By setting $\frac{\partial Q}{\partial a} = 0$, show that $a = \dfrac{\sum_{i=1}^{n} y_i - b \sum_{i=1}^{n} x_i}{n}$.

d. Substitute this in the expression for $\frac{\partial Q}{\partial b}$, set equal to 0 and show that

$$b = \frac{n \sum_{i=1}^{n} x_i y_i - \sum_{i=1}^{n} x_i \sum_{i=1}^{n} y_i}{n \sum_{i=1}^{n} x_i^2 - \left(\sum_{i=1}^{n} x_i \right)^2}$$

e. For the data in Part 1, show that this formula gives $b = 1$. Then use the result of 2c to show that $a = 2$.

The coefficients given by the formulas in 2d and 2c determine the least squares regression line for the set of data.

f. Show that if $n = 2$, the formula in 2d simplifies to $b = \dfrac{y_2 - y_1}{x_2 - x_1}$.

Explain the significance of this result.

Part 3: Regression through the origin

Suppose y represents the force required to stretch a spring x meters beyond its natural length. Since no force is required to stretch the spring 0 meters, then y must be 0 when x is 0. This means the regression line is of the form $y = bx$, where b is the spring constant.

a. Let $r_i = y_i - bx_i$ be the vertical distance between the points and the line and let $Q = \sum_{i=1}^{n} r_i^2$. (Note that Q is a function of b only.)

Show that the value of b that minimizes Q is $b = \dfrac{\sum_{i=1}^{n} x_i y_i}{\sum_{i=1}^{n} x_i^2}$.

b. The data below represent several measurements of force and displacement for a given spring. Use the result of 3a to estimate the spring constant.

Displacement(x)	2	4	6	8	10	12
Force(y)	5.9	11.7	17.7	23.6	29.4	35.1

Part 4: Non-linear regression

Sometimes, a plot of the data indicates that the underlying relationship between x and y is not linear. For example, the following data are the cooking times (y, measured in hours) for turkeys of various sizes (x, measured in pounds).

Size(x)	5	7	10	13	15	18	20
Time(y)	2	2.7	3.4	4.1	4.5	5.2	5.4

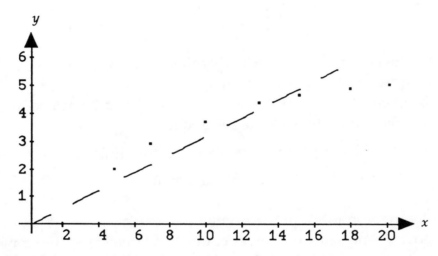

Therefore, fitting a regression line of the form $y = a + bx$ is inappropriate. A better choice might be a non-linear relationship of the form $y = ax^b$.

a. Use logarithms to change $y = ax^b$ into a linear equation whose intercept is $\log(a)$ and whose slope is b. (The logarithms may be natural or base 10 or any other base. Just be consistent.)

b. Modify the results of 2c and 2d to get least squares estimates of $\log(a)$ and b.

c. Assuming the relationship is of the form $y = ax^b$, use 4b to determine a and b for the data above.

d. Many cookbooks suggest cooking turkey 20 minutes per pound. If this were true, what would the value of b have to be? Is this what you got? Why are there so many overcooked turkeys?

PROJECT 13.3

DIVERGENCE AND CURL

OBJECTIVE: In this chapter, we defined the gradient of a function of two variables as $\nabla f(x, y) = \langle f_x(x, y), f_y(x, y) \rangle$. We then determined under what conditions a given vector field $F(x, y) = \langle P(x, y), Q(x, y) \rangle$ is the gradient of some function ϕ (that is, conditions that make F conservative). In this project, we will extend this to three dimensions. Specifically, let $F(x, y, z) = \langle P(x, y, z), Q(x, y, z), R(x, y, z) \rangle$ be a three-dimensional field. What must be true about the functions P, Q and R so that F is the gradient of some function $\phi(x, y, z)$? In the process, we will define two new operations, the **curl** and the **divergence**, and investigate some of their properties.

PROCEDURE:

Part 1: Conservative vector fields

Let $F(x, y, z) = \langle P(x, y, z), Q(x, y, z), R(x, y, z) \rangle$ where P, Q and R are nice functions. Suppose F is conservative and $\phi(x, y, z)$ is a potential function for F. Then $\phi_x(x, y, z) = P(x, y, z)$, $\phi_y(x, y, z) = Q(x, y, z)$ and $\phi_z(x, y, z) = R(x, y, z)$.

a. Assuming ϕ is very nice, write two different expressions for ϕ_{xy}, for ϕ_{yz} and for ϕ_{xz}.

b. Argue that F is conservative if and only if $R_y = Q_z$, $P_z = R_x$ and $P_y = Q_x$.

c. Show that $F(x, y, z) := \langle 2xy, x^2 + z^2, 2zy \rangle$ is conservative.

d. Determine whether $F(x, y, z) := \langle \sin(y), -x \cos(y), 1 \rangle$ is conservative.

e. Determine a potential function for the vector field in 1c.

Part 2: The curl of a vector field

Let $F(x, y, z) = \langle P(x, y, z), Q(x, y, z), R(x, y, z) \rangle$. The **curl** of F is the three-dimensional vector field

$$\text{curl } F = \langle R_y - Q_z, P_z - R_x, Q_x - P_y \rangle.$$

(The curl is also denoted $\nabla \times F$.)

a. Determine the curl of $F(x, y, z) := \langle x^2 y, 2x + 5yz, xyz^3 \rangle$.

b. Argue that F is conservative if and only if curl $F = 0$, the zero vector.

c. Let $F(x, y, z) := \langle xyz, y, z \rangle$. Determine curl(curl F).

d. Let $f(x, y, z)$ be a scalar function. Show that $\operatorname{curl}(\nabla f) = 0$ (assuming f is very nice).

e. Let $F(x, y, z) := \left\langle \dfrac{-x}{r^3}, \dfrac{-y}{r^3}, \dfrac{-z}{r^3} \right\rangle$, where $r = \sqrt{x^2 + y^2 + z^2}$. This is a three-dimensional inverse-square vector field. (See Sections 12.5 and 13.4 for a discussion of the two-dimensional case.) Show that $\operatorname{curl} F = 0$.

Part 3: The divergence of a vector field

Another operation on vector fields is the **divergence**. Let $F(x, y, z) := \langle P(x, y, z), Q(x, y, z), R(x, y, z) \rangle$. Then $\operatorname{div} F = \dfrac{\partial P}{\partial x} + \dfrac{\partial Q}{\partial y} + \dfrac{\partial R}{\partial z}$.

(The divergence is also denoted $\nabla \cdot F$.) Note that the divergence of a vector field is a scalar quantity (which is consistent with the dot product notation). A field whose divergence is 0 is said to be **solenoidal**.

a. Determine $\operatorname{div} F$ where F is the vector field in 2a.

b. Show that $\operatorname{div}(\operatorname{curl} F) = 0$ if F has nice components.

c. Let $F(x, y, z)$ be a vector field and $f(x, y, z)$ be a scalar function. Show that $\operatorname{div}(fF) = f \operatorname{div} F + \nabla f \cdot F$.

d. Let F be a three-dimensional inverse-square field as in 2e. Show that $\operatorname{div} F = 0$.

Part 4: Harmonic functions

Let F be a vector field that is both conservative and solenoidal and let ϕ be a potential function for F. Then ϕ is said to be **harmonic**. The inverse-square field is an example of such a field (see 2e and 3d).

a. Show that $\phi(x, y, z) := \dfrac{1}{\sqrt{x^2 + y^2 + z^2}} = \dfrac{1}{r}$ is a potential function for the inverse-square field and, thus, ϕ is harmonic. (See Section 13.4.)

b. Show, in general, that ϕ is harmonic if $\phi_{xx} + \phi_{yy} + \phi_{zz} = 0$. (This equation is known as **Laplace's equation**.)

c. Show that the function $\phi(x, y, z) := e^{-\sqrt{\lambda^2 + \mu^2}\, x} \sin(\lambda y) \sin(\mu z)$ is harmonic.

d. More generally, show that any function of the form $\phi(x, y, z) := X(x)Y(y)Z(z)$, where X satisfies $X'' = -(\lambda^2 + \mu^2)X$, Y satisfies $Y'' = \lambda^2 Y$ and Z satisfies $Z'' = \mu^2 Z$ is harmonic.

CHAPTER 14

MULTIPLE INTEGRATION

14.1 VOLUME

In Chapters 2 and 6, we studied the problem of finding the area of a region in the xy-plane bounded by a non-negative function $y = f(x)$ and the x-axis, over the interval $[a, b]$. We partitioned the interval $[a, b]$ into n equal subintervals, each of length $\Delta x = \dfrac{b - a}{n}$, and constructed rectangles. Then we approximated the area of the region by computing the sum of the areas of the rectangles. Specifically, let x_j be the x-value at the right side of the jth subinterval. (Actually x_j could be *any* x-value in the jth subinterval.) Then, $S(n) := \sum_{j=1}^{n} f(x_j) \Delta x$ is the sum of the areas of the rectangles. The exact area is obtained by letting n approach ∞; that is,

$$A = \lim_{n \to \infty} \sum_{j=1}^{n} f(x_j) \Delta x .$$

There are other applications of this idea such as finding the distance travelled by a particle given its velocity, or the total mass of an object given its density.

More generally, we can define the Riemann sum $S(n) := \sum_{j=1}^{n} f(x_j) \Delta x$ for any continuous function (not necessarily non-negative). Upon taking the limit as n approaches ∞, we get the definite integral of f over the interval $[a, b]$. In other words,

$$\int_a^b f(x) \, dx = \lim_{n \to \infty} \sum_{j=1}^{n} f(x_j) \Delta x .$$

Although the definite integral is defined as the limit of a Riemann sum, in practice it is not computed this way. Rather, we attempt to invoke the Fundamental Theorem of Calculus which reduces the problem of evaluating the definite integral to one of finding an antiderivative of f. (Of course, if f has no simple antiderivative, then we must go back to the definition or some numerical method of evaluating the definite integral.)

◻ In this chapter, we will look at the three-dimensional analog of the area problem, namely the problem of finding volume. In particular, let T be the solid bounded above by the non-negative function $z = f(x, y)$ and below by the xy-plane over some bounded region R in the xy-plane. See Figure 14.1. Our objective is to find the volume of T.

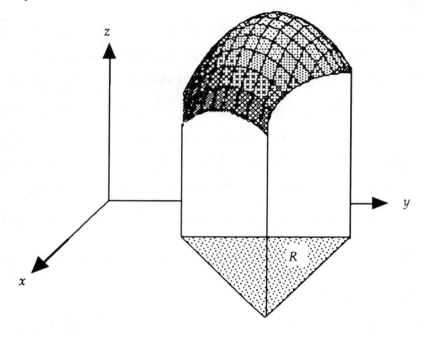

Fig. 14.1

As you might expect, we will first approximate the volume of T by chopping it into n small pieces and adding up the volumes of the pieces. Then we get the exact volume by letting n approach ∞. The first question is: How shall we chop it into pieces?

Before we consider the general case in which R is an arbitrary closed region, let's consider the special case in which R is a rectangle with sides parallel to the coordinate axes. Assume that R is bounded by the lines $x = a, x = b, y = c$ and $y = d$. Partition the interval $[a, b]$ on the x-axis into m equal segments of length $\Delta x = \dfrac{b-a}{m}$ and the interval $[c, d]$ on the y-axis into n equal segments of length $\Delta y = \dfrac{d-c}{n}$. This partitions R into a "rectangular grid" of mn subregions. See Figure 14.2.

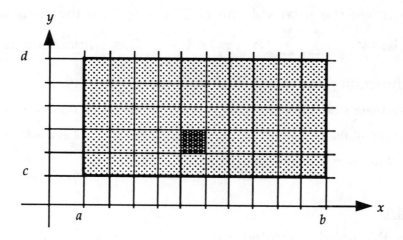

Fig.14.2

Let C_{ij} designate the subrectangle in the ith column (starting from the left) and j^{th} row (starting from the bottom). For example, the dark rectangle in the figure above would be C_{52}. Let ΔA_{ij} denote the area of C_{ij}. Here, $\Delta A_{ij} = \Delta x\, \Delta y$, for all i and j.

This partitioning of R also partitions the solid T into pieces that resemble rectangular prisms, except that the top surface need not be flat. (If you'd like to do an experiment that mimics this process, take a potato and cut it in half so that it sits flat on the counter. Then cut the potato into French fries.) A typical prism is shown in Figure 14.3.

Fig. 14.3

Let (x_i, y_j) be any point in C_{ij}. Since the volume of a rectangular prism is given by (height)(area of base) and the height is approximately the function value at that point, then the volume of the rectangular prism in column i, row j is *approximately* $f(x_i, y_j)\Delta A_{ij}$.

To approximate the total volume of T, we add up the volumes of all the prisms; that is, $V \approx \sum\limits_{j=1}^{n} \sum\limits_{i=1}^{m} f(x_i, y_j) \Delta A_{ij}$. This summation is a Riemann sum for the function f and we shall denote it $S(m, n)$.

Note: To evaluate a double summation, work from the inside out. Start with $j = 1$ and compute the sum of all the terms for $i = 1$ to $i = m$. Then set $j = 2$ and add in the sum of all the terms for $i = 1$ to $i = m$. Continue until $j = n$.

EXAMPLE 14.1:

Let T be the solid bounded by $f(x, y) := x + y$ over the rectangle bounded by $x = 1$, $x = 3$, $y = 2$ and $y = 5$. Approximate the volume of T by partitioning the interval $[1, 3]$ on the x-axis into $m = 4$ equal parts and the interval $[2, 5]$ on the y-axis into $n = 3$ equal parts as shown in Figure 14.4. Evaluate the function at the upper right corner of each subrectangle.

We have $\Delta x = \dfrac{3-1}{4} = \dfrac{1}{2}$ and $\Delta y = \dfrac{5-2}{3} = 1$, from which $\Delta A_{ij} = \Delta x \Delta y = \dfrac{1}{2}$. The partition points on the x-axis are $\{1, 1.5, 2, 2.5, 3\}$ and on the y-axis are $\{2, 3, 4, 5\}$. The upper right corner of C_{11} is $(1.5, 3)$; the upper right corner of C_{12} is $(2, 3)$, etc.

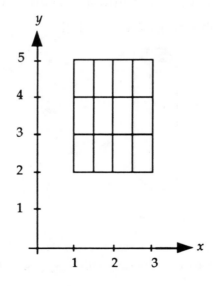

Fig. 14.4

The desired Riemann sum is:

$$S = \sum_{j=1}^{3} \sum_{i=1}^{4} f(x_i, y_j) \Delta A_{ij} = \frac{1}{2} \sum_{j=1}^{3} \sum_{i=1}^{4} (x_i + y_j)$$

$$= \frac{1}{2}[(1.5 + 3) + (2 + 3) + (2.5 + 3) + (3 + 3) + (1.5 + 4) + (2 + 4) + (2.5 + 4)$$

$$+ (3 + 4) + (1.5 + 5) + (2 + 5) + (2.5 + 5) + (3 + 5)] = 37.5 \quad \blacklozenge$$

TEST YOUR UNDERSTANDING

1. For the solid T in Example 14.1, compute the approximate volume by using the same partition but by choosing the function value at the *lower left* corner of each subrectangle.

2. For the solid T in Example 14.1, compute the approximate volume obtained by partitioning the interval $[1, 3]$ of the x-axis into 2 equal parts and the interval $[2, 5]$ on the y-axis into 3 equal parts. (Use the upper right corners to evaluate f.)

3. Compute the approximate volume of the solid T bounded by $f(x, y) := xy$ over the rectangle bounded by $x = 0, y = 0, x = 4$ and $y = 2$. Use $m = 2$ subintervals on the x-axis and $n = 2$ subintervals on the y-axis and evaluate f at the *center* of each subrectangle.

To get the exact volume, we make the subrectangles smaller and smaller. That is, we let Δx and Δy both approach 0 or, equivalently, let m and n approach ∞ in the Riemann sum. This leads to the following:

DEFINITION: Let R be the rectangular region bounded by $x = a$, $x = b$, $y = c$ and $y = d$ and let f be continuous on R. The **double integral of** $f(x, y) \, dA$ **over the region R** is

$$\iint\limits_R f(x, y) \, dA = \lim_{m, n \to \infty} \sum_{j=1}^{n} \sum_{i=1}^{m} f(x_i, y_j) \, \Delta A_{ij},$$

where $\Delta A_{ij} = \Delta x \, \Delta y = \left(\dfrac{b - a}{m} \right)\left(\dfrac{d - c}{n} \right)$ for all i, j.

When f is non-negative over R, then $\iint\limits_R f(x, y) \, dA$ represents the volume of the solid T bounded above by the surface $z = f(x, y)$ over the region R.

We shall not attempt to use this definition to compute any double integrals. (Remember we did one example in Chapter 6 for a function of one variable. That was difficult enough; it is surely more difficult to compute it for functions of two variables.) Rather, in the next section, we will derive an analog to the Fundamental Theorem of Calculus that will make the evaluation of double integrals easier. This new theorem, called Fubini's theorem, reduces the double integral problem to one of finding antiderivatives.

◻ Now let's consider what happens if R is not a rectangle. Assuming R is bounded, then it is possible to enclose it in a rectangle which can then be "chopped up" as before. (See Figure 14.5.)

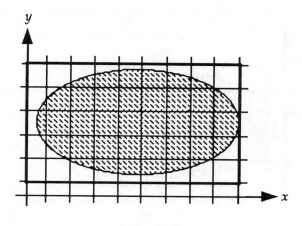

Fig. 14.5

Note that some of the pieces of R cut off by the grid--the ones on the boundary--are not rectangular. In other words, some of the rectangles C_{ij} are not fully contained in R. (Indeed, if R has some "dents" or "holes" in it, some of the rectangles may not intersect R at all.)

This introduces two minor problems which we need to address. First, we need to be careful about where we pick the point (x_i, y_j) in rectangle C_{ij}. Previously, we said we could pick any point; now we need to have (x_i, y_j) in R (since f may not be defined outside R). Secondly, when we add up the terms in the Riemann sum, we'll agree that we should only include terms corresponding to rectangles that intersect R.

The notation used in the definition indicates that we should add in a term for every rectangle; unfortunately, there is no simple, unambiguous way of modifying it to indicate that we may want to leave some terms out. Since we won't be using the definition to do any calculations, this notational deficiency should not cause any problems.

Except for these modifications, the definition of the double integral remains the same; that is, $\iint\limits_{R} f(x,y)\, dA = \lim\limits_{m,n \to \infty} \sum\limits_{j=1}^{n} \sum\limits_{i=1}^{m} f(x_i, y_j)\, \Delta A_{ij}$. By including all rectangles that intersect R, we are really approximating the boundary of R by a jagged line. (See Figure 14.6.) As Δx and Δy become smaller, the boundary "smooths out".

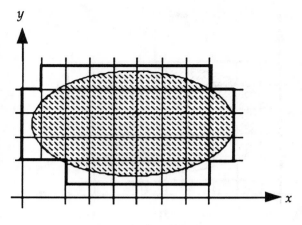

Fig. 14.6

Many properties of single integrals can be extended to double integrals.

THEOREM 14.1:

(a) $\iint\limits_{R} [f(x,y) + g(x,y)]\, dA = \iint\limits_{R} f(x,y)\, dA + \iint\limits_{R} g(x,y)\, dA$

(b) $\iint\limits_{R} cf(x,y)\, dA = c\iint\limits_{R} f(x,y)\, dA$

(c) If we divide R into two non-overlapping pieces R_1 and R_2, then

$$\iint\limits_{R} f(x,y)\, dA = \iint\limits_{R_1} f(x,y)\, dA + \iint\limits_{R_2} f(x,y)\, dA .$$

The proof of this theorem follows directly from the definition of the double integral and we omit it.

EXERCISES FOR SECTION 14.1:

1. Compute the approximate volume of the solid T bounded by $z = x^2 + y^2$ over the rectangle bounded by $x = 1, x = 4, y = 0$ and $y = 2$. Use $m = 3$ subintervals on the x-axis and $n = 2$ subintervals on the y-axis. Evaluate the function at the *upper left* corner of each rectangle.

2. Re-do Exercise 1 by evaluating the function at the
   (a) upper right corner of each rectangle   (b) center of each rectangle.

3. Let R be the region in the diagram below.

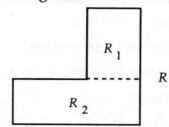

If $\displaystyle\iint_{R_1} f(x,y)\,dA = 7$ and $\displaystyle\iint_{R_2} f(x,y)\,dA = 5$, determine:

(a) $\displaystyle\iint_{R_2} 3f(x,y)\,dA$ (b) $\displaystyle\iint_{R_1} 4f(x,y)\,dA - \iint_{R_2} 6f(x,y)\,dA$ (c) $\displaystyle\iint_{R} f(x,y)\,dA$

4. Given $f(1, 1) = 6, f(1, 2) = 4, f(3, 1) = 5$ and $f(3, 2) = 2$, estimate $\displaystyle\iint_{R} f(x,y)\,dA$, where R is the rectangle bounded by $x = 0, x = 4, y = 0$ and $y = 3$.

PROBLEMS FOR SECTION 14.1:

1. Argue that $\displaystyle\iint_{R} 1\,dA = $ area of R.

2. A function $f(x, y)$ is said to be **x-odd** if $f(-x, y) = -f(x, y)$ for all x, y. Let R be the rectangle bounded by $x = 2, x = -2, y = 0$ and $y = 6$, and let f be any continuous x-odd function. What is $\displaystyle\iint_{R} f(x,y)\,dA$? Explain.

3. Some stuff (as in Section 13.7) is growing on a rectangular dish. The density of stuff at the point (x, y) is $\rho(x, y) := 2xy$. If the dish is bounded by $x = 0, x = 3, y = 0$ and $y = 4$, approximate the total mass of stuff by dividing the x-interval [0, 3] into 3 equal parts and the y-interval [0, 4] into 2 equal parts and using the center of each subrectangle.

TYU Answers for Section 14.1

  1. 28.5   2. 39   3. 16

14.2 ITERATED INTEGRALS AND FUBINI'S THEOREM

As we stated in the last section, it is very difficult to use the definition of the double integral to evaluate such an integral. Rather, we need something like the Fundamental Theorem of Calculus to convert the integral into an antiderivative which can be easily evaluated. Fortunately, such a theorem, called **Fubini's theorem**, exists. It is useful when the region R over which we are integrating is of a special type.

For now, suppose R is the rectangle bounded by $x = a, x = b, y = c$ and $y = d$ and that f is a continuous, non-negative function defined on R. (R does not have to be a rectangle nor does f have to be non-negative in order for Fubini's theorem to hold; it's just easier to illustrate in this case. We'll relax these restrictions somewhat a bit later.) Let T be the solid bounded above by $z = f(x, y)$ and below by the xy-plane over R. Partition the interval $[c, d]$ on the y-axis into subintervals of width Δy. At each subdivision point, construct a plane parallel to the xz-plane and perpendicular to xy-plane. This cuts T into thin slices. A typical slice is shown in Figure 14.7. (In keeping with our potato analogy of the last section, we have now made potato chips, rather than French fries.)

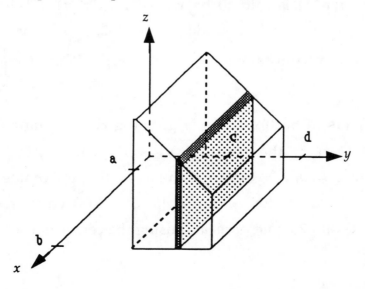

Fig. 14.7

The volume of T can be calculated by adding up the volume of all the slices. The volume of a slice is approximately the product of its thickness and the area of one of its faces. Let V_j = volume of the slice drawn at the point y_j on the y-axis. Then:

(1) $V_j = A(y_j) \, \Delta y$

where $A(y_j)$ is the area of the face of the slice.

The total volume V can be obtained by adding up the volume of the slices and taking the limit as $n \to \infty$; that is,

(2) $V = \lim\limits_{n \to \infty} \sum\limits_{j=1}^{n} V_j = \lim\limits_{n \to \infty} \sum\limits_{j=1}^{n} A(y_j) \, \Delta y$.

The limit of this Riemann sum defines a definite integral; hence,

(3) $V = \displaystyle\int_{c}^{d} A(y) \, dy$.

To get $A(y_j)$, let's confine ourselves to the plane $y = y_j$. The upper boundary of the face is the curve formed by the intersection of the surface $z = f(x, y)$ and the plane $y = y_j$--that is, the curve $z = f(x, y_j)$. Therefore, we can get the area by integrating z with respect to x over the interval $[a, b]$. Specifically,

(4) $A(y_j) = \displaystyle\int_{a}^{b} f(x, y_j) \, dx$.

Substituting Eq.(4) into Eq.(3) gives:

(5) $V = \displaystyle\int_{c}^{d} \left\{ \int_{a}^{b} f(x, y) \, dx \right\} dy$.

Thus, in order to get the volume of T, first integrate $f(x, y)$ with respect to x, substitute $x = b$ and $x = a$ and subtract. Then take the result (which may still be a function of y), integrate with respect to y, substitute $y = d$ and $y = c$ and subtract. This type of calculation in which we first integrate with respect to one of the variables and then with respect to the other is called an **iterated integral**. Generally, we omit the braces and write Eq.(5) as

$$V = \int_c^d \int_a^b f(x, y)\, dx\ dy$$

where we agree that we work "from the inside out". In other words, by writing dx followed by dy, we mean to integrate first with respect to x, then with respect to y.

As long as R is a rectangle, our choice to integrate x first is arbitrary. We could have partitioned the interval $[a, b]$ on the x-axis into subintervals, thus slicing T with planes parallel to the yz-plane. The area of the face of the slice at x_j is $A(x_j) = \int_c^d f(x_j, y)\, dy$ and the total volume of T is given by $V = \int_a^b \int_c^d f(x, y)\, dy\ dx$.

EXAMPLE 14.2:

Evaluate $\int_0^2 \int_1^3 6xy^2\, dx\ dy$.

First, treating y as a constant, we have:

$$\int_0^2 \int_1^3 6xy^2\, dx\ dy = 3x^2 y^2 \Big|_{x=1}^{x=3} = 27y^2 - 3y^2 = 24y^2.$$

Then, $\int_0^2 24y^2\, dy = 8y^3 \Big|_{y=0}^{y=2} = 64$. ♦

EXAMPLE 14.3:

Determine the exact volume of the solid in Example 14.1.

Since the region of integration is rectangular, we have $V = \int_2^5 \int_1^3 (x + y)\, dx\ dy$.

$$\int_1^3 (x + y)\, dx = \left(\frac{x^2}{2} + xy\right)\Big|_{x=1}^{x=3} = 4 + 2y.$$

$$\int_2^5 (4 + 2y)\, dy \;=\; \left(4y + y^2\right)\Big|_{y=2}^{y=5} = 31.$$

Compare this to our approximation of 37.5 and to the approximation we obtained in Example 14.1 and TYU's #1 and 2.   ◆

TEST YOUR UNDERSTANDING

1. Evaluate the integral in Example 14.2 in the "reverse order"; that is, by integrating y first.

2. Evaluate each of the following:

   (a) $\displaystyle\int_{-2}^{2}\int_{1}^{3} (3x + 4y)\, dx\; dy$ (b) $\displaystyle\int_{0}^{1}\int_{0}^{2} \frac{1}{x^2 + 1}\, dy\; dx$

3. Determine the volume of the solid bounded above by $z = x/y$ over the rectangle bounded by $x = 2, x = 4, y = 1$ and $y = 2$.

▫ Now let's see what happens if R is not a rectangle. When we computed $A(y_j)$ in Eq.(4), we integrated from $x = a$ to $x = b$ for every j. In other words, the limits of integration for x were the same for every slice. This is not necessarily true when the boundary of R is not a rectangle. It is possible that the limits of integration for x may differ from slice to slice.

Suppose R is the region bounded by $x = g(y)$, $x = h(y)$, $y = c$ and $y = d$, where we assume that $h(y) > g(y)$ for $c \le y \le d$. See Figure 14.8.

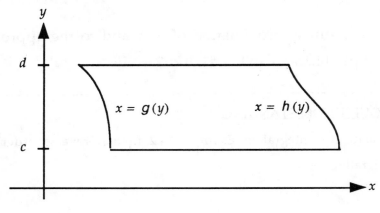

Fig. 14.8

To get the area of the face of the slice drawn at y_j, we have to integrate $z = f(x, y_j)$ from $x = g(y_j)$ to $x = h(y_j)$; that is,

(6) $\qquad A(y_j) = \int_{g(y_j)}^{h(y_j)} f(x, y_j)\, dx$.

The rest of the derivation remains unchanged. Hence, the volume of T is given by:

(7) $\qquad V = \int_c^d \int_{g(y)}^{h(y)} f(x, y)\, dx\; dy$.

This iterated integral is evaluated exactly as the one in Eq.(5). First integrate with respect to x, substitute $x = h(y)$ and $x = g(y)$ and subtract. Then integrate the result (which will be a function of y alone) with respect to y, substitute $y = d$ and $y = c$ and subtract. Notice that the lower limit of integration for x is the left side of the region and the upper limit is the right side. The lower limit of integration for y is the bottom of the region and the upper limit is the top.

EXAMPLE 14.4:

Evaluate $\int_1^3 \int_y^{2y} x^2 y^4 \, dx \, dy$ and sketch the region of integration.

Treating y as a constant, we have for the inner integral:

$$\int_y^{2y} x^2 y^4 \, dx = \frac{x^3 y^4}{3} \Big|_{x=y}^{x=2y} = \frac{(2y)^3 y^4}{3} - \frac{y^3 y^4}{3} = \frac{7y^7}{3}$$

Then, $\int_1^3 \frac{7y^7}{3} \, dy = \frac{7y^8}{24} \Big|_{y=1}^{y=3} = \frac{7(6561-1)}{24} \approx 1913.3$

The region of integration is bounded by the lines $x = y$ on the left, $x = 2y$ on the right, $y = 1$ on the bottom and $y = 3$ on top, as pictured in Figure 14.9.

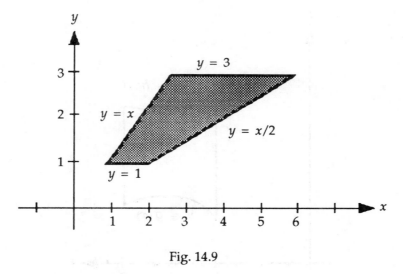

Fig. 14.9

♦

It is very important to realize that, for regions of this type, we cannot easily switch the order of integration as we could for rectangular regions. To see why, look at the picture in Example 14.4. Since there are points in R with x-values from 1 to 6, we would have to partition the interval $[1, 6]$ on the x-axis. For slices at x-values between 1 and 2, the y-values go from $y = 1$ to $y = x$. For slices between $x = 2$ and $x = 3$, they go from $y = \frac{x}{2}$ to $y = x$. For slices between $x = 3$ and $x = 6$, they go from $y = \frac{x}{2}$ to $y = 3$.

Thus, we would need three separate integrals to cover all of R. This is the kind of complication we would like to avoid, if at all possible. (Sometimes it is not possible, in which case we'll just have to persevere.)

◻ Conversely, suppose R were bounded by $y = g(x), y = h(x), x = a$ and $x = b$, as in Figure 14.10. Now we must partition the interval $[a, b]$ on the x-axis and draw slices parallel to the y-axis. The area of the face of the slice drawn at x_j is $A(x_j) = \int_{g(x_j)}^{h(x_j)} f(x_j, y)\,dy$ and the total volume of T is

$V = \int_a^b \int_{g(x)}^{h(x)} f(x, y)\,dy\,dx$. Notice again that the lower limit of integration for y is the bottom of the region and the upper limit is the top; the lower limit for x is the left side of the region and the upper limit is the right.

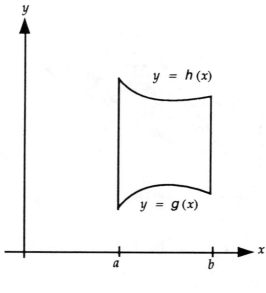

$y = h(x)$

$y = g(x)$

Fig. 14.10

One rule you should always remember: In order to evaluate an iterated integral, the <u>outer limits of integration must be constants</u>. The inner limits of integration may be functions of the outer variable (i.e. the last one to be integrated).

We are now prepared to state Fubini's theorem.

THEOREM 14.2 (FUBINI'S THEOREM): Let $f(x, y)$ be continuous on some region R in the xy-plane.

(a) If R is bounded by $y = g(x)$, $y = h(x)$, $x = a$ and $x = b$ where $h(x) \geq g(x)$ for $a \leq x \leq b$, then $\displaystyle\iint\limits_{R} f(x, y)\, dA = \int_{a}^{b} \int_{g(x)}^{h(x)} f(x, y)\, dy\ dx$.

(b) If R is bounded by $x = g(y)$, $x = h(y)$, $y = c$ and $y = d$ where $h(y) \geq g(y)$ for $c \leq y \leq d$, then $\displaystyle\iint\limits_{R} f(x, y)\, dA = \int_{c}^{d} \int_{g(y)}^{h(y)} f(x, y)\, dx\ dy$.

This says that if R is of a certain shape, then we can evaluate the double integral of $f(x, y)$ by using an appropriate iterated integral. Specifically, if R has a "horizontal top and bottom" as in Figure 14.8, then we can use an iterated integral with x as the inner variable (that is, $dx\ dy$); if R has "vertical sides" as in Figure 14.10, we can use an iterated integral with y as the inner variable (that is, $dy\ dx$).

TEST YOUR UNDERSTANDING

    4. Evaluate the following iterated integrals:

        (a) $\displaystyle\int_{0}^{2} \int_{y+1}^{3} (x + y)\, dx\ dy$ (b) $\displaystyle\int_{-2}^{2} \int_{x^2}^{4} xy\, dy\ dx$

    Before we do some examples, here are some guidelines that you may find helpful.

1. Always draw the region over which the integral is defined. This is VERY IMPORTANT!! It is very difficult to set up the limits of integration properly without a picture in front of you.

2. Determine the order in which you will iterate the integral--that is, which variable you will integrate first. Often the choice is dictated by the region of integration. Integrals over regions resembling Figure 14.8 must be set up as $dxdy$; those resembling Figure 14.10 must be set up as $dydx$. There are, however, many regions in which it is possible to set up the integration in either order. (Clearly, this is true for rectangles but there are many others as well.) In this case, the choice may be determined by the integrand. It is certainly easier to evaluate $\int \sqrt{1+y^3}\, dx$ than to evaluate $\int \sqrt{1+y^3}\, dy$. So, we might choose to integrate $dxdy$ here, although the "outer integration" may turn out to be nasty anyway. That depends on the inner limits of integration.

3. The limits of integration are *always* bottom to top for y and left to right for x.

EXAMPLE 14.5:

Evaluate $\displaystyle\iint\limits_{R} 2xy\, dA$, where R is the region bounded by $y = x^2, y = 4$, $x = 0$ and $x = 1$.

To sketch R, first draw the region bounded below by the parabola $y = x^2$ and above by the horizontal line $y = 4$. R is the slice of this region between the vertical lines $x = 0$ and $x = 1$. See Figure 14.11.

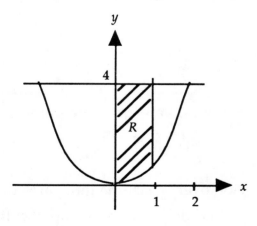

Fig. 14.11

Since R has vertical sides, then we should set up the integral with y as the first variable of integration. For any fixed x between 0 and 1, the y-values go from $y = x^2$ at the bottom to $y = 4$ at the top. Thus, $\iint\limits_R 2xy\, dA =$

$\int_0^1 \int_{x^2}^4 2xy\, dy\, dx$. The inner integral is:

$$\int_{x^2}^4 2xy\, dy = xy^2 \Big|_{y=x^2}^{y=4} = x(4^2) - x(x^2)^2 = 16x - x^5.$$

Therefore, $\iint\limits_R 2xy\, dA = \int_0^1 \left(16x - x^5\right) dx = \left(8x^2 - \dfrac{x^6}{6}\right)\Big|_{x=0}^{x=1} = \dfrac{47}{6}$.   ♦

EXAMPLE 14.6:

Evaluate $\iint\limits_R \left(2x + 3y^2\right) dA$, where R is bounded by $y = \sqrt{x}$, $y = 0$ and $y = x - 2$, as shown in Figure 14.12.

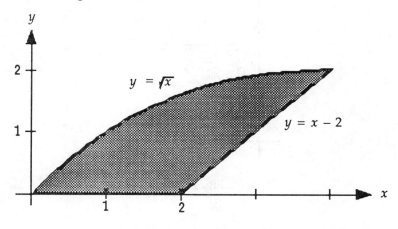

Fig. 14.12

This is a region with only "three sides". However, since it has a horizontal bottom, we can iterate the integral with x as the inner variable. Fix a y-value between 0 and 2 (the interval of the y-axis covered by R). The x-values go from the parabola over to the line. Since these are limits of integration for x, they must be expressed in terms of y. Observe that if $y = \sqrt{x}$, then $x = y^2$ on the left and if $y = x - 2$, then $x = y + 2$ on the right.

Therefore, $\iint\limits_R \left(2x + 3y^2\right) dA = \int_0^2 \int_{y^2}^{y+2} \left(2x + 3y^2\right) dx\, dy$.

The inner integral is:

$$\int_{y^2}^{y+2} \left(2x + 3y^2\right) dx = \left(x^2 + 3xy^2\right)\big|_{x\,=\,y^2}^{x\,=\,y+2}$$

$$= (y+2)^2 + 3(y+2)y^2 - (y^2)^2 - 3y^2y^2$$

$$= 4 + 4y + 7y^2 + 3y^3 - 4y^4.$$

Therefore, $\displaystyle\iint_R \left(2x + 3y^2\right) dA = \int_0^2 \left(4 + 4y + 7y^2 + 3y^3 - 4y^4\right) dy$

$$= \left(4y + 2y^2 + \frac{7}{3}y^3 + \frac{3}{4}y^4 - \frac{4}{5}y^5\right)\Big|_{y\,=\,0}^{y\,=\,2} = \frac{316}{15}. \quad \blacklozenge$$

EXAMPLE 14.7:

Evaluate $\displaystyle\iint_R e^{x+y}\, dA$, where R is the region bounded by $y = x$, $x = 0$
and $y = 1$, as shown in Figure 14.13.

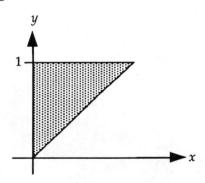

Fig. 14.13

Again we have a three-sided region. Since the top is horizontal and one side is vertical, we can integrate in either order. Let's set it up with x first. For each y-value in the interval $[0, 1]$, the x-values run from the y-axis on the left to the line $y = x$ on the right--in other words, from $x = 0$ to $x = y$. Thus, $\displaystyle\iint_R e^{x+y}\, dA = \int_0^1 \int_0^y e^{x+y}\, dx\, dy$.

To evaluate the inner integral, note that $e^{x+y} = e^x e^y$.

$$\int_0^y e^{x+y}\,dx \;=\; e^y \int_0^y e^x\,dx \;=\; e^y\, e^x\,\Big|_{x=0}^{x=y} \;=\; e^{2y} - e^y.$$

Hence, $\displaystyle \iint_R e^{x+y}\,dA \;=\; \int_0^1 \left(e^{2y} - e^y\right) dy \;=\; \frac{1}{2}\,e^{2y} - e^y\,\Big|_{y=0}^{y=1} \;=\; \frac{1}{2}\,e^2 - e + \frac{1}{2}\,.$

Suppose we had chosen to integrate with respect to y first. Then for each x in the interval $[0, 1]$, the y-values run from $y = x$ on the bottom to $y = 1$ on the top. Thus, $\displaystyle \iint_R e^{x+y}\,dA \;=\; \int_0^1 \int_x^1 e^{x+y}\,dy\,dx$. We leave it to you to show that the answer is the same. $\qquad\blacklozenge$

EXAMPLE 14.8:

Evaluate $\displaystyle \iint_R \sin(y^2)\,dA$, where R is the same region as in Example 14.7.

Since the region of integration has not changed, then the limits of integration on the iterated integral will not change either. Thus, $\displaystyle \iint_R \sin(y^2)\,dA \;=\; \int_0^1 \int_0^y \sin(y^2)\,dx\,dy$. The inner integral is:

$$\int_0^y \sin(y^2)\,dx \;=\; x\,\sin(y^2)\,\Big|_{x=0}^{x=y} \;=\; y\,\sin(y^2).$$

Thus, $\displaystyle \iint_R \sin(y^2)\,dA \;=\; \int_0^1 y\,\sin(y^2)\,dy \;=\; \frac{-1}{2}\cos(y^2)\,\Big|_{y=0}^{y=1} \;=\; \frac{1 - \cos(1)}{2} \approx .2298.$

Suppose we tried to iterate in the other order; that is, $\displaystyle \iint_R \sin(y^2)\,dA \;=\;$ $\displaystyle \int_0^1 \int_x^1 \sin(y^2)\,dy\,dx$. Immediately, we see a problem. It is not possible to evaluate the inner integral $\displaystyle \int_x^1 \sin(y^2)\,dy$ in closed-form. Thus, even though the region of integration allows us to iterate the integral in either order, the integrand forces us to integrate x first. $\qquad\blacklozenge$

EXAMPLE 14.9:

Write an iterated integral that can be used to determine the volume of the solid bounded by $z = y$ over the region R bounded by $y = x^2$ and $y = x + 6$, as shown in Figure 14.14.

Note that $z > 0$ for all x and y, so the volume is given by the double integral

$$V = \iint_R y \, dA \, .$$

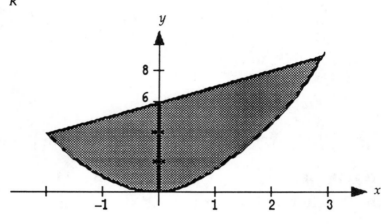

Fig. 14.14

First note that the curves intersect whenever $x^2 = x + 6$; that is, when $x = 3$ and $x = -2$. Since there are no straight sides to this region, we have to think a little harder about the order of integration. If we slice the region with horizontal slices at y-values in the interval $[0, 9]$, then some of them will go from the line to the parabola; others will go between two halves of the parabola. This means we would need two separate iterated integrals to cover the entire region.

On the other hand, if we slice the region with vertical slices, then every slice goes from the parabola to the line. So, we can cover the region with one iterated integral with y as the inner variable. Specifically, for any x in the interval $[-2, 3]$, y goes from x^2 to $x + 6$. Thus, the volume can be computed by $V = \int_{-2}^{3} \int_{x^2}^{x+6} y \, dy \, dx \, .$ ♦

----

5. Evaluate the integral in Example 14.9.

6. Evaluate $\iint\limits_R f(x,y)\,dA$ for each of the following:

(a) $f(x,y) := y$, where R is bounded by $y = 2x$, $y = 0$ and $x = 3$

(b) $f(x,y) := \cos(2x + 5y)$, where R is bounded by $x = y$, $x = 3y$, $y = 0$ and $y = \pi$

◻ So far, we have constructed the iterated integral from a description of R. It is also important to be able to construct R from a given iterated integral.

EXAMPLE 14.10:

Sketch the region of integration for the iterated integral $\int_{-4}^{1} \int_{3x}^{4-x^2} f(x,y)\,dy\ dx$.

We work from the inside out. First draw the line $y = 3x$ (the bottom) and the parabola $y = 4 - x^2$ (the top). Note that they intersect when $4 - x^2 = 3x$ or, upon solving, when $x = -4$ or $x = 1$. Hence, R is the entire region bounded by the line and the parabola. See Figure 14.15.

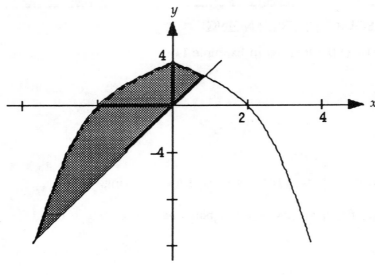

Fig. 14.15

EXERCISES FOR SECTION 14.2:

1. Sketch the region of integration for each of the following iterated integrals:

   (a) $\displaystyle\int_{-2}^{1}\int_{x^2}^{2-x} f(x,y)\,dy\,dx$ (b) $\displaystyle\int_{0}^{2}\int_{x^3}^{12-x^2} f(x,y)\,dy\,dx$

   (c) $\displaystyle\int_{0}^{2}\int_{y^2-1}^{3} f(x,y)\,dx\,dy$ (d) $\displaystyle\int_{-1}^{1}\int_{0}^{\sqrt{1-y^2}} f(x,y)\,dx\,dy$

2. Evaluate each iterated integral:

   (a) $\displaystyle\int_{1}^{3}\int_{-x}^{x} 2xy\,dy\,dx$ (b) $\displaystyle\int_{1}^{2}\int_{1}^{3x} \frac{1}{(x+y)^2}\,dy\,dx$

   (c) $\displaystyle\int_{0}^{1}\int_{0}^{x} e^{x^2}\,dy\,dx$ (d) $\displaystyle\int_{1}^{2}\int_{-y^2}^{0} \sqrt{x+y^2}\,dx\,dy$

   (e) $\displaystyle\int_{-\pi/2}^{\pi/2}\int_{0}^{\tan(y)} \cos(y)\,dx\,dy$ (f) $\displaystyle\int_{0}^{1}\int_{0}^{x^{2/3}} e^x\,\sqrt{y}\,dy\,dx$

3. Find the volume bounded by $z = 8 - 2y$ over the region $0 \le y \le 4$, $0 \le x \le 2$.

4. Find the volume of the tetrahedron in the first octant bounded by $z = 6 - 2x - y$ and the coordinate planes.

5. Find the volume of the solid in the first octant bounded by $z = xy$, $y = x$ and $x = 1$.

6. Express each of the following as an iterated integral in the reverse order:

(a) $\int_0^3 \int_0^{2y} f(x,y)\, dx\ dy$ (b) $\int_0^2 \int_1^{e^x} f(x,y)\, dy\ dx$ (c) $\int_0^1 \int_x^{2-x} f(x,y)\, dy\ dx$

7. Evaluate $\int_0^1 \int_y^1 \sin(x^2)\, dx\ dy$.

8. Evaluate $\iint\limits_R xy\ dA$, where R is the triangle with vertices $(0, 0)$, $(2, 0)$ and $(1, 4)$.

PROBLEMS FOR SECTION 14.2:

1. A solid is bounded by $z = k^2 - y^2, z = 0, x = 0$ and $x = 3$. For what value of k will this solid have a volume of 256?

2. Find the volume of the solid bounded by $z = \dfrac{1}{(x+1)^2(y+1)^2}$, $x \geq 0, y \geq 0$.

3. Express in terms of a, b and c, the volume in the first octant bounded by the plane $\frac{x}{a} + \frac{y}{b} + \frac{z}{c} = 1$, where a, b and c are positive.

4. The **average value** of a function over a region R is defined by $f_{av} = \dfrac{1}{\text{area } R} \iint\limits_R f(x,y)\, dA$. Find the average value of $f(x,y) := xy$ over the triangle bounded by $y = 2x, y = 0$ and $x = 2$.

5. The **surface area** of the surface $z = f(x, y)$ over some region R is given by

$$S = \iint\limits_R \sqrt{1 + [f_x(x,y)]^2 + [f_y(x,y)]^2}\ dA .$$

Determine the surface area of $f(x, y) := 2y + x^2$, where R is the triangle with vertices $(0, 0)$, $(1, 0)$ and $(1, 1)$.

1. $\int_0^2 6x y^2\, dy = 2xy^3 \big|_{y=0}^{y=2} = 16x$; $\int_1^3 16x\, dx = 8x^2 \big|_{x=1}^{x=3} = 64$

2. (a) 48   (b) $\pi/2$ 3. 6 ln(2)   4. (a) 6 (b) 0   5. 250/3   6. (a) 18 (b) –4/77

14.3 CHANGE OF VARIABLES FOR DOUBLE INTEGRALS

Consider the definite integral $\int_0^2 f(x)\,dx$, where f is a continuous function. Suppose we introduce a new variable $u = \sqrt{x}$, or equivalently, $x = u^2$. Then $dx = 2u\,du$, $u = 0$ when $x = 0$ and $u = 4$ when $x = 2$. Hence, $\int_0^2 f(x)\,dx = \int_0^4 f(u^2)\,2u\,du$. If $u = e^x$, then $x = \ln(u)$, $dx = \frac{1}{u}\,du$, $u = 1$ when $x = 0$ and $u = e^2$ when $x = 2$. Thus, $\int_0^2 f(x)\,dx = \int_1^{e^2} f(\ln(u))\frac{1}{u}\,du$.

More generally, consider the integral $\int_a^b f(x)\,dx$ and suppose u is related to x by the function $x = g(u)$. Then $dx = g'(u)\,du$ and

(6) $$\int_a^b f(x)\,dx = \int_c^d f(g(u))\,g'(u)\,du,$$

where c is the value of u corresponding to $x = a$ and d is the value of u corresponding to $x = b$; that is, $a = g(c)$ and $b = g(d)$.

Let's look at Eq.(6) from the point of view of Riemann sums. Suppose we partition the interval $[c, d]$ of u-values into n equal subintervals of length Δu and let u_j and u_{j+1} be any two consecutive partition points. Their corresponding x-values are $x_j = g(u_j)$ and $x_{j+1} = g(u_{j+1})$. If Δu is sufficiently small, then $x_{j+1} - x_j \approx g'(u_j)(u_{j+1} - u_j)$ or, in other words,

(7) $$\Delta x_j \approx g'(u_j)\Delta u.$$

For example, suppose $x = u^2$ is defined on the u-interval $[0, 2]$. Partition $[0, 2]$ into 8 equal parts of length $\Delta u = \frac{1}{4}$; the partition points are at $\{0, .25, .5, .75, 1, 1.25, 1.5, 1.75, 2\}$. The corresponding x-interval $[0, 4]$ is partitioned at $\{0, .0625, .25, .5625, 1, 1.5625, 2.25, 3.0625, 4\}$. Note that these subintervals are not of equal length. See Figure 14.16.

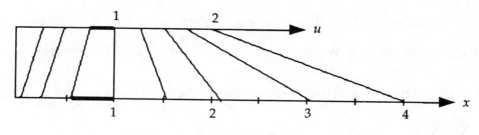

Fig. 14.16

Eq.(7) says that the length of the subinterval $[x_j, x_{j+1}]$ is approximately $g'(u_j)\Delta u = 2u_j(\frac{1}{4}) = \frac{u_j}{2}$. For instance, for $j = 3$, the interval $[.5625, 1]$ is of length $.4375$ which is approximately the same as $\frac{u_3}{2} = .375$.

Recall that $\int_a^b f(x)\,dx = \lim_{n \to \infty} \sum_{j=1}^{n} f(x_j)\Delta x$ by definition. When we originally stated this definition, we required that the interval $[a, b]$ be partitioned into n equal parts. This isn't necessary; it is permissible for the parts to be of unequal length as long as the lengths of all the subintervals go to 0 as n approaches infinity. Hence, we can write $\int_a^b f(x)\,dx = \lim_{n \to \infty} \sum_{j=1}^{n} f(x_j)\Delta x_j$, where Δx_j is the length of the jth subinterval. Now, using Eq.(7), we get $\lim_{n \to \infty} \sum_{j=1}^{n} f(x_j)\Delta x_j = \lim_{n \to \infty} \sum_{j=1}^{n} f(g(u_j))g'(u_j)\Delta u$ or, equivalently, $\int_a^b f(x)\,dx = \int_c^d f(g(u))g'(u)\,du$.

Thus, the function g, which transforms u-values into x-values, also changes the distance between points. The "scaling factor"--that is, the factor by which we must multiply the distance between u-values to get the distance between corresponding x-values--is approximately $g'(u)$. This, in turn, multiplies the terms in the Riemann sum and, consequently, the integral by the same factor. Note that, unless g is a linear function, the scaling factor is not constant but rather depends on the u-values being considered.

◻ In this section, we'll explore an equivalent idea for double integrals. In particular, suppose we want to evaluate $\iint\limits_R f(x,y)\,dA$, where R is some region of the xy-plane. By definition, $\iint\limits_R f(x,y)\,dA =$ $\lim\limits_{m,n \to \infty} \sum\limits_{j=1}^{n} \sum\limits_{i=1}^{m} f(x_i, y_j)\,\Delta A_{ij}$, again the limit of a Riemann sum. Typically, if R is of a special type, we evaluate the double integral by invoking Fubini's Theorem, which replaces the double integral by an iterated integral.

In some cases, either f or R may be sufficiently complicated so that iterating the integral in either order is messy or impossible. If so, then we may introduce new variables, u and v, where we assume that there are two functions g and h such that $x = g(u,v)$ and $y = h(u,v)$. Further, there is some region S in the uv-plane which is transformed by the functions g and h into the region R of the xy-plane.

Let's look at an example where such a transformation might help. Suppose R is the rectangle $ABCD$ bounded by the lines $x + y = 2$, $x + y = 6$, $x - y = -1$ and $x - y = 2$, as shown in Figure 14.17.

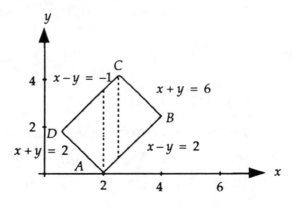

Fig. 14.17

If we were to try to integrate over this region in one of the standard ways (say $dy\,dx$), we would need to partition the rectangle into three pieces, as indicated by the dotted lines.

A cleverer approach is to define new variables $u = x + y$ and $v = x - y$. This is a one-to-one transformation since upon adding, we get $u + v =$

$2x$, from which $x = \dfrac{u + v}{2}$. Substitution in the first equation gives $y = \dfrac{u - v}{2}$. The vertices of R have xy-coordinates $A(2, 0)$, $B(4, 2)$, $C(5/2, 7/2)$ and $D(1/2, 3/2)$, respectively. The corresponding points on the uv-plane are $A'(2, 2)$, $B'(6, 2)$, $C'(6, -1)$ and $D'(2, -1)$. Every point along AB satisfies $x - y = 2$ or, equivalently, $v = 2$ and, hence, is transformed into a point along $A'B'$. Since a similar argument can be made for the other edges of R, we conclude that R is transformed into S, a rectangle with vertices A', B', C' and D'. Therefore, we can integrate from $u = 2$ to $u = 6$ and from $v = -1$ to $v = 2$. Depending on the exact nature of the integrand, this is potentially a much simpler calculation. See Figure 14.18.

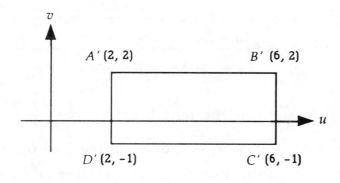

Fig. 14.18

◻ We now need to determine what effect this transformation has on the Riemann sum. In particular, what "scaling factor" do we need to include in the integrand (comparable to $g'(u)$ in the single variable case)?

Partition S into subrectangles by partitioning the interval $[2, 6]$ on the u-axis into equal pieces of length Δu and the interval $[-1, 2]$ on the v-axis into equal pieces of length Δv. Choose any one of these subrectangles and denote its vertices as $M'(u, v)$, $N'(u + \Delta u, v)$, $P'(u + \Delta u, v + \Delta v)$ and $Q'(u, v + \Delta v)$. (See Figure 14.19.) The area of $M'N'P'Q'$ is $\Delta u \Delta v$.

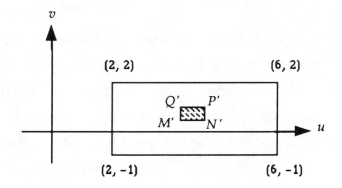

Fig. 14.19

The point in the xy-plane corresponding to M' is $M\left(\dfrac{u+v}{2}, \dfrac{u-v}{2}\right)$. The point corresponding to N' is $N\left(\dfrac{u+\Delta u+v}{2}, \dfrac{u+\Delta u-v}{2}\right)$, the point corresponding to P' is $P\left(\dfrac{u+\Delta u+v+\Delta v}{2}, \dfrac{u+\Delta u-v-\Delta v}{2}\right)$ and the point corresponding to Q' is $Q\left(\dfrac{u+v+\Delta v}{2}, \dfrac{u-v-\Delta v}{2}\right)$. The length of MN is $\sqrt{\left(\dfrac{\Delta u}{2}\right)^2+\left(\dfrac{\Delta u}{2}\right)^2} = \dfrac{\Delta u}{\sqrt{2}}$ and the length of NP is $\sqrt{\left(\dfrac{\Delta v}{2}\right)^2+\left(\dfrac{\Delta v}{2}\right)^2} = \dfrac{\Delta v}{\sqrt{2}}$. Hence, the area of $MNPQ$ is $\dfrac{\Delta u\ \Delta v}{2}$, one-half the area of $M'N'P'Q'$. In this case, because the transformation from uv-coordinates to xy-coordinates is linear, then the scaling factor $\dfrac{1}{2}$ is the same for all subrectangles. In general, the scaling factor should depend on u and v. We'll look at the general case soon.

Now, the double integral $\displaystyle\iint\limits_R f(x,y)\,dA = \lim_{m,n \to \infty} \sum_{j=1}^{n}\sum_{i=1}^{m} f(x_i, y_j)\,\Delta A_{ij} =$

$\displaystyle\lim_{m,n \to \infty} \sum_{j=1}^{n}\sum_{i=1}^{m} f\left(\frac{u_i+v_j}{2}, \frac{u_i-v_j}{2}\right)\frac{\Delta u\ \Delta v}{2} = \int_{-1}^{2}\int_{2}^{6} f\left(\frac{u+v}{2}, \frac{u-v}{2}\right)\left(\frac{1}{2}\right)du\ dv$.

EXAMPLE 14.11:

Evaluate $\displaystyle\iint\limits_R xy\,dA$, where R is the rectangle considered above.

$$\iint\limits_R xy\,dA = \int_{-1}^{2}\int_{2}^{6}\left(\frac{u+v}{2}\right)\left(\frac{u-v}{2}\right)\left(\frac{1}{2}\right)du\ dv = \frac{1}{8}\int_{-1}^{2}\int_{2}^{6}\left(u^2-v^2\right)du\ dv$$

$$= \frac{1}{8} \int_{-1}^{2} \left(\frac{208}{3} - 4v^2 \right) dv = 196.$$

$\diamond$

¤ Before proceeding to the general case, we need the following:

DEFINITION: Suppose $x = g(u, v)$ and $y = h(u, v)$. The **Jacobian of x and y with respect to u and v** is defined by

$$J(u, v) = g_u(u, v)h_v(u, v) - g_v(u, v)h_u(u, v)$$
$$= \frac{\partial x}{\partial u} \frac{\partial y}{\partial v} - \frac{\partial x}{\partial v} \frac{\partial y}{\partial u}.$$

The Jacobian is often denoted $\dfrac{\partial(x, y)}{\partial(u, v)}$.

Note: Those readers who are familiar with matrices will note that the Jacobian is the determinant of the 2 x 2 matrix consisting of the partial derivatives of x and y with respect to u and v--that is, the matrix $\begin{bmatrix} g_u & g_v \\ h_u & h_v \end{bmatrix}$.

In our example, $g_u(u, v) = \frac{1}{2}$, $g_v(u, v) = \frac{1}{2}$, $h_u(u, v) = \frac{1}{2}$, $h_v(u, v) = -\frac{1}{2}$, so $J(u, v) = (\frac{1}{2})(-\frac{1}{2}) - (\frac{1}{2})(\frac{1}{2}) = -\frac{1}{2}$ the absolute value of which, not coincidentally, is the scaling factor that appeared in the double integral. The reason that $J < 0$ is that the transformation reverses the order of the vertices; in Figure 14.17, vertices A, B, C and D are in counterclockwise order while in Figure 14.18, vertices A', B', C' and D' are in clockwise order.

TEST YOUR UNDERSTANDING

1. Compute the Jacobian for each of the following:

    (a) $x = u - v^2, y = u + v$ (b) $x = u/v, y = v/u$

    (c) $x = uv, y = u^2 + v^2$

2. Suppose $u = \dfrac{x^2 + y^2}{2}$ and $v = \dfrac{x^2 - y^2}{2}$. Solve for x and y in terms of u and v and compute $J(u, v)$, assuming x and y are ≥ 0.

Now for the main result:

THEOREM 14.3: Let the equations $x = g(u, v)$, $y = h(u, v)$ define a one-to-one transformation from a region S in the uv-plane to a region R in the xy-plane. If f is a continuous function on R and the Jacobian $J(u, v)$ is continuous and non-zero on S, then $\displaystyle\iint\limits_{R} f(x, y)\, dA \quad =$

$\displaystyle\iint\limits_{S} f(g(u, v), h(u, v)) \, |J(u, v)| \, du \; dv$.

Note that there is an absolute value sign on the Jacobian. This is needed because the Jacobian is a scale-change factor for area and since area is a positive quantity, the scale factors ought to be positive.

EXAMPLE 14.12:

Evaluate $\displaystyle\iint\limits_{R} 49(x + y)\, dA$, where R is the parallelogram bounded by the lines $2x - y = 1$, $2x - y = -2$, $x + 3y = 0$ and $x + 3y = 1$, as shown in Figure 14.20.

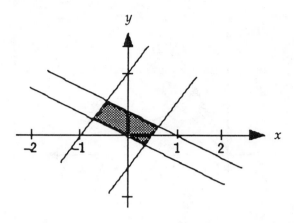

Fig. 14.20

The boundaries of R suggest that the transformation $u = 2x - y, v = x + 3y$ might be helpful. Upon multiplying the second equation by 2 and subtracting from the first, we get $u - 2v = -7y$, from which $y = \dfrac{2v - u}{7}$. Substitution in the second equation gives $x = v - 3y = v - 3\left(\dfrac{2v - u}{7}\right) = \dfrac{v + 3u}{7}$.

The Jacobian of this transformation is $J(u, v) = \dfrac{3}{7}\left(\dfrac{2}{7}\right) - \dfrac{1}{7}\left(\dfrac{-1}{7}\right) = \dfrac{1}{7}$.

Since $49(x + y) = 49\left[\left(\dfrac{v + 3u}{7}\right) + \left(\dfrac{2v - u}{7}\right)\right] = 7(3v + 2u)$, then by Theorem 14.3, we have:

$$\iint_R 49(x + y)\, dA = \int_0^1 \int_{-2}^1 7(3v + 2u)\tfrac{1}{7}\, du\ dv = \int_0^1 \int_{-2}^1 (3v + 2u)\, du\ dv$$

$$= \int_0^1 (9v - 3)\, dv = \dfrac{3}{2}. \qquad \blacklozenge$$

EXAMPLE 14.13:

Evaluate $\displaystyle\iint_R x^3 y\, dA$, where R is the region in the first quadrant bounded by the lines $y = x$ and $y = 2x$ and the hyperbolas $xy = 1$ and $xy = 4$, as shown in Figure 14.21.

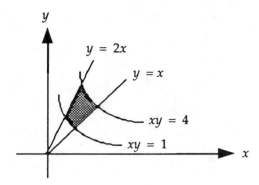

Fig. 14.21

Since the straight sides of R can be rewritten as $\frac{y}{x} = 1$ and $\frac{y}{x} = 2$, we might try letting $u = xy$ and $v = \frac{y}{x}$. Then $uv = y^2$, from which $y = \sqrt{uv}$. (We can restrict ourselves to the positive square root since y is positive in the first quadrant. This makes the transformation one-to-one over R.) Upon substitution, we get $x = \frac{u}{y} = \frac{u}{\sqrt{uv}} = \sqrt{\frac{u}{v}}$.

The partial derivatives are: $\frac{\partial x}{\partial u} = \frac{1}{2}\left(\frac{u}{v}\right)^{-1/2}\left(\frac{1}{v}\right)$, $\frac{\partial x}{\partial v} = \frac{1}{2}\left(\frac{u}{v}\right)^{-1/2}\left(\frac{-u}{v^2}\right)$, $\frac{\partial y}{\partial u} = \frac{1}{2}(uv)^{-1/2}(v)$ and $\frac{\partial y}{\partial v} = \frac{1}{2}(uv)^{-1/2}(u)$

Hence, the Jacobian of the transformation is $J(u, v) = \frac{1}{4v} + \frac{1}{4v} = \frac{1}{2v}$.

Thus, $\iint\limits_{R} x^3y \; dA = \int_1^2 \int_1^4 \left(\frac{u}{v}\right)^{3/2}(uv)^{1/2}\frac{1}{2v} \; du \; dv = \int_1^2 \int_1^4 \frac{u^2}{2v^2} \; du \; dv$

$= \int_1^2 \frac{21}{2v^2} \; dv = \frac{21}{4}$.

We could also evaluate this integral by using the transformation $u = xy$, $v = y$. This implies $x = \frac{u}{v}$, $y = v$. Then along the line $y = x$, we have $v = \frac{u}{v}$. That is, $u = v^2$, or $v = \sqrt{u}$. Similarly, along the line $y = 2x$, we have $u = \frac{v^2}{2}$, so that $v = \sqrt{2u}$. The Jacobian of the transformation is $J(u, v) = \frac{1}{v}$ and, hence,

$$\iint\limits_{R} x^3y \; dA = \int_1^4 \int_{\sqrt{u}}^{\sqrt{2u}} \left(\frac{u}{v}\right)^3 v \left(\frac{1}{v}\right) dv \; du .$$

The region of integration in the uv-plane is pictured in Figure 14.22.

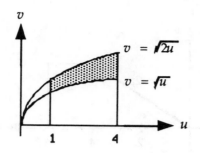

Fig. 14.22

We leave it as an exercise for you to show that you get the same answer.   ♦

In both examples above, we chose a transformation that converts the region R into one over which Fubini's theorem will allow us to integrate easily. Sometimes, we choose a transformation that simplifies the integrand.

EXAMPLE 14.14:

Evaluate $\displaystyle\iint_R y(x+y)\sin(x+y)^2\,dA$, where R is the trapezoid bounded by $y=x$, $x+y=6$, $y=0$ and $y=2$, as shown in Figure 14.23.

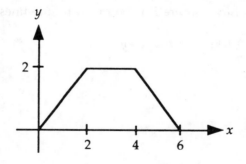

Fig. 14.23

The integrand would be greatly simplified by letting $u=x+y$ and $v=y$. This implies $x=u-y=u-v$ and $y=v$. The Jacobian is easily seen to be $J(u,v)=1$.

If $y=x$, then $u-v=v$ or $u=2v$. The other boundaries of R are $v=0$, $v=2$ and $u=6$. The region of integration in the uv-plane is pictured in Figure 14.24.

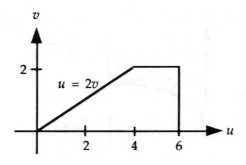

Fig. 14.24

Hence,

$$\iint\limits_{R} y(x+y)\sin(x+y)^2\,dA \;=\; \int_0^2 \int_{2v}^6 uv\,\sin(u^2)\,du\;dv$$

$$=\;\int_0^2 \left[\frac{-v\,\cos(36)+v\,\cos(4v^2)}{2}\right]dv$$

$$=\;-\cos(36)+\frac{\sin(16)}{16}\;\approx\;.10997 \qquad\qquad \blacklozenge$$

TEST YOUR UNDERSTANDING

3. Evaluate each of the following integrals by making the indicated change of variables.

(a) $\displaystyle\iint\limits_{R} y(x-y)\,dA$, where R is bounded by the lines $y=x,\,y=x-4,\,y=0$ and $y=3$; let $u=y,\,v=x-y$

(b) $\displaystyle\iint\limits_{R} \frac{\sqrt{x+y}}{x}\,dA$, where R is the triangle bounded by the lines $y=0,\,y=x$ and $x=4$; let $u=x$ and $v=x+y$

(c) $\iint\limits_R 1\, dA$, where R is the region in the first quadrant bounded by $xy = 1$, $xy = 4$, $y = x$ and $y = 4x$; let $u = xy$ and $v = y$.

4. Determine the volume bounded by $f(x, y) := \left(\dfrac{x - 3y}{x + 4y}\right)^2$ over the parallelogram whose sides are $x - 3y = 0$, $x - 3y = 6$, $x + 4y = 4$ and $x + 4y = 8$.

POLAR COORDINATES

Suppose the region R over which we are integrating is the circle $x^2 + y^2 = 1$. While it is possible to evaluate a double integral over R as an iterated integral in xy-coordinates, the inner limits of integration will be a bit messy and may make the outer integration impossible. For regions of this type, it may be more prudent to switch to polar coordinates.

Recall from Chapter 10 that the rectangular and polar coordinates of a point are related by the formulas $x = r\cos(\theta)$ and $y = r\sin(\theta)$. The partial derivatives are $\dfrac{\partial x}{\partial r} = \cos(\theta)$, $\dfrac{\partial y}{\partial r} = \sin(\theta)$, $\dfrac{\partial x}{\partial \theta} = -r\sin(\theta)$ and $\dfrac{\partial y}{\partial \theta} = r\cos(\theta)$ from which the Jacobian is $J(r, \theta) = [\cos(\theta)][r\cos(\theta)] - [\sin(\theta)][-r\sin(\theta)] = r(\cos^2(\theta) + \sin^2(\theta)) = r$.

Suppose R is a region in the xy-plane that is conveniently described in polar coordinates by $r = g(\theta)$, $r = h(\theta)$, $\theta = \alpha$ and $\theta = \beta$, where $h(\theta) > g(\theta) > 0$ whenever $\alpha < \theta < \beta$. See Figure 14.25 for an example.

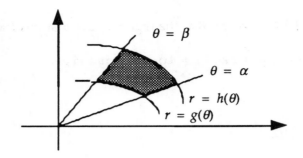

Fig. 14.25

Then to evaluate the double integral of some continuous function f over this region, we can change to polar coordinates. Invoking Theorem 14.3, we have:

$$\iint_R f(x,y)\, dA \; = \; \int_\alpha^\beta \int_{g(\theta)}^{h(\theta)} f(r\,\cos(\theta), r\,\sin(\theta))\, r\, dr\, d\theta.$$

Note the presence of the factor r in the integral on the right; this is the Jacobian.

EXAMPLE 14.15:

Evaluate $\displaystyle \int_0^4 \int_0^{\sqrt{16-y^2}} y\, dx\, dy$ by converting to polar coordinates.

The region of integration is the portion of the circle $x^2 + y^2 = 16$ that lies in the first quadrant. See Figure 14.26. In polar coordinates, this is bounded by $r = 0, r = 4, \theta = 0$ and $\theta = \pi/2$.

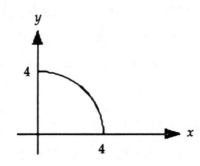

Fig. 14.26

The integrand $y = r\,\sin(\theta)$ and the $dx\, dy$ becomes $r\, dr\, d\theta$. Hence,

$$\int_0^4 \int_0^{\sqrt{16-y^2}} y \ dx \ dy = \int_0^{\pi/2} \int_0^4 r^2 \sin(\theta) \ dr \ d\theta = \int_0^{\pi/2} \frac{64}{3} \sin(\theta) \ d\theta$$
$$= \frac{64}{3}. \qquad \blacklozenge$$

EXAMPLE 14.16:

Evaluate $\iint\limits_R \sqrt{x^2+y^2} \ dA$, where R is the region described by the polar function $r = \sin(\theta)$ in Figure 14.27.

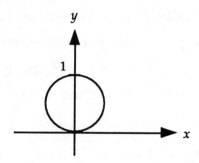

Fig. 14.27

Since $x^2 + y^2 = r^2$ and $r \geq 0$ on R, then $\sqrt{x^2+y^2} = r$. Also, note that the entire circle is traced for $0 \leq \theta \leq \pi$. Hence,

$$\iint\limits_R \sqrt{x^2+y^2} \ dA = \int_0^{\pi} \int_0^{\sin(\theta)} r \cdot r \ dr \ d\theta = \int_0^{\pi} \int_0^{\sin(\theta)} r^2 \ dr \ d\theta$$

$$= \int_0^{\pi} \frac{\sin^3(\theta)}{3} \ d\theta = \int_0^{\pi} \frac{\sin(\theta)[1-\cos^2(\theta)]}{3} \ d\theta = \frac{-\cos(\theta)}{3} + \frac{\cos^3(\theta)}{9} \Big|_0^{\pi}$$
$$= \frac{4}{9}. \qquad \blacklozenge$$

- -

TEST YOUR UNDERSTANDING

5. Evaluate each of the following by converting to polar coordinates:

(a) $\int_0^1 \int_0^{\sqrt{1-x^2}} xy \ dy \ dx$

(b) $\int_{-2}^2 \int_0^{\sqrt{4-x^2}} \sin(x^2+y^2) \ dy \ dx$

(c) $\iint\limits_{R} (x+y)\,dA$, where R is the region bounded by the lines $y = 0, y = x$
and the circle $x^2 + y^2 = 9$.

¤ We can argue geometrically that we need the Jacobian in the integrand. Consider the "polar rectangle" with vertices whose polar coordinates are (r, θ), $(r + \Delta r, \theta)$, $(r + \Delta r, \theta + \Delta\theta)$ and $(r, \theta + \Delta\theta)$, as shown in Figure 14.28. Using some facts from geometry, we can show that the area of this region is $\frac{1}{2}(r + \Delta r)^2\Delta\theta - \frac{1}{2}r^2\Delta\theta = \dfrac{(r+\Delta r)+r}{2}(r + \Delta r - r)\Delta\theta = \bar{r}\,\Delta r\,\Delta\theta$, where $\bar{r}$ is the average of r and $r + \Delta r$. Clearly, as $\Delta r \to 0, \bar{r} \to r$. Hence, the scaling factor for the area is r, the Jacobian.

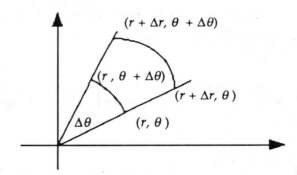

Fig. 14.28

We conclude this section with an example which is important to the study of probability and statistics.

EXAMPLE 14.17:

Evaluate $I = \displaystyle\int_{-\infty}^{\infty} e^{-x^2}\,dx$.

You should be convinced that there are no simple closed-form antiderivatives for $f(x) := e^{-x^2}$ and, hence, the Fundamental Theorem of Calculus does not help us here.

Since the variable used in an integrand is really a placeholder (or dummy),

then $I = \int_{-\infty}^{\infty} e^{-y^2} dy$, as well. It follows that

$$I^2 = \int_{-\infty}^{\infty} e^{-x^2} dx \int_{-\infty}^{\infty} e^{-y^2} dy = \int_{-\infty}^{\infty} \int_{-\infty}^{\infty} e^{-x^2-y^2} dx \, dy .$$

Now convert to polar coordinates. The region of integration is the entire xy-plane which is equivalent to integrating r from 0 to ∞ and θ from 0 to 2π. Hence, $I^2 = \int_0^{2\pi} \int_0^{\infty} e^{-r^2} r \, dr \, d\theta$. The inner integral, although improper, converges to $\frac{1}{2}$, so that $I^2 = \int_0^{2\pi} \frac{1}{2} d\theta = \pi$. Therefore, $\int_{-\infty}^{\infty} e^{-x^2} dx = \sqrt{\pi}$.

Note: Throughout this example, we have assumed that I converges. For a proof that it converges, see Problem 3 at the end of this section. ◆

EXERCISES FOR SECTION 14.3:

1. Determine the Jacobian for each of the following:

(a) $x = 3u + 2v$, $y = 5u - v$ (b) $x = uv^2$, $y = vu^2$

(c) $x = e^{u+v}$, $y = e^{u-v}$ (d) $x = \cos(u)\sin(v)$, $y = \sin(u)\cos(v)$

2. Consider the transformation defined by $u = 2x, v = \dfrac{1}{x+y}$.

(a) Solve for x and y in terms of u and v.

(b) Determine the Jacobian $J(u, v)$.

3. Complete the integral in the discussion following Example 14.12 and show that the answer is the same as Example 14.12.

4. Evaluate the following by making the indicated change of variables:

(a) $\displaystyle\iint_R 4xy \, dA$, where R is the square with vertices $(0, 0)$, $(1, 1)$, $(2, 0)$ and

$(1, -1)$;   let $u = x + y, v = x - y$

(b) $\displaystyle\iint_R 1 \, dA$, where R is the region bounded by $xy = 2, xy = 4, y = 1$

and $y = 4$; let $u = xy, v = y$

5. Determine the volume of the solid bounded above by $f(x, y) :=$ $\sqrt{(x - y)(x + 4y)}$ over the parallelogram bounded by $y = x, y = x - 5$, $x + 4y = 5, x + 4y = 0$.

6. Evaluate each of the following:

   (a) $\iint\limits_R (x^2 + y^2)\, dA$, where R is the region bounded by the circle $r = 2$.

   (b) $\iint\limits_R (x^2 + y^2)\, dA$, where R is the region bounded by the cardioid $r =$ $1 + \cos(\theta)$.

   (c) $\iint\limits_R (x^2 + y^2)\, dA$, where R is the region bounded by the circle $r = 2$ and the line $r \sin(\theta) = 1$.

7. Determine the volume of the solid bounded by the circular paraboloid $z = 4 - x^2 - y^2$ and the xy-plane.

8. Determine the volume of the solid in the first octant bounded by $z = xy$ and the circle $x^2 + y^2 = 1$.

9. Determine the volume of the solid bounded by $z = y^2$ above the ring between circles of radius 2 and 3 centered at the origin.

PROBLEMS FOR SECTION 14.3:

1. Use integration in polar coordinates to show that the volume of a sphere of radius R is $V = \frac{4}{3} \pi R^3$.

2. Triangle OAB is bounded by the lines $y = 2x, y = \frac{1}{2}x$ and $x + y = 3$. (O is the origin.)

   (a) Determine the coordinates of the vertices A and B of the triangle.

   (b) Compute the length of the perpendicular from O to AB and use it to find the area of the triangle.

   (c) Let $u = x + y, v = \frac{y}{x}$. Show that this is equivalent to $x = \frac{u}{1 + v}$, $y = \frac{uv}{1 + v}$.

   (d) Show that the Jacobian of the transformation in (c) is $J(u, v) = \frac{u}{(1 + v)^2}$.

(e) Use this transformation to evaluate a double integral whose value is the area of the triangle. Confirm your answer to (b).

3. In Example 14.17, we showed that $I = \int_{-\infty}^{\infty} e^{-x^2} dx = \sqrt{\pi}$. The calculation presumes that I converges. Here we show that it indeed does converge.

(a) Show that if $H = \int_{0}^{\infty} e^{-x^2} dx$ converges, then $I = 2H$.

(b) Show that $e^{-x^2} \le e^{-x}$, for $x \ge 1$ and hence H converges if $\int_{0}^{\infty} e^{-x} dx$ converges.

(c) Show that $\int_{0}^{\infty} e^{-x} dx$ converges.

(d) Conclude that I converges.

TYU Answers for Section 14.3

1. (a) $J = 1 + 2v$ (b) $J = 0$ (c) $J = 2v^2 - 2u^2$ 2. $x = \sqrt{u + v}$, $y = \sqrt{u - v}$,

$J = \dfrac{-1}{2\sqrt{u^2 - v^2}}$ 3. (a) 36   (b) $\dfrac{32(2^{3/2} - 1)}{9} \approx 6.5$ (c) 3 ln(2)   4. $V = 9/7$

5. (a) $\dfrac{1}{8}$ (b) $\dfrac{\pi[1 - \cos(4)]}{2} \approx 2.598$ (c) 9

14.4 LINE INTEGRALS

In Chapter 13, we defined the concept of a vector field; namely, it is a function that associates a two-dimensional vector with each point on the xy-plane. We write $F(x, y) = \langle P(x, y), Q(x, y) \rangle$, where P and Q are scalar functions representing the components of the vector field F. There are many examples of vector fields in physics; some of the common ones are force fields and velocity fields.

Consider the following problem: An object in the xy-plane is acted on by the force field $F(x, y)$. How much work is done by moving the object along a curve C from the point $A(x_1, y_1)$ to the point $B(x_2, y_2)$? See Figure 14.29.

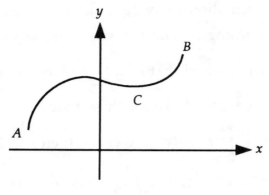

Fig. 14.29

Recall that if an object is subject to a constant force F parallel to the direction of motion, then the work done by moving it in a straight line from $x = a$ to $x = b$ is given by $W = (b - a)F$. In Chapter 6, we showed that if the force is not constant but is a function of x, then the work done is given by $W = \int_a^b F(x)\,dx$.

Our problem is complicated by the fact that the force is a vector, that it depends on both the x- and y-coordinates of the object and that the motion is not confined to one dimension. We can, however, still use the idea of a Riemann sum to calculate the total amount of work done; we just have to be a little more careful about how we do it.

First assume that C is the curve traced by the vector function $r(t) = \langle x(t), y(t) \rangle$ and that $r(a) = (x_1, y_1)$ and $r(b) = (x_2, y_2)$. In other words, a particle travelling along C will be at point A when $t = a$ and at point B when $t = b$. Partition the time interval $[a, b]$ into n equal subintervals of length Δt, as we have always done. Let (x_j, y_j) be the point on the curve corresponding to $t = t_j$ and let $\Delta r_j = r(t_{j+1}) - r(t_j) = \langle x_{j+1} - x_j, y_{j+1} - y_j \rangle = \langle \Delta x_j, \Delta y_j \rangle$ be the vector connecting the points (x_j, y_j) and (x_{j+1}, y_{j+1}). See Figure 14.30.

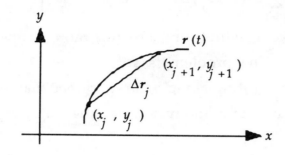

Fig. 14.30

If Δt is small, then we can assume that the force at any point along this segment is approximately constant $F(x_j, y_j)$. Moreover, the work done by moving the particle from (x_j, y_j) to (x_{j+1}, y_{j+1}) is the product of the distance moved and the component of the force *in the direction of motion*.

It is not hard to show (see, for example, Problem 6 at the end of Section 9.1) that the component of a vector v in the direction of a vector w is just $v \cdot u$, where $u = \dfrac{w}{\|w\|}$ is a unit vector in the direction of w. Thus, the component of the force F in the direction of Δr_j is $F \cdot \dfrac{\Delta r_j}{\|\Delta r_j\|}$. The distance moved is approximately $\|\Delta r_j\|$ since the length of the vector is approximately the length of the curve. Therefore, the work done by moving the particle from (x_j, y_j) to (x_{j+1}, y_{j+1}) is approximately $\Delta W_j = F(x_j, y_j) \Delta r_j$.

To get the total work done, we'll add up all the ΔW_j and take the limit as $n \to \infty$:

$$W = \lim_{n \to \infty} \sum_{j=1}^{n} F(x_j, y_j) \Delta r_j .$$

This would look like the definition of a definite integral except that the quantity after the summation sign is the dot product of two vectors, not the product of two scalar quantities. However, $F(x_j, y_j) \Delta r_j = P(x_j, y_j) \Delta x_j + Q(x_j, y_j) \Delta y_j$. Hence,

$$W = \lim_{n \to \infty} \sum_{j=1}^{n} \left[P(x_j, y_j) \Delta x_j + Q(x_j, y_j) \Delta y_j \right].$$

This looks more like a definite integral (or, more properly, the sum of two definite integrals). The problem is still that we have a function of two variables and are integrating along a curve, rather than a segment of an axis. Nevertheless, we have some motivation for the following:

DEFINITION: Let $F(x, y) = \langle P(x, y), Q(x, y) \rangle$ be a vector field and let C be the curve in the xy-plane traced by the vector function $r(t) = \langle f(t),$ $g(t) \rangle$ from A to B. The **line integral** of F along C is

$$\int_C F \cdot dr = \lim_{n \to \infty} \sum_{j=1}^{n} F(x_j, y_j) \Delta r_j \,, \text{ where } \Delta r_j = \langle \Delta x_j, \Delta y_j \rangle.$$

Note: We sometimes write a line integral in terms of its components; since $dr = \langle f'(t) \, dt, g'(t) \, dt \rangle = \langle dx, dy \rangle$, then $\int_C F \cdot dr = \int_C P \, dx + Q \, dy$. Also, it would be more accurate to call these "curve integrals" but we shall not do so.

Therefore, the total work done by moving the object from point A to point B along the curve C is $W = \int_C F \cdot dr$.

In order for the line integral to exist, we must require that $r(t)$ be **smooth**. This means that $r'(t)$ must be continuous and $r'(t) \neq 0$ for all t between a and b. If $r(t)$ is represented by the parametric equations $x = f(t)$, $y = g(t)$, then smoothness is equivalent to having $f'(t)$ and $g'(t)$ be continuous and not both be 0 simultaneously. For example, the curve defined by $x = t^3$, $y = t^3$ is not smooth at $t = 0$ since $f'(0) = g'(0) = 0$. This may be somewhat counterintuitive since C is equivalent to the line $y = x$ which certainly "looks" smooth. In essence, smoothness is an algebraic property of the parameterization of C and not a geometric property of C itself.

If C is not smooth, then it may be possible to break it down into a finite number of smooth pieces, in which case we say it is **piecewise smooth**. The example above is piecewise smooth since it is smooth for all $t > 0$ and for all $t < 0$.

Suppose that C is the union of a finite number of smooth pieces C_1, $C_2,...,C_m$. Then the line integral of F along C is just the sum of the line integrals along each piece; that is, $\displaystyle\int_C F \cdot d\,r \;=\; \sum_{j=1}^{m} \int_{C_j} F \cdot d\,r$.

Recall that curves defined by vector functions (i.e. parametrically) have an **orientation**. In other words, a particle moves along C in a specific direction as t increases. When talking about line integrals, we must keep the orientation in mind. In fact, it's not hard to believe that reversing the orientation changes the sign of the value of the line integral. Specifically, if we let $\overline{C}$ represent the same curve as C oriented in the opposite direction, then $\displaystyle\int_{\overline{C}} F \cdot d\,r \;=\; -\int_C F \cdot d\,r$.

◻ We now face the problem of evaluating line integrals. Surely, we don't want to resort to the definition. What we need is a shortcut.

It turns out that there are three techniques that can be used to evaluate line integrals. The first, and most general, involves making use of the parameterization of C to re-express the line integral as an ordinary integral in t. This can get a bit messy if C is complicated, thus making the parameterization difficult. The second approach applies to the special case when F is the gradient of some function of two variables--that is, when F is conservative. In this case, then the line integral can be evaluated by finding a potential function for F, plugging in the endpoints of C and subtracting. We shall call this the Fundamental Theorem of Line Integrals (what else?). Finally, if C is a simple, closed curve, meaning that it encloses a bounded region and does not cross itself, then there is a theorem called Green's Theorem that converts the line integral along C into an equivalent double integral over the region enclosed by C. We shall look at each of the techniques in turn.

PARAMETERIZATION

Let $F(x, y) := \langle xy, x + y \rangle$ and let C be the curve joining the points $A(0, 1)$ and $B(4, 5)$ and parameterized by $x = t^2, y = 2t + 1$. Note that A and B correspond to $t = 0$ and $t = 2$, respectively. See Figure 14.31.

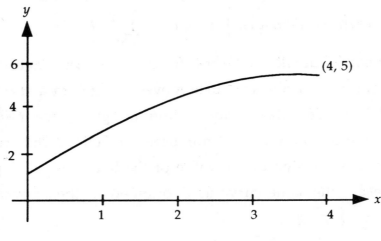

Fig. 14.31

To integrate F along C, we express everything in terms of the parameter t. The components of F are $P(x, y) := xy = t^2(2t + 1)$ and $Q(x, y) := x + y = t^2 + 2t + 1$. The differentials are $dx = 2t\, dt$ and $dy = 2\, dt$. Thus,

$$P\, dx + Q\, dy = 2t^3(2t + 1) + 2(t^2 + 2t + 1) = 4t^4 + 2t^3 + 2t^2 + 4t + 2$$

and
$$\int_C P\, dx + Q\, dy = \int_0^2 \left(4t^4 + 2t^3 + 2t^2 + 4t + 2\right) dt$$

$$= \frac{4t^5}{5} + \frac{t^4}{2} + \frac{2t^3}{3} + 2t^2 + 2t \,\Big|_{t=0}^{t=2} = \frac{764}{15}\ .$$

¤ A question should occur to you at this point. Our definition of the line integral includes only the vector field F and the curve C. It does not mention any parameters. Therefore, we should hope that the value of the line integral to be independent of the parameterization of C, as long as the parameterization is smooth. In other words, if we parameterize C some other way, we should get the same answer for the line integral. Let's try it.

Note that, by eliminating t, C has the xy-equation $x = \left(\frac{y-1}{2}\right)^2$. So, another parameterization for C is $x = \left(\frac{t-1}{2}\right)^2$, $y = t$, in which case the points A and B correspond to $t = 1$ and $t = 5$, respectively. Then, $P(x,y) = t\left(\frac{t-1}{2}\right)^2$, $Q(x,y) = t + \left(\frac{t-1}{2}\right)^2$, $dx = \frac{t-1}{2} dt$ and $dy = 1\, dt$, and

$$\int_C P\, dx + Q\, dy = \int_1^5 \left[t\left(\frac{t-1}{2}\right)^3 + \left(t + \left(\frac{t-1}{2}\right)^2 \right) \right] dt$$

$$= \int_1^5 \frac{t^4 - 3t^3 + 5t^2 + 3t + 2}{8}\, dt$$

$$= \left. \frac{t^5}{40} - \frac{3t^4}{32} + \frac{5t^3}{24} + \frac{3t^2}{16} + \frac{t}{4} \right|_{t=1}^{t=5} = \frac{764}{15}$$

as before.

EXAMPLE 14.18:

Evaluate $\int_C F \cdot d\,r$ where $F(x,y) := \langle y, -x \rangle$ and C is the curve defined by $r(t) := \langle e^t, t \rangle$, for $0 \le t \le 2$, as shown in Figure 14.32.

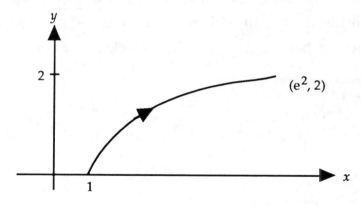

Fig. 14.32

We have $P(x,y) := y = t$, $Q(x,y) := -x = -e^t$, $dx = e^t\, dt$ and $dy = 1\, dt$. Thus, $\int_C F \cdot d\,r = \int_0^2 (t\, e^t - e^t)\, dt$. Using integration by parts or a table of integrals, we get:

$$\int_0^2 \left(t\, e^t - e^t \right) dt \;=\; (t-2)e^t \,\Big|_{t=0}^{t=2} \;=\; 2. \qquad\qquad \blacklozenge$$

EXAMPLE 14.19:

Evaluate $\displaystyle\int_C F \cdot d\,r$ where $F(x,y) := \langle xy, -x^2 \rangle$ and C is the top half of the circle $x^2 + y^2 = 1$ traversed clockwise, as shown in Figure 14.33.

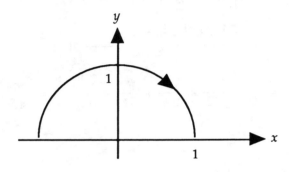

Fig. 14.33

The first thing we need to do is parameterize C. There are several ways to do this. We could let $x = t$, in which case $y = \sqrt{1-t^2}$. As t goes from -1 to 1, we trace the top half of the circle in a clockwise direction. Then, $dx = dt$ and $dy = \dfrac{-t}{\sqrt{1-t^2}}\,dt$ and

$$\int_C F \cdot d\,r \;=\; \int_{-1}^{1} \left(t\,\sqrt{1-t^2} + \frac{t^3}{\sqrt{1-t^2}} \right) dt \;=\; \int_{-1}^{1} \frac{t}{\sqrt{1-t^2}}\, dt$$

$$=\; -\sqrt{1-t^2}\,\Big|_{t=-1}^{t=1} \;=\; 0.$$

Another approach is to recall from Chapter 9 that $x = \sin(t)$, $y = \cos(t)$, $-\pi/2 \le t \le \pi/2$ parameterizes this semi-circle in a clockwise direction. Then,

$$\int_C F \cdot d\,r \;=\; \int_{-\pi/2}^{\pi/2} \left[\sin(t)\cos^2(t) + \sin^3(t) \right] dt \;=\; \int_{-\pi/2}^{\pi/2} \sin(t)\left[\cos^2(t) + \sin^2(t) \right] dt$$

$$=\; \int_{-\pi/2}^{\pi/2} \sin(t)\, dt \;=\; 0. \qquad\qquad \blacklozenge$$

EXAMPLE 14.20:

Evaluate $\int_C F \cdot d\,r$ where $F(x, y) := \langle x^2 + 1, xy \rangle$ and C is the closed curve consisting of $y = x^2$ and $y = 4$ oriented counterclockwise, as shown in Figure 14.34.

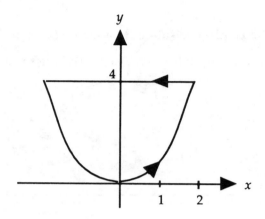

Fig. 14.34

Here, C consists of two smooth pieces. The parabolic part C_1 can be parameterized by $x = t, y = t^2$, for $-2 \le t \le 2$. The horizontal top C_2 can be parameterized by $x = -t, y = 4$, for $-2 \le t \le 2$. Thus,

$$\int_C F \cdot d\,r = \int_{C_1} F \cdot d\,r + \int_{C_2} F \cdot d\,r.$$

$$\int_{C_1} F \cdot d\,r = \int_{-2}^{2} \left((t^2 + 1)(1) + t^3(2t) \right) dt = \int_{-2}^{2} \left(2t^4 + t^2 + 1 \right) dt = \frac{524}{15}.$$

$$\int_{C_2} F \cdot d\,r = \int_{-2}^{2} \left((t^2 + 1)(-1) - 4t\,(0) \right) dt = \frac{-28}{3}.$$

Thus, $\int_C F \cdot d\,r = \frac{524}{15} - \frac{28}{3} = \frac{128}{5} = 25.6$. ♦

- -

TEST YOUR UNDERSTANDING

1. Evaluate each of the following line integrals:

   (a) $\int_C (2x + y)\,dx + xy\,dy$ where C is the line $y = x + 3$ from $(-1, 2)$ to $(2, 5)$.

(b) $\displaystyle\int_C 2x^3y\,dx + (3x+y)\,dy$ where C is the parabola $x = y^2$ from $(1, -1)$ to $(1, 1)$.

2. An object in the xy-plane is subject to a force $F(x,y) := \langle y, x \rangle$. How much work is done by moving the object from $(0, 0)$ to $(2, 4)$ along the parabola $y = x^2$?

FUNDAMENTAL THEOREM OF LINE INTEGRALS

The Fundamental Theorem of Calculus says that if f is continuous on $[a, b]$ and F is an antiderivative of f, then $\displaystyle\int_a^b f(x)\,dx = F(b) - F(a)$. It replaces the problem of integration with one of antidifferentiation and the successful use of this theorem hinges on finding F.

Before stating an analogous result for line integrals, let's review a few facts about vector fields from Chapter 13. A vector field $F(x, y) = \langle P(x, y), Q(x, y) \rangle$ is said to be **conservative** if it is the gradient of some function--that is, if there exists a function $\Phi(x, y)$ such that $\nabla \Phi = F$. The function Φ is called a **potential function** (or, "antigradient" if you like) of F. Furthermore, it is easily shown that, assuming P and Q are nice enough, F is conservative if and only if $P_y(x, y) = Q_x(x, y)$ for all x, y.

THEOREM 14.4 (FUNDAMENTAL THEOREM OF LINE INTEGRALS): Let C be a curve in the xy-plane connecting the points $A(u_1, v_1)$ and $B(u_2, v_2)$. Let $F(x, y) = \langle P(x, y), Q(x, y) \rangle$ be a vector field whose components are continuous in some region containing C. If F is a conservative vector field and Φ is a potential function of F, then

$$\int_C F(x, y) \cdot dr = \Phi(u_2, v_2) - \Phi(u_1, v_1).$$

PROOF: Assume C is smooth and that it can be represented by the parametric equations $x = x(t)$ and $y = y(t)$. Then,

$$F = \nabla \Phi = \left\langle \Phi_x(x(t), y(t)), \Phi_y(x(t), y(t)) \right\rangle \text{ and } dr = \left\langle \frac{dx}{dt}, \frac{dy}{dt} \right\rangle dt$$

from which

$$\int_C F \cdot dr = \int_a^b \left\langle \Phi_x(x(t), y(t)), \Phi_y(x(t), y(t)) \right\rangle \cdot \left\langle \frac{dx}{dt}, \frac{dy}{dt} \right\rangle dt$$

$$= \int_a^b \left[\Phi_x(x(t), y(t)) \frac{dx}{dt} + \Phi_y(x(t), y(t)) \frac{dy}{dt} \right] dt \; .$$

By the chain rule, the expression in square brackets is the derivative of Φ with respect to t. Hence, by the (old) Fundamental Theorem of Calculus,

$$\int_C F \cdot dr = \int_a^b \frac{d\Phi}{dt} dt = F(x(b), y(b)) - F(x(a), y(a))$$

$$= \Phi(u_2, v_2) - \Phi(u_1, v_1).$$

This theorem says that in order to evaluate the line integral of a *conservative* vector F field along some curve C, just evaluate a potential function of F at both ends of the curve and subtract. Admittedly, this is of limited usefulness since it is highly unlikely that an arbitrary vector field will be conservative.   However, there are several important examples of conservative vector fields in physics for which this theorem will have interesting ramifications.

Notice that the theorem doesn't depend on the curve C itself but rather only on the endpoints A and B. This leads to the following:

COROLLARY 1: The line integral of a conservative vector field depends only on the endpoints of the curve and not on the curve itself.

Furthermore, if the curve is closed--that is, if $A = B$--then $\Phi(a_2, b_2) = \Phi(a_1, b_1)$ and the value of the integral is 0. Hence, we have:

COROLLARY 2: The line integral of a conservative vector field along any closed path C is 0.

EXAMPLE 14.21:

Evaluate $\int_C F \cdot dr$ where $F(x, y) := \langle 2xy, x^2 \rangle$ and C is any curve from $(1, 2)$ to $(5, 6)$.

With $P(x, y) := 2xy$ and $Q(x, y) := x^2$, we have $P_y(x, y) := 2x = Q_x(x, y)$ and, hence, F is conservative. Furthermore, $\Phi(x, y) := x^2 y$ is a potential function for F. Therefore, $\int_C F \cdot dr = \Phi(5, 6) - \Phi(1, 2) = 150 - 2 = 148$. ♦

- -

TEST YOUR UNDERSTANDING

3. Is the Fundamental Theorem of Line Integrals applicable to the vector field

$F(x, y) := \langle e^x \cos(y), - e^x \sin(y) \rangle$? Explain.

4. Evaluate each of the following line integrals:

(a) $\int_C y \cos(xy)\, dx + x \cos(xy)\, dy$ where C is any simple curve from $(1, \pi/2)$ to $(\pi/2, -1)$

(b) $\displaystyle\int_C \frac{x}{\sqrt{x^2+y^2}}\,dx + \frac{y}{\sqrt{x^2+y^2}}\,dy$ where C is any simple curve from (3, 4) to

    (6, 8) not passing through the origin

(c) $\displaystyle\int_C \left(4x^3y^2 + 2xy^4\right)dx + \left(2x^4y + 4x^2y^3\right)dy$ where C is the triangle whose

    vertices are (1, 0), (3, 0) and (2, 4).

In Chapter 13, we showed that any force (such as gravitational force) that obeys the inverse square law is conservative. Thus, the work done by moving an object from point A to point B in such a force field is independent of the path taken from A to B. Moreover, if the object is moved from point A along a path and back to the same point A, then the total work done is 0. So, for example, if you lift a book from the table and then put it back down in the same place, you have done no work (assuming no friction).

GREEN'S THEOREM

The last method of evaluating line integrals applies when the curve along which we are integrating is of a special type. It must be:

(a) simple--meaning that it does not cross itself

(b) closed--meaning that it starts and ends in the same place

(c) piecewise smooth--meaning that it can be written as the union of smooth arcs. Figure 14.35 shows a simple, closed, piecewise smooth curve consisting of 3 smooth arcs.

Fig. 14.35

Every simple closed curve encloses a bounded region. We will say that the curve is traversed in the **positive direction** if the enclosed region remains to the left as you go around. Roughly speaking this is equivalent to going counterclockwise (although it might be hard to tell time on such an oddly-shaped clock).

Green's Theorem relates the line integral of a vector field along C to a double integral over the region R bounded by C.

THEOREM 14.5 (GREEN'S THEOREM): Let $F(x, y) = \langle P(x, y), Q(x, y) \rangle$ be a vector field for which P and Q are nice in some region containing

$$R. \quad \text{Then,} \oint_C F \cdot d\,r = \iint_R \left(\frac{\partial Q}{\partial x} - \frac{\partial P}{\partial y} \right) dA$$

Note: The loop on the line integral means "integrate around C in the positive direction".

A general proof of Green's Theorem is messy and beyond the scope of this book. We can, however, prove a special case in which C is the rectangle bounded by $x = a, x = b, y = c$ and $y = d$, as shown in Figure 14.36.

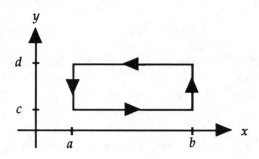

Fig. 14.36

If so, then

$$\iint\limits_{R} \left(\frac{\partial Q}{\partial x} - \frac{\partial P}{\partial y}\right) dA = \int_{c}^{d} \int_{a}^{b} \left(\frac{\partial Q}{\partial x} - \frac{\partial P}{\partial y}\right) dx \; dy$$

$$= \int_{c}^{d} \int_{a}^{b} \frac{\partial Q}{\partial x} dx \; dy - \int_{c}^{d} \int_{a}^{b} \frac{\partial P}{\partial y} dx \; dy$$

$$= \int_{c}^{d} \int_{a}^{b} \frac{\partial Q}{\partial x} dx \; dy - \int_{a}^{b} \int_{c}^{d} \frac{\partial P}{\partial y} dy \; dx$$

$$= \int_{c}^{d} \left[Q(b,y) - Q(a,y)\right] dy - \int_{a}^{b} \left[P(x,d) - P(x,c)\right] dx \; .$$

Now start over with the line integral. The bottom edge of the rectangle can be parameterized by $\{x = t, y = c, a \leq t \leq b\}$ and the right edge can be parameterized by $\{x = b, y = t, c \leq t \leq d\}$. The top edge would be parameterized by $\{x = t, y = d, a \leq t \leq b\}$ if we were moving left to right. However, since we are moving right to left, we will change the sign on the integral representing this edge. Similarly, the left edge would be parameterized by $\{x = a, y = t, d \leq t \leq c\}$ if we were moving bottom to top so we'll change the sign here also. Thus,

$$\oint_{C} F \cdot d\,r = \int_{a}^{b} P(t,c)\,dt + \int_{c}^{d} Q(b,t)\,dt - \int_{a}^{b} P(t,d)\,dt - \int_{c}^{d} Q(a,t)\,dt$$

$$= \int_{a}^{b} \left[P(t,c) - P(t,d)\right] dt + \int_{c}^{d} \left[Q(b,t) - Q(a,t)\right] dt$$

which is what we have above. The proof is complete.

EXAMPLE 14.22:

Use Green's theorem to evaluate the line integral in Example 14.20.

Since $P(x, y) := x^2 + 1$ and $Q(x, y) := xy$, then $\dfrac{\partial P}{\partial y} = 0$ and $\dfrac{\partial Q}{\partial x} = y$.

The region R is bounded by $y = x^2$ and $y = 4$. Thus, $\displaystyle\oint_C F \cdot d\,r =$

$$\int_{-2}^{2} \int_{x^2}^{4} y\ dy\ dx = \int_{-2}^{2} \left(8 - \frac{x^4}{2}\right) dx = 25.6, \text{ as we got before.} \qquad \blacklozenge$$

EXAMPLE 14.23:

Evaluate $\displaystyle\oint_C F \cdot d\,r$, where $F(x, y) := \langle x^2 + y^2, x^2 - y^2 \rangle$ and C is the rectangle bounded by $x = 0, x = 3, y = 0$ and $y = 5$, oriented counterclockwise.

To evaluate the line integral directly would require 4 integrals, one for each side of the rectangle. However, Green's theorem reduces this to one double integral. Since $P_y(x, y) := 2y$ and $Q_x(x, y) := 2x$, then

$$\oint_C F \cdot d\,r = \int_{0}^{3} \int_{0}^{5} (2x - 2y)\ dy\ dx = \int_{0}^{3} (10x - 25)\ dx = -30. \qquad \blacklozenge$$

Note that if F is conservative, then $\dfrac{\partial Q}{\partial x} = \dfrac{\partial P}{\partial y}$ and the integral on the right side of Green's theorem will be 0. This is consistent with the second corollary of the last section in which we said that the line integral of any conservative vector field around any closed curve is 0.

TEST YOUR UNDERSTANDING

5. Evaluate each line integral by using Green's theorem to convert it to an equivalent double integral:

   (a) $\displaystyle\int_C 2xy\ dx + (x + y)\ dy$ where C is the boundary of the region bounded by
   $y = 4 - x^2$ and the x-axis traversed counterclockwise.

(b) $\displaystyle\int_C (y-x)\,dx + (2x+y)\,dy$ where C is the boundary of the region bounded

by $y = x^2$ and $y = x$ traversed counterclockwise.

So far, we have used Green's theorem to evaluate line integrals by converting them to double integrals. It can also be used in reverse--that is, to evaluate double integrals by converting them to an equivalent line integral, as the next example illustrates.

EXAMPLE 14.24:

Evaluate $\displaystyle\iint_R y\,dA$, where R is the region bounded by the semi-circle $y = \sqrt{1-x^2}$ and the x-axis, as shown in Figure 14.37.

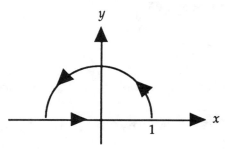

Fig. 14.37

We could set this up as an iterated integral

$$\iint_R y\,dA = \int_{-1}^{1}\int_0^{\sqrt{1-x^2}} y\,dy\,dx = \int_{-1}^{1} \frac{1-x^2}{2}\,dx = \frac{2}{3}.$$

Or, we could invoke Green's theorem. To do so, we need to find two functions P and Q such that $Q_x - P_y = y$. There are infinitely many choices. One possibility is $Q(x,y) := 0$ and $P(x,y) := -\dfrac{y^2}{2}$.

The boundary of R consists of two pieces, the semi-circle and its diameter (the x-axis). Since $y = 0$ along the x-axis, $P(x, y) := 0$ there so the line integral along this segment will be 0. The semi-circle can be parameterized by $x = -\sin(t), y = \cos(t)$. (Verify.) Hence, along the semi-circle, we have $P(x, y) := \dfrac{\cos^2(t)}{2}$ and $dx = -\cos(t)\, dt$. Thus,

$$\iint_R y\, dA = \int_{-\pi/2}^{\pi/2} \left\langle \frac{-\cos^2(t)}{2}, 0 \right\rangle \cdot \langle -\cos(t), -\sin(t) \rangle\, dt = \int_{-\pi/2}^{\pi/2} \frac{\cos^3(t)}{2}\, dt =$$

$$-\frac{\sin^3(t)}{6} + \frac{\sin(t)}{2} \Bigg|_{t=-\pi/2}^{t=\pi/2} = \frac{2}{3}. \qquad \blacklozenge$$

In this example, we were able to evaluate the integral by invoking Fubini's theorem because the region is "nice". However, if the region of integration is not one of the two types covered by Fubini's theorem, then we cannot easily convert the double integral into an iterated integral. If so, then it might be that the region is bounded by a simple closed piecewise smooth curve, in which case Green's theorem applies.

EXAMPLE 14.25:

Evaluate $\displaystyle\iint_R 2xy\, dA$, where R is the region bounded by the graph of $x = 1 - t^2, y = 3t - 3t^3$, for $-1 \le t \le 1$, as shown in Figure 14.38.

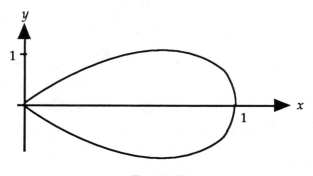

Fig. 14.38

Note that the curve is at (0, 0) when $t = -1$ and $t = 1$ and at (1, 0) when $t = 0$. Furthermore $y > 0$ for $0 < t < 1$. This implies that the curve is traversed counterclockwise.

Although this region is technically of the type covered by Fubini's theorem, we cannot easily convert the parametric representation into an xy-equation as we would need to set up an iterated integral. Hence, let's invoke Green's theorem. We need to find two functions P and Q such that $Q_x - P_y = 2xy$. Again there are infinitely many choices; we'll try $P(x, y) := 0$ and $Q(x, y) := x^2y$.

Substituting for x, y, dx and dy in terms of t, we have:

$$\iint_R 2xy \ dA = \int_{-1}^{1} \left(1 - t^2\right)^2 \left(3t - 3t^3\right)\left(3 - 9t^2\right) dt$$

$$= \int_{-1}^{1} \left(27t^9 - 90t^7 + 108t^5 - 54t^3 + 9t\right) dt = 0$$

because the integrand is odd and the interval is symmetric about $t = 0$. ◆

EXERCISES FOR SECTION 14.4:

1. Evaluate each of the following line integrals by parameterization:

(a) $\int_C x^2y \ dx + x \ dy$, where C is the straight line from (0, 0) to (1, 2)

(b) $\int_C x^2y \ dx + x \ dy$, where C is the parabola $y = 2x^2$ from (0, 0) to (1, 2)

(c) $\int_C x^2y \ dx + x \ dy$, where C is the parabola $y = 2x^2$ from (−1, 2) to (1, 2)

(d) $\int_C \left(x^2 + y^2\right) dx - x \ dy$, where C is the quarter circle $x^2 + y^2 = 1$ in the first quadrant

(e) $\int_C x^2 \ dx + xy \ dy$, where C is the ellipse defined by $x = 3\sin(t)$, $y = 2\cos(t)$, for $0 \le t \le 2\pi$.

2. Evaluate each of the integrals below by using the Fundamental Theorem of Line Integrals, if possible. If not possible, indicate why.

(a) $\int_C e^y \ dx + xe^y \ dy$ along any path from (3, ln(2)) to (−1, 0)

(b) $\int_C (3x - y + 5) dx - (x + 4y - 3) dy$ along any path from (2, 2) to (3, 5)

(c) $\displaystyle\int_C x^2 y\,dx + 8x^3 y^2\,dy$ along any path from $(0, 0)$ to $(2, 4)$

(d) $\displaystyle\int_C 2x\sin(y)\,dx + x^2\cos(y)\,dy$ around the triangle with vertices $(0, 1)$, $(2, 5)$ and $(-2, 5)$

3. For each integral in Exercise 2 that is not path independent, choose any two paths through the given points, evaluate the line integral and show that the results are different.

4. Evaluate each of the following using Green's Theorem:

(a) $\displaystyle\int_C x^2\,dx + xy\,dy$ counterclockwise around the triangle with vertices $(0, 0)$, $(1, 0)$ and $(1, 2)$

(b) $\displaystyle\int_C (e^x + y)\,dx + e^y\,dy$, where C is the boundary of the region enclosed by $y = x^2$ and $y = x$, traversed counterclockwise

(c) $\displaystyle\int_C \ln(1 + y)\,dx - \frac{xy}{1+y}\,dy$, where C is the boundary of the region enclosed by $y = 4 - x^2$ and the x-axis, traversed counterclockwise

5. A particle moves along the curve $x = t, y = 1/t, 1 \le t \le 3$ while subject to the force $F(x, y) := \langle x^2 + xy, y - x^2 y\rangle$. Calculate the work done.

6. Evaluate the integral in Example 14.24 by converting to polar coordinates.

PROBLEMS FOR SECTION 14.4:

1. Let C be a closed curve and let R be the region enclosed by C.

(a) Show that the area of R can be obtained by evaluating the line integral
$$\frac{1}{2}\int_C -y\,dx + x\,dy\,.$$

(b) Use 1(a) to find the area enclosed by the ellipse whose parametric representation is $x = a\cos(t), y = b\sin(t), 0 \le t \le 2\pi$.

2. Let $F(x, y, z) = \langle P(x, y, z), Q(x, y, z), R(x, y, z) \rangle$ be a three-dimensional vector field. We can define the line integral $\int_C F \cdot dr = \int_C P\ dx + Q\ dy + R\ dz$, where C is the curve traversed by the three-dimensional vector function $r(t)$.

    Evaluate $\int_C xz\ dx + x^2 y\ dy + 2yz\ dz$, where C is defined parametrically by $x = t, y = t^2, z = 1/t$, for $1 \le t \le 2$.

3. Let $F(x, y) = \langle P(x, y), Q(x, y) \rangle$ be a vector field for which $P(x, y) = u(x)$ and $Q(x, y) = v(y)$; that is, the horizontal component of F depends only on x and the vertical component depends only on y. Use Green's theorem to show that the line integral of F along any simple, closed curve C is 0.

4. Evaluate $\int_C (e^x - y^3)\ dx + (\cos(y) + x^3)\ dy$, where C is the circle of radius 1 centered at the origin traversed counterclockwise.

TYU Answers for Section 14.4

   1. (a) 21 (b) 26/9   2. 8   3. Yes, F is conservative   4. (a) –2 (b) 5 (c) 0

   5. (a) 32/3 (b) 1/6

QUESTIONS TO THINK ABOUT

1. State and explain the definition of a double integral in terms of Riemann sums.

2. State and explain Fubini's theorem and why it is useful. When does it apply?

3. Explain the role of the Jacobian in the transformation of variables technique for evaluating double integrals.

4. Describe three methods of evaluating line integrals. Make sure to include any conditions necessary for the method to apply.

Index

We ask your indulgence using this index. In some cases, editing after the index was created has moved a referent to a near-by page. If you cannot find the term you were seeking on the page listed in the index, try the previous and succeeding several pages.

Page references that begin with the letter "p" refer to the projects at the ends of chapters. For example, the page reference "p6.3" refers to Project 6.3; that is the third project at the end of Chapter 3.